THIS GREAT AND WIDE SEA

D0962381

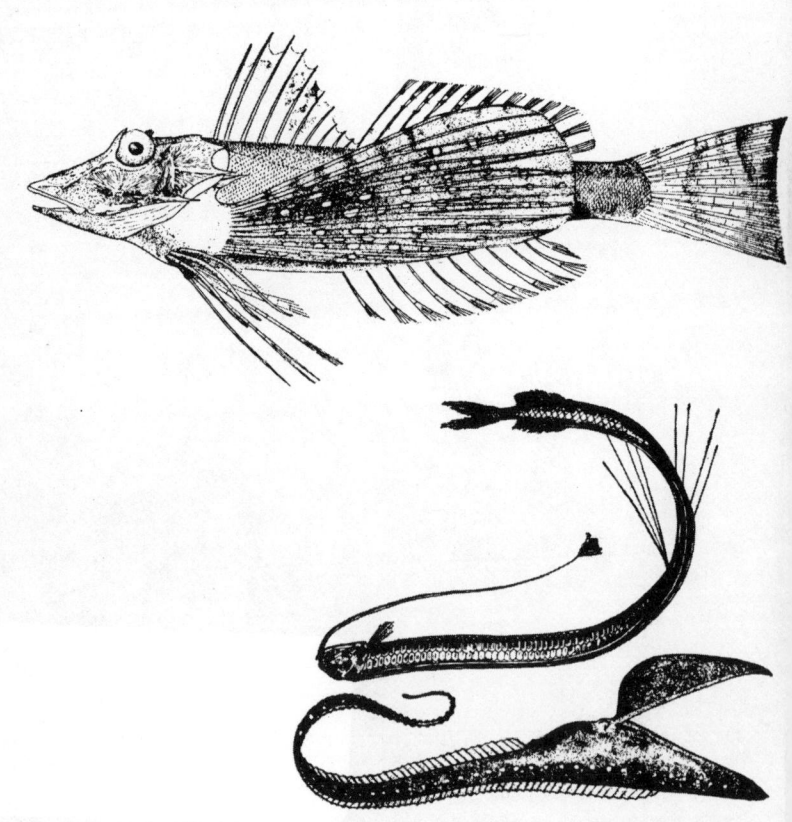

R. E. Coker

This great and wide
sea

*An Introduction to
Oceanography and
Marine Biology*

❧

HARPER TORCHBOOKS / The Science Library

HARPER & BROTHERS, NEW YORK

$P_{ref}ace$

I N UNDERTAKING TO DEAL WITH SO BROAD A SUBJECT AS THE SEAS IN their physical, dynamic, and biological aspects, and to do this in a single small volume, I realize only too well the difficulties and the dangers. Yet three general purposes have urged me to the task. First, and of least general significance, is the fact that, as a teacher of biology, and of aquatic biology particularly, I have personally felt the need for a relatively brief, comprehensive, and not too technical presentation of some of the basic phenomena of the ocean as a place of life for plants and animals. For an even elementary understanding of the relations of temperature, light, gases, circulation, and marine life, it was necessary to delve into many authoritative treatises, some of which were not easily read, even so far as one not highly trained in mathematics and physics could read them at all. The results of a great deal of effort are here put into print in the hope that others of like need may profit with less expenditure of labor.

A second general motive was based on the belief that a more widespread "sea-consciousness" must prevail in the future. There may well be persons not specializing in the sciences who want to know more about the seas over which so many will voyage by sea-ship or by airship. It may be interesting to them—it may even, on occasion, be useful to them—to understand a little of the conditions underlying some of the surprisingly anomalous states of temperature, water-movement, and organic life so frequently encountered here and there about the world. It is presumed, too, that there are those who, out of mere intellectual curiosity, will want to gain a better picture of that major portion of the earth's surface which is occupied by salt water.

Finally, in respect to motivation, let it be said that, although the book has, of necessity, its eclectic features, it is definitely not intended to be a mere compilation of interesting facts about the seas. The broader underlying and directive purpose may or may not have been accomplished in some small measure. Personally, I have been impressed with the *unity* of the seas; they form a single dynamic mechanism, world-wide in operation and in influence. Yet it is not an independent mechanism; on the contrary, it is obviously and measurably affected by outside forces, particularly by the rotation of the earth and by the celestial movements of sun and moon. It is influenced also by direct income and outgo of radiant solar energy. Furthermore, there are vital interchanges of energy between sea and atmosphere and land: through radiation, through vapor formation, along with its distribution and condensation, through the indirect effects of geological processes, and through photosynthesis and other biological phenomena. Perhaps this may sound complex and forbidding in the reading at this stage; there is the hope, however, that it will seem to work out more simply as one passes from topic to topic in the following pages. We may even need sometimes to guard against thinking it all simpler and more fully comprehensible than it is.

A very large volume would be necessary to do full justice to the general idea, which, of course, is not new; yet either voluminousness or a high degree of technicality in the presentation would defeat the major purpose. The justification for a small and nontechnical volume, if it has one, rests on the effort to assemble data from many areas of oceanographic study, put them in as simple terms as possible, and point out a good many of the linkages. Connections between physical conditions and interrelations of biological and physical phenomena will be emphasized. Obviously, repetitions are necessary; it is hoped that there may not seem to be excessive reiteration. The book attempts to enable the reader with little or no technical training to grasp a good many of the interrelations. Certainly, the ordinary person does not want to give a lifetime to the study of the sea; but he may like to follow for at least a few hours a short path leading to a point of vision of the sea as a whole—a point from which a glimpse may be had of physical, chemical, dynamic, and biological phenomena as completely inter-related. The relations are intricate, to be sure; let us not underrate their complexity. Yet even to those who are barely initiated, the general character of the relations can be grasped to an extent that brings a definite measure of intellectual satisfaction.

The materials assembled and correlated in this volume have been derived in small part from personal experience, in far greater part from books and papers too numerous to mention. A selected bibliography on page 301 to 303 lists a few publications to which the writer is more particularly indebted, besides some popular or semi-popular works that should be of interest to the general reader. Sources to which only an occasional reference is made are cited in footnotes. No apology need be offered for a fairly free use of quotations. Direct quotations from writers of special experience and knowledge may sometimes be reassuring to the reader who must realize that no one can have full grasp of the whole field of oceanography. Explicit credit is given for a good many unquoted statements; but it may well be assumed that in such a work, unless the whole text were littered with citations, the "debits" for facts and ideas must greatly exceed the "credits" by acknowledgement.

A dozen friends have given help by reading chapters of the manuscript, or the whole, and detecting some errors of fact or form—although, doubtless, not all. Professor Thurlow C. Nelson of Rutgers University gave valuable suggestions in connection with the earlier chapters. These were read also by two graduate students, Misses Catherine Henley and Carrie Ola Hughes, each of whom was genuinely helpful. Another student, Miss Flossie Martin, contributed materially to the historical chapters. Dr. Harden F. Taylor, recently president of the Atlantic Coast Fisheries Company as well as a competent biologist and technologist, has kindly read the entire manuscript and offered many valuable criticisms and comments. Professor W. C. Allee of the University of Chicago has made useful comments in respect to the chapters dealing with marine biology. I am grateful, indeed, to all of these and to several colleagues in the University of North Carolina: Professors Karl Fussler, in the Department of Physics, and R. W. Bost, Head of the Department of Chemistry, have read several of the chapters on physical and chemical oceanography and have checked some slips; Captain E. E. Hazlett, U. S. N., Retired, Professor Samuel Emory of the Department of Geology and Geography, and Professors C. D. Beers, D. P. Costello, C. S. Jones, and Nelson Marshall of the Department of Zoology have been good enough to read large parts or all of the manuscript and have given aid in the detection of errors. The author alone is responsible for the ideas expressed and for such errors or defects as remain.

R.E.C.

Contents

	Page
Preface	V
Introduction: Meaning of Oceanography . . .	3

Part I. History and Geography

1. *Discovery of the Seas* . . . . . . | 11
2. *Beginnings of Oceanography* . . . . . | 17
3. *Pioneers in Oceanography* . . . . . | 19

   Edward Forbes, 1815-1854—Matthew Fontaine Maury, 1806-1873—The "Challenger" and Sir Wyville Thomson, 1830-1882—Sir John Murray, 1841-1914—Palumbo and the Closing Net—Victor Hensen, Carl Chun, and the Prince of Monaco—Hans Lohmann and the Centrifuge —Recent European Oceanographic Expeditions—Shore Stations Across the Atlantic

4. *Oceanography in America* . . . . . | 40

   Early American Oceanographic Research—Alexander Agassiz, 1835-1910—The "Albatross," 1882-1924, and "The Fish Commission"—Hydrographic Office, U. S. Navy—United States Coast and Geodetic Survey—Recent American Oceanographic Research—Oceanography in Canada—Summary of Historical Review.

Page

5. *Sea and Land* 57

Some Gross Features of the Ocean—Some Interrelations of the Oceans—Continuity and Contrasts—Depth and Topography—Interrelations of Sea and Land

Part II. CHEMISTRY AND PHYSICS

6. *The Sea as a Solution* 77

Chemical Nature of Sea Water—Inorganic Substances in Solution—Collection of Samples and Analysis—Distribution of Salinity—Effect of Salt on Circulation—Organic Substances in Solution and Their Distribution—Gases in Solution—Utilization of Materials in Solution

7. *Some Physical Properties of Sea Water* . . . 94

Temperature—How Temperature in the Deep is Taken—Temperature and Life in the Sea—Viscosity—Influence of Viscosity on Organisms in the Sea—Density—Pressure

8. *Deposits at the Bottom of the Sea* 112

9. *Sea Water in Motion: General Plans of Circulation* . 120

Broad Features of Circulation and Methods of Observation—The Atlantic Ocean—The Pacific Ocean—The Indian Ocean—The Antarctic Ocean—The Arctic Ocean—Conclusion

10. *Sea Water in Motion: Water Moved by the Winds* . 138

Horizontal Currents—Upwelling—Waves

11. *Sea Water in Motion: Tides and Other Movements* . 146

The Tide—Internal Waves—"Tidal Waves"—Biological Relations of Waves, Tides, and Upwelling

12. *The Sea and the Sun* 160

The Sea a Dynamic Body—The Sea as a Reservoir of Heat—How the Seas are Warmed and Cooled—The Penetration of Radiation

Part III. LIFE IN THE SEA

13. *Life in the Seas: General Conditions* . . . 177

Modes of Living and Habitats—Some Relations to
Physical Conditions—No Hiding Place—Metabolism of
the Sea—Summary

14. *Pasturage of the Sea* 197

Premium on Simplicity—Kinds of Plants—Summary

15. *Drifting Life: The Plankton* 208

Universality of Plankton—Conditions Governing Distribution by Regions and by Depth

16. *Composition of the Plankton* 219

Protozoa — Sponges (Porifera) — Coelenterata — Comb
Jellies (Ctenophora)—Flatworms (Platyhelminthes)—
Round Worms (Nemathelminthes)—Moss Animalicules
(Bryozoa) — Brachiopoda — Arrow-worms (Chaetog-
natha)—Segmented Worms (Annelida)—Echinodermata
—Mollusca—Arthropoda—Summary for Chapters 15
and 16

17. *Life on the Bottom: The Benthos* 240

Stationary Life: The Edreobenthos — Life near the
Shores: The Littoral—Deep-Sea Life: Benthic—How the
Bottom Fauna is Taken—Benthonic Animals Useful to
Man—Summary

18. *Life at Large: The Nekton* 255

Barriers to Distribution—Zones of Life—Kinds of Fishes
—Useful Fishes—Capture of Fish in the Depths—Summary

19. *More About Life at Large: The Nekton* . . . 281

Some Features of the Natural History of Fishes—Mol-
lusks: The Squid—Some Lower Vertebrates—Sea Fowl—
Sea Otters, Sea Lions, and Sea Cows—The Whales—
Summary

Selected Bibliography 301

Index 305

Illustrations

Figures

		Page
1	Map of the world, showing all oceans . . .	58
2	Map of northern and southern hemispheres . .	64
3	Distribution of the deeps	66
4	Map showing location of canyons and principal furrows off the Mid-Atlantic states	68
5	Map of the Hudson canyon and vicinity . . .	68
6	Schematic representation of the Continental Shelf, Edge, and Slope	72
7	Schematic representation of the distribution of temperatures by depth and latitude	97
8	The pelagic oozes	116
9	Ocean currents	121
10	Diagram showing the plan of the standard automatic tide gage	147
11	Varieties of pelagic sargassum	200
12	A Dinoflagellate	203
13	Coccolithophores	204
14	The protozoan, *Globigerina bulloides* D'Orbigny .	220
15	Free-swimming pteropod mollusks	226
16	Giant ostracod	229
17	Copepods	231

		Page
18	Old-type Blake trawl	249
19	Sea Robin	268
20	Bat fish	270
21	Oceanic fishes	271
22	Diagram of a purse seine	275
23	Diagram of steam-trawler with otter trawl . .	278

Plates

Between pages 30-31

1 Woods Hole Oceanographic Institution
2 Scripps Institution of Oceanography
3 The research vessel ARGO
4 U.S. Fish and Wildlife Service Biological Station, North Carolina
5 ATLANTIS under sail

Between pages 142-143

6 Sandfall
7 Tide-predicting machine
8 Read-out Equipment
9 Standard automatic tide gage
10 Lowering of temperature probe
11 Sea-mount
12 Nansen bottle
13 Six-tone crane for lowering heavy equipment in ocean
14 Underwater camera
15 Lowering chain dredge from research vessel HORIZON

Between pages 222-223

16 Clarke quantitative plankton sampler
17 Attaching meter net to towing cable for collecting plankton
18 Towing plankton net near the surface
19 Hauling in quantitative plankton net
20 Heavy catch in plankton net
21 Sea Spider, three brittle-stars and various tracks on sea floor

22 Living Coral
23 Cleaned skeleton of living coral
24 Plankton: diatoms
25 Plankton: copepod
26 Plankton: dinoglagellate
27 Plankton: radiolarian protozoan
28 Diver examining coral beds
29 Living sponge attached to a shell
30 Cleaned skeleton of sponge
31 Spider crab
32 Isaacs-Kidd midwater trawl

THIS GREAT AND WIDE SEA

The earth is full of Thy riches;
So is this great and wide sea,
Wherein are things creeping innumerable,
Both small and great beasts.
There go the ships:
There is that Leviathan,
Whom Thou has made to play therein.

(Psalm CIV)

Introduction

I N RECENT YEARS, AND ALMOST WITHOUT OUR AWARENESS, THE SEAS have crept upon us; it might be said, they have crowded upon us—into our consciousness. Always we have known the oceans were there, but for most of us they were remote. They were places for recreation—bathing, fishing, boating. They were highways for travel and for commerce. They were protective walls about our homelands, insuring us, we imagined, the opportunity to live our lives without fear of molestation, though there could be distant peoples less sensible than we, and less devoted to peaceful and constructive pursuits.

All the time, of course, but without our thinking much about it, the seas significantly influenced every individual life; they were mute but powerful forces acting on the whole structure of human society. They affected climate and weather; and this was economically and socially significant. They yielded tasty and commercially valuable foods, and oils, fertilizers, salt, pearls, and sponges; in so doing, they often governed movements of populations and development of cities. As avenues of trade between peoples of different continents and islands, they facilitated the world-wide distribution of a thousand comforts, conveniences, and luxuries, and the profitable disposal of farm and factory surpluses. Thus they had great significance in the lives of all; yet for such as were not actually seafarers, there was little need for particular concern about those great bodies of water. It was enough to know that the seas floated useful ships, nourished marketable oysters, crabs, and fish, and kept potentially hostile folks away.

Almost suddenly, our conception of the oceans has undergone drastic change. If we had thought of them as *separating* barriers, we now see them as *connecting* links between all the continents and islands. It is not only that the lands have become so interdependent that whatever happens in one seriously to modify the fortunes of life there, may quickly affect all others around the globe. The broad waters are actual *links*. The protective walls, as we civilians once saw them, now appear as wide avenues for invasion—in either direction. Ready and royal avenues they are too. Spatially, the Japanese made by sea far greater and more rapid advances toward us and our allies than ever the Germans did by land against France or Russia. We, when we had regained our strength, proceeded eastward and westward at speeds, measured in miles per annum, far greater over water than over land. This is definitely not a military disquisition: no longer should a civilian have the temerity to measure the protective value of seas against that of hills and valleys; mentally, however, he notes that, not only for ships, as navy men have always known, but also for armies and munitions, for planes and rockets, the seas are not now "set as a bound that they may not pass over."

In still other ways the seas have lost significance as barriers. They no longer retard the passage of the spoken word. Every day vocal language flies through the air, over and beyond the seas, to encircle the globe with virtual instantaneity of passage. Human bodies are transported from continent to continent, or even completely around the world, with a time schedule of mere hours. Furthermore, planes not only fly above the ocean; they make it their landing field.

Let us not think, either, that the "ships of the air" have no concern with the seas except as something not to be collided with inopportunely. Nothing that moves through the air, whether it be over sea or over land, is even halfway independent of oceanic phenomena. Heat and cold, rains and snows, storms, hurricanes, upcurrents and down-currents—all these anywhere may have greater or less dependence upon the dynamics of the sea. To the air-minded —and who is not so now?—one does not need to argue the importance of meteorology—yet, meteorology and oceanography are indissolubly associated. In short, the seas are no longer what they were when all rapid transport was by craft floating on water or by vehicles with wheels demanding a solid substratum for traction.

More than ever, then, the seas have come into our lives in ways that are appreciable. They are still avenues for pleasure and for profit, but they are also highways for defensive and offensive logistics. Much more important for our thought in times of peace is the fact that the basic conditions of our ordinary lives are governed to no little extent by what takes place at and beneath the surface of the sea. If we now begin to see the lands of our globe as "One World," socially regarded, we might also come to sense more generally the fact that land and sea and atmosphere are *one world*.

We might then be interested in some of the facts and the principles of the relationships between the great components of an integrated physical sphere. The interest has a sounder basis because the integration does not stop with the physical or material structure. In many ways, both simple and complex, the interrelations of sea, land, and atmosphere have intimate ties with the world of organisms of land and water; and they have impacts upon the economic and social life of man.

WHAT IS OCEANOGRAPHY?

As the study of the sea in all its aspects, oceanography is not a science in itself but is rather a correlation of various sciences—geographical, geological, physical, chemical, and biological, along with some astronomy and with mathematics unlimited. The pursuit and the correlation of such diversified studies are directed toward learning what really goes on in a continuous, but varied, circulating, and turbulent medium which covers some three-fourths of the earth's surface. To some, oceanography embraces the physical studies, leaving the biological phenomena involved to the special field of hydrobiology. Others would make the former term more inclusive and subdivide oceanography into hydrobiology and hydrography; yet the latter term seems inadequate to cover the necessary geographical, physical, and chemical features. Why not just say *oceanography* and distinguish, when necessary, its biological and physical approaches? Everywhere it is becoming more difficult to draw sharp lines between the different standard divisions of the natural sciences, such as between chemistry and physics, between biology and chemistry, or between biology and geology. If this statement has validity in the broad field of science, it is particularly true in respect to the oceans. Hardly any phenomenon of the sea is capable of satisfactory analysis without coordination of all the fundamental natural sciences.

The geologist is concerned with topography and sediments; but the sediments may be largely biological products, and topography partly the effect of biological phenomena (coral islands, for example); the nature of the bottom materials is governed in great part, too, by physical and chemical phenomena. Physical and chemical conditions are certainly dependent upon geological history and formations. They depend also upon meteorological conditions; on the other hand, the meteorologist cannot escape the consideration of oceanographical and geological phenomena. Biological patterns in the sea derive to a great extent from geographical, chemical, and physical conditions, and these patterns contribute to an understanding of physical conditions as expressed in currents and drifts. These are only suggestions of the close interlocking of the several fields of science in the one great pattern presented to the oceanographer. For our purpose it will suffice to regard oceanography as the study of the sea in all of its aspects.

What has activated the study of the oceans? Perhaps the problems of navigation first played a leading part in directing oceanographical studies, when it became apparent that knowledge of currents and drifts could shorten periods of sailing between ports, and make navigation safer through facilitating avoidance of areas of storm, calms, or icebergs. Certainly it required no special acumen to recognize the practical value of accurate knowledge of depths and shoals, reefs and rocks, in continental regions. Fairly recently (1912) the tragic loss of the "Titanic," after collision with an iceberg, and the drowning of hundreds of its passengers and crew, led to the establishment of the International Ice Patrol, with its program of cooperative research, conducted in the North Atlantic under the immediate direction of the U.S. Coast Guard. Problems of empire, of naval efficiency, and of success in international wars have come into the picture in various ways. The oceans loom large in the visions of those who specialize in geopolitics.

A second and cogent motive for the study of the sea was afforded by the needs of the fisheries, particularly in the northeast Atlantic region, around Norway, in the North Sea, about the British Isles and off the northeast coast of America. Centers of population have been determined by the distribution of herring and other commercial fishes, the distribution of these fishes governed by populations of copepods and other small organisms, and the distribution of the microscopic life controlled, in turn, by currents and other physical phenomena in the sea; hence, the inevitably close link between oceanography and fisheries science.

Some of the most productive of the cruises in exploration of the oceans have had as primary objectives the study of the biology of the sea or other purely scientific objectives. Again, very significant contributions to knowledge of the ocean have been made in connection with the study of terrestrial magnetism by the Carnegie Institution of Washington.

Often the possibility of contribution to a scientific understanding of oceanographic phenomena has been regarded as secondary to more practical basic purposes. A sentence from the intructions to Lieutenant Wilkes commanding the United States Exploring Expedition, 1838-41, is illustrative. "Although the primary object of the Expedition is the promotion of the great interests of commerce and navigation, yet you will take all occasions, not incompatible with the great purposes of your undertaking, to extend the bounds of science and to promote the acquisition of knowledge."[1]

Certainly there are oceanographic institutions and there have been oceanic cruises whose first emphasis and "great purposes" are, or were, the study of physical and biological oceanography in its purely scientific aspects. Nevertheless, the financial support for such expensive operations—and they are always costly—is generally based on some faith that ultimately there will be substantial benefits to navigation and commerce, to national safety or to empire.

---

1. Max Meisel, *Bibliography of American Natural History. The Pioneer Century, 1769-1865,* II, 652.

I

HISTORY AND GEOGRAPHY

CHAPTER 1

Discovery of the Seas[1]

ARLY MAN COULD NOT HAVE CONCEIVED, EVEN APPROXIMATELY, of the oceans as we know them today. Lacking means and implements for extended navigation, an individual or a community could see only a small part of the total area of sea or land. As long as there were not effective means of communication, what little knowledge was gained in different coastal communities could not be interchanged for synthesis and analysis, even if such habits of mind had prevailed. Furthermore, most people of the ancient world left no record of what they saw or knew. It happens, then, that our knowledge of early concepts of world geography derives chiefly from the Greeks and the Egyptians; we may well be impressed with the capacity of the cultivated human mind of ancient times, armed only with skill in mathematics and with curiosity concerning the movements of visible celestial bodies, to picture the whole earth even as little wrongly as they did (p. 13, below).

In the time of Homer, about 1000 B.C., the world was considered to be a relatively flat disk of land around a part of the Mediterranean, with some islands. An early concept, attributed to the Babylonians, pictured an area of land surrounded by a broad ocean which in turn was encircled by the Dawn. Even the early naturalistic observers had some belief in the great breadth, endurance, and dominance of the waters. An ancient poet and philosopher, one of whose writings became a part of the Psalms of David and was considered by the

1. With substantial acknowledgements to Marmer, *The Sea;* Herdman, *Founders of Oceanography;* Murray and Hjort, *The Depths of the Ocean;* and other sources.

great naturalist Humboldt to be the finest poem of nature ever written, pictured the earth as securely anchored in the sea: the waters had even covered the whole earth but had been forced by an Almighty power to recede from the lands and to remain at the boundaries fixed for them.[2]

Going back to the Greeks, the poetry of Hesiod, ten centuries B.C., contains references to lands out in the oceans, the Isles of the Blessed, the Hesperides, and others. Plato, in the fourth and third centuries B.C., gives us the story of the great island of Atlantis, presumed to have been located in the Atlantic Ocean. The Greeks are supposed to have learned of Atlantis 150 years earlier and to have received through an Egyptian priest records dating back for nine millennia. By their own prowess in battle, according to the story, the Greeks saved European civilization from the might of the rulers of Atlantis, which a great earthquake subsequently destroyed in a day and night. It vanished beneath the sea, we are told, but the questions of its actual or fictitious existence, its location and the causes of its disappearance lie in the field of speculation or imagination and may always rest there.

The Atlantic Ocean was undoubtedly known to many early mariners who voyaged some distance out from the Mediterranean to reach England, probably Ireland, and possibly the Canaries. The Phoenicians are believed to have sailed far out in the Atlantic and into the Sargasso Sea, that great area of dark blue, translucent, and highly saline water, with innumerable scattered patches of sea weed (sargassum or "gulf weed"), which is surrounded by the north equatorial current on the south, by the Gulf Stream on the west and north, and by the Canaries current on the east and southeast. Herodotus tells us also of Phoenician mariners who, starting from the Red Sea, worked their way around Africa to return through the Straits of Gibraltar (the Pillars of Hercules) and the Mediterranean.

The conception of the world as a sphere, as improbable as that idea must always seem to a casual observer, is not recent. No one

---

2. "Who layeth the beams of his chambers in the waters . . . who laid the foundations of the earth that it should not be removed forever. Thou coveredst it with the deep as with a garment: the waters stood above the mountains. At Thy rebuke they fled; at the voice of Thy thunder they hasted away. They go up by the mountains; they go down by the valleys unto the place which Thou hast founded for them. Thou hast set a bound that they may not pass over; that they turn not again to cover the earth."—Psalm CIV.

had sailed around the globe when the historian Herodotus, in the fifth century B.C., summarized knowledge of the earth as a sphere, divided, somewhat as we now divide it, into five zones. The middle torrid zone and the outer cold zones were thought to be too extreme in temperature for human habitation.

Pytheas, navigator and geographer, a contemporary of Alexander the Great, in the fourth century B.C., voyaged to the British Isles, determined latitude and longitude, and related the tides to the moon.

It is remarkable indeed that, even in the third century B.C., the learned Eratosthenes gave the circumference of the earth as approximately what we know it to be today, about 25,000 miles, that he drew lines for latitude and longitude corresponding in a general way to our parallels and meridians, and that he suggested the possibility of sailing around the globe were it not for the vast extent of the Atlantic Sea. The geographer Strabo, at the beginning of the Christian Era, is said to have measured the depth of the Mediterranean near Sardinia to a depth of 1,000 fathoms, more than a mile, but how did he do it? Widely traveled and steeped in the knowledge of Alexandria, Strabo accepted Eratosthenes' idea of the world as a sphere with a circumference of 25,000 miles and the earlier concept of the five zones; he supposed that the inhabited land extended about one-third the way around the earth, and suggested that there might be other continents as yet unknown.

In the second century, Ptolemy in Egypt, "last of the classical oceanographers," prepared his map of the world, which was to be the standard geography for a very long time. He exaggerated the east and west extent of the inhabited world and accepted a substantially reduced estimate of the circumference of the earth, some 18,000 miles. Perhaps his errors were actually fortunate in that they encouraged the idea of reaching India by a westward voyage far shorter and simpler than it subsequently proved to be.

Unfortunately the early promising trend in understanding of terrestrial relations soon went into reverse. The inhabitants of Europe had to live through a millenium of non-scientific and supposedly scriptural interpretation of world geography by those who remained ignorant of ancient learning. The earth again became flat in the minds of men who presumed to guide human thought.

Even during the long centuries of relative intellectual darkness, there were daring voyages on the Atlantic, particularly by the Vikings who discovered Iceland, Greenland, and North America. The geographical knowledge gained by these bold sea-going tourists had relatively little significance only because it never came to the attention of those who were writing the books or making geopolitical plans for the countries of Europe. Ancient knowledge, still preserved by the Arabians, had yet to come back to those who could engage in great voyages of discovery and who, happily or unhappily, cherished ambitions of empire. Modern knowledge of terrestrial geography is rooted, then, not in those individually magnificent voyages of the Vikings, but rather in the revival of the old ideas of the Greeks and in the world-tours that they prompted. Most notable of these geographical expeditions were: the rounding of the Cape of Good Hope and return to Portugal by Bartholomeu Diaz in 1487, the discovery of America by Columbus in 1492, the voyage of Vasco da Gama around the Cape of Good Hope and all the way to India in 1499, the discovery of the eastern shore of the Pacific by Balboa in 1513, the first crossing of the Pacific by Magellan about 1520-21, and the completion in 1522 of the first circumnavigation of the earth. Magellan, himself, was killed in the Philippines, but Sebastian del Cano, commanding the "Victoria," continued westward to Spain. John Fiske can be charged with little exaggeration in his characterization (in a school history) of the voyages of Columbus and Magellan. That of Columbus was "the most daring thing that had ever been done . . . Columbus was the first to bid good-bye to the land and steer straight into the trackless ocean in reliance upon a scientific theory"; "Magellan, in spite of mutiny, scurvy and starvation, crossed the vast Pacific in the most astonishing voyage that ever was made."

Even up to the present time there have been "astonishing" voyages and travels in exploration of the remote and more difficult areas of the surface of the earth. Among such were the voyages in search of the Northwest Passage by Martin Frobisher, heading westward in 1576, '77, and '78, by Davis in 1585, '86, and '87, by Hudson and Baffin in the early part of the next century, by Bering and Cook more than a century later, and by Ross, Parry, and Franklin in the nineteenth century. Presumably, from the records discovered, Franklin completed the passage, but he never lived to obtain the high monetary reward which went to McClure returning to England after a search for the lost Franklin and his party; McClure had made the Northwest Passage, in 1853, although he had had to travel partly over ice. It was only in the present century that the Northwest Passage was actually *sailed* by Roald Amundsen, starting from Norway in 1903 and arriving at Nome, Alaska, a little over three years later. Meantime, in 1878-79 Baron Nordenskiöld had completed the Northeast Passage from Sweden to the Pacific through the Bering Sea and Bering Strait.

Efforts of equal or greater daring and hardship were the polar expeditions. Let us mention, at least, those made in search of the North Pole: by the Scoresbys, father and son, in, respectively, 1806 and 1820; by Parry, 1819-25; by the British Markham and the American Greeley fifty years later; by Fridtjof Nansen with "the drift of the 'Fram'" in 1893-96; and, finally, by Peary in voyages between 1886 and 1909. Peary actually reached the North Pole on April 6, 1909.

Close approaches to the South Pole came much later; yet long ago a valuable foundation of knowledge of that part of the earth's surface had been laid with the penetration of the Antarctic region and circumnavigation of the South Sea by "that truly scientific navigator," Captain James Cook, in 1773, through the explorations of Bellinghausen and Wedell in the first quarter of the nineteenth century, and of Sir James Ross about 1840, by the United States Exploring Expedition (Wilkes Expedition, 1838-42), and by the cruise of the "Challenger" in 1874. About the "Challenger" more will be said later. Of course, the South Pole is on land.

We have also the great voyages and treks of Scott, from 1902, of Shackleton in and after 1909, and of Roald Amundsen, who attained the South Pole on December 14, 1911. Four days more than a month after Amundsen had completed the primary quest, Captain Scott and four of his party, approaching from another direction, reached the same position to find the markers and notes of Amundsen. The record of the heroic, but uncompleted return journey of Scott and his companions and the subsequent discovery of their frozen bodies and their well-kept records is already a classic of history. Truly the expeditions of those who sought the "passages" or the poles, with the greatest possible display of endurance, exertion, courage, and faith, whether they returned alive or perished in the effort, rank second to none in the almost superhuman achievements of man in efforts to complete our knowledge of the globe on which we live.

For the early mariners and explorers we have mentioned, the sea served only as a highway. We are now concerned more with those voyagers whose curiosity led them to look on the sea as in itself an object of biological and physical study. Of such were many of the Arctic and Antarctic explorers. To Scoresby, Wilkes, Nansen, Amundsen, Peary, and Shackleton, we owe much scientific knowledge. Captain Ross employed the dredge to obtain bottom-dwelling animals in the Antarctic. Particularly notable, and the subject of later reference, will be some of the studies of Nansen. Quite recently we have had the extensive explorations in the Antarctic by Captain Richard Byrd and his expedition, with its great collection of scientific data and of materials for intensive studies by others. Not all the grist that is brought to the mill of oceanography is ground in a single day: the published or tabulated data and the specimens taken may be the subject of thoughtful and meticulous consideration by various specialists during a considerable period of time.

CHAPTER 2

Beginnings of Oceanography

T HE TITLE "FOUNDER OF OCEANOGRAPHY" IS SOMETIMES GIVEN to Edward Forbes (1815-54), sometimes to our own Maury (1806-73), and sometimes to others. There is no one founder, but many. We have already said that oceanography is not a science in itself but rather a system of application of all the sciences in a comprehensive and interrelated study of the seas in all their aspects and relationships.

For the beginnings of comprehensive knowledge of conditions within the sea we should perhaps go back to some who are not thought of as oceanographers in any special sense. William Scoresby, to whom reference has previously been made as an early seeker of the North Pole, made soundings and also dipped "colored" waters in the Greenland Sea to find many diatoms, which seemed to have something to do with the movements of whales. A quarter of a century later, Ehrenberg found skeletons of diatoms and radiolarian protozoa, both in the surface water and on the bottom. He concluded with Alexander von Humboldt that the whole sea was filled with microscopic life. Neither Scoresby nor Ehrenberg knew what diatoms were, nor did anyone, until the English botanist Hooker in 1847 recognized diatoms from Antarctic waters as microscopic plants, which he believed to play somewhat the same role in nutrition of animals in the sea as did the green plants on land for terrestrial animals.

Hooker is said to have been the first to recognize the significance of diatoms in the formation of bottom deposits beneath the polar sea. The Danish naturalist Örstedt found great quantities of a blue-green microscopic plant (Trichodesmium) giving color to the waters of warmer regions and playing in the open water community there a part like to that of the diatoms in colder waters. It is to *Tri-chodesmium erythraeum*, actually red, that the color of the Red Sea is attributed. Lohmann (1912) gives to Ehrenberg, Hooker, and Örstedt credit for two fundamental concepts of biological and geological oceanography: the significance of microscopic plants in the organic community in the sea, and the notable part played by minute plants and radiolarian animals in the formation of bottom deposits.

The observations and reasoning of Charles Darwin on the voyage of the "Beagle" (1831-36) deserve passing mention especially for his study of the origin of coral islands and reefs.

Strangely enough, early naturalists were generally slow to employ nets or other mechanical straining devices for exploration of the freely drifting organic communities of the sea. Some merely dipped water to see what was afloat or adrift. Credit has commonly been given to the great German physiologist and teacher, Johannes Müller, for discovering the possibilities in intensive collecting of the drifting organisms, first by pouring dipped sea water through a net of fine gauze and then by towing such a net from a moving boat. Actually, Müller had been anticipated in this technique by Charles Darwin, Vaughan Thompson, and, doubtless, several others.[1] Müller did, however, succeed in imparting to other naturalists generally his great enthusiasm for the net, which soon revealed virtually a whole new world of life. The inauguration of the townet as an instrument for hydrobiology might almost be compared in significance with the invention of the wheel or of the sail as implements for transportation. Yet for a long time the townet remained chiefly a means for the discovery of new species or of new stages in the life histories of animals having pelagic eggs or larvae. We shall return later to a consideration of the broader use of the net in expeditions of the British "Challenger," the German "National" and "Valdivia," the American "Albatross," and others.

1. Dr. Robert Gurney of Oxford, England, has kindly given me some early references to the use of townets of bunting or muslin.

CHAPTER 3

Pioneers in Oceanography

Edward Forbes, 1815-1854

THE NAMES MENTIONED SO FAR ARE THOSE OF MEN WHO HAVE made observations, discoveries, or inventions forming an important part of the foundation of modern oceanographic research. They were naturalists, but not oceanographers in the sense of being among the pioneers who engaged in comprehensive studies of the sea as a whole, or of some substantial part of it, with the purpose of integrating oceanic observations and attempting generalizations respecting the oceans. Perhaps the real pioneer of oceanography was the short-lived Manx naturalist, Edward Forbes. Of mixed descent, Scotch, English, and Manx, he had as a child remarkable precocity and as an adult exceptionally comprehensive knowledge, true originality, and notable capacity for achievement. He is reported to have written at the age of twelve a manuscript "Manual of British Natural History in All Its Departments." Later, as a medical student in Edinburgh, he was rated an extreme idler and he failed to report for his examination. He may have been an idler as a medical student, but he could never have been inactive as a naturalist. He went his own way and that proved to be a uniquely valuable one. He was later to be professor of botany in King's College, curator for the Geological Society, and paleontologist of the Geological Survey, all at one time. Still later he was to be appointed to the distinguished Chair of Natural History in the University of Edinburgh (where he had declined to take his examinations!).

He occupied that chair only a few months before his untimely death.[1]

Forbes exerted a profound influence in the fields of botany, geology, zoology, paleontology, and oceanography. He seems to have been a stimulating teacher, a jovial and witty companion, and a genuine thinker. He was a pioneer in the systematic use of the scientific dredge in shallow water, and in the study of zones of organic life in the sea and on land. The dredge as an instrument of scientific collection was not original with him; it had been invented, or modified from the fishermen's oyster dredges, by Italian investigators about 1750, and modified again by the Dane, O. F. Müller, about 1799. Forbes used the dredge freely in waters adjacent to the British Isles and also in the Aegean Sea where he collected from a depth of 200 fathoms, or about one quarter of a mile. As a result of the work in the Aegean, he defined eight zones of depth, characterized by distinctive communities of animals. "About 1850 Forbes prepared his remarkable map of distribution of marine life over the oceans of the world, and of homoiozoic belts, which was probably the first attempt to divide the oceans into provinces on scientific grounds." [2]

Naturally the early hypotheses about zones were not all supported by later evidence. We now know that Forbes's belief in a lifeless deep was quite erroneous. Nevertheless, as Herdman has remarked, his theories "have had a position and an influence in the history of science, have been an inspiration to many both in his own generation and since, and have led up to and guided the very researches which have, in some cases, resulted in more correct views. His theory of the 'azoic zone' in the sea, that no life existed below 300 fathoms, based upon his observations in the Eastern Mediterranean, was justified by the facts known at the time, but required to be modified later on when the deep-sea dredging expeditions, which Forbes's work had stimulated, made known that an abundant living fauna extended down to the greatest depths of the abysses." [3]

Matthew Fontaine Maury, 1806-1873

Oceanography as an organized study is generally and properly dated from an American, Lieutenant Matthew Fontaine Maury,

1. Dr. Joel Hedgpeth includes a most interesting account of Forbes in "A Century at the Seashore," *The Scientific Monthly*, LXI, 1945.
2. Herdman, *op. cit.*, pp. 29-30.
3. *Ibid.*, pp. 30-31.

"Pathfinder of the Sea," who published in 1855 what is frequently called the first textbook on oceanography. He entitled it *The Physical Geography of the Sea*, adopting a characterization by Baron von Humboldt of the system of research that Maury had already inaugurated. As an officer of the U. S. Navy, Maury had voyaged widely, even circumnavigating the globe, and had become "Officer in Charge of Depot of Charts and Instruments," the Depot being precursor to the Naval Hydrographic Office (cf. p. 45 below). It was in this position that he began the accumulation and compilation of data regarding winds and currents, enlisting the aid of mariners of all types of ships and finally those of all nationalities. In appraising the work of Maury, we must keep in mind that up to his time there was little correlated knowledge of wind and weather, tides and currents, such as every sailor needs. Each mariner learned "the hard way." Trade secrets of sailing were sometimes cherished to the disadvantage of all.[4] Much of the story is best told by quotations from Maury's own book.

"By putting down on a chart the tracks of many vessels on the same voyage, but at different times, in different years, and during all seasons, and by projecting along each track the winds and currents daily encountered, it was plain that navigators hereafter, by consulting this chart, would have for their guide the results of the combined experience of all whose tracks were thus pointed out."[5]

"The results of the first chart, however, though meagre and unsatisfactory, were brought to the notice of navigators; their attention was called to the blank spaces, and the importance of more and better observations than the old sea-logs generally contained was urged upon them.

"They were told that if each one would agree to cooperate in a general plan of observations at sea, and would send regularly, at the end of every cruise, an abstract log of their voyage to the National Observatory at Washington, he should, for so doing, be furnished, free of cost, with a copy of the charts and sailing directions that might be founded upon those observations. . . .

"The quick, practical mind of the American ship-master took hold of the proposition at once. . . .

4. Murray mentions a publication of James Rennell in 1832 summarizing the knowledge of North Atlantic currents on the basis of sailors' observations.

5. M. F. Maury, *The Physical Geography of the Sea*, p. vii.

"So in a little while, there were more than a thousand navigators engaged day and night, and in all parts of the ocean, in making and recording observations according to a uniform plan, and in further- ing this attempt to increase our knowledge as to the winds and cur- rents of the sea, and other phenomena that relate to its safe naviga- tion and physical geography."[6]

Maury's work attracted international attention. The President of the British Association, meeting in Liverpool in 1854, attempted a calculation of the annual saving effected by those charts and sailing directions to the commerce of the United States and the estimate ran into millions, because "the sailing directions have shortened the pas- sage to California 30 days, to Australia 20, and to Rio Janeiro 10."

Maury recognized the importance of the scientific study of the sea, and he was, besides, a man of notable energy and enthusiasm with a rare gift of expression to aid his practical persuasive powers. The rhetorical aspect of his book, the text of which opens with the short sentence, "There is a river in the ocean," [7] has been the occa- sion of comment, and perhaps sometimes of disparagement. Al- though it is now the fashion in scientific writings and textbooks to be sparing of rhetoric (and sometimes, it would seem, to be wary of clarity), it can hardly be questioned that Maury's style of expres- sion, combining rhetoric, clarity, and piety, was one of his most ef- fective implements of trade. He readily commanded the general co- operation of shipmasters, who were no addicts of science or letters. One of them wrote him: "For myself, I am free to confess that for many years I commanded a ship, and, although never insensible to the beauties of nature upon the sea or land, I yet feel that, until I took up your work, I had been traversing the ocean blindfolded."[8]

It was at Maury's instance that the government of the United States invited "all the maritime states of Christendom" to a confer- ence intended to promote a uniform system of observations at sea. The representatives of ten nations, including all the leading states

6. *Ibid.*, p. ix.

7. "There is a river in the ocean. In the severest droughts it never fails, and in the mightiest floods it never overflows. Its banks and its bottoms are of cold water, while its current is of warm. The Gulf of Mexico is its fountain, and its mouth is in the Arctic Sea. It is the Gulf Stream. There is in the world no other such ma- jestic flow of waters. Its current is more rapid than the Mississippi or the Amazon, and its volume more than a thousand times greater."—Maury, *op. cit.*, p. 25.

8. *Ibid.*, p. xiii.

with maritime interests, met in Brussels in 1853 and recommended a plan of observation to be followed on board the vessels of all "friendly" nations. Nine other nations subsequently joined in, to enter the circle of oceanographic friendship. "Thus," as Maury comments with some enthusiasm, "the sea has been brought regularly within the domains of philosophical research, and crowded with observers."[9]

Great as was Maury's achievement in enlisting the interest and aid of thousands of observers and in making every ship at sea, and every spot on the ocean passed over by each ship, a locus of oceanic observation with respect to winds, currents, climates, etc., this was not his best contribution to the germinating science of oceanography. His greatest service was in what he did with the vast quantity of assembled data, his work of integration and of deduction. His book is still well worth reading as a whole with the understanding that the facts and conclusions in many cases are not now acceptable in the light of subsequent and more precise observations and of a far better understanding of many oceanic phenomena. A glance at the list of contents gives some indication of the comprehensive scope of his work, as we see chapters upon the Gulf Stream, the atmosphere, currents of the sea, the depths of the ocean, winds, climates, drifts, storms, etc.

From data obtained by the use of a sounding apparatus with detachable weight prepared by Midshipman Brooke, Maury prepared the first bathymetrical map of the North Atlantic ocean, with contour lines shown at the one, two, three, and four thousand fathom lines. The bottom deposits obtained were examined by experts.

Maury's name is frequently associated with the Gulf Stream, first mapped roughly by Benjamin Franklin. Of course, the great movement of water long known as the Gulf Stream, has, in the light of more comprehensive information, come to be known as being much more complex than could have been suspected in Maury's time. As we shall see later, it is now regarded as a system of movements, only part of which is presently designated as the Gulf Stream. But Maury's comprehension of the dynamics of the seas extended far beyond the mapping of particular currents. He showed a profound grasp of the fact that the sea is a single dynamic mechanism, with "a system of oceanic circulation as complete, as perfect and as har-

9. *Ibid.*, p. x.

monious as is that of the atmosphere or the blood." "When, therefore, we take into consideration the fact that, as a general rule, sea water is, with the exceptions above stated, everywhere and always the same, and that it can only be made so by being well shaken together, we find grounds on which to base the conjecture that the ocean has its system of circulation, which is probably as complete and not less wonderful than is the circulation of blood through the human system."[10]

He finds the average water in the Pacific Ocean to have the same analysis as the average water of the Atlantic. It is as if "the two samples had been taken from the same bottle after having been well shaken." "This fact, as to uniformity of components, appears to call for the hypothesis that sea water which today is in one part of the ocean will, in the process of time, be found in another part the most remote. It must, therefore, be carried about by currents; and as these currents have their offices to perform in the terrestrial economy, they probably do not flow by chance, but in obedience to physical laws. . . ." And, again: "Nay, having reached this threshold, and taken a survey of the surrounding ocean, we are ready to assert, with all the confidence of knowledge, that the sea has a system of circulation for its waters."[11]

The first intercontinental cable was laid down on lines suggested by Maury and he was "the first scientist to foresee the possibility of daily weather reports."[12] Maury's work for the Hydrographic Office was interrupted when, at the outbreak of the Civil War in 1861, he went with his state, Virginia, to join the Confederacy, in which he served as commodore in the navy.

The "Challenger" and Sir Wyville Thomson, 1830-1882

It may be seen that, of the two great pioneers we have considered so far, Forbes concerned himself primarily with what we would now call hydrobiology and Maury with the beginnings of physical oceanography. It was only a little before Forbes's death and the publication of Maury's text that the invention of the Müller net (p. 18, above) introduced the possibility of adequate study of the micro-

10. *Ibid.,* p. 180.
11. *Ibid.,* p. 181–82.
12. Naval Hydrographic Office. *Special Notice to Mariners. One Hundredth Anniversary Number, 1830–1930.* Washington, 1930. Pp. 18. This is finely printed and illustrated with reproductions of photographs, colored charts, etc.

scopic life of the sea as a highly important phase of oceanography. The study of the small drifting organisms, which can be assembled by a concentrating mechanism, such as the nets of fine-meshed gauze, not only yields important biological knowledge, but it also contributes to knowledge of the movements of masses of water, of stratification of waters of different origins, and of other physical phenomena.

The first world-wide use of the Müller net, and the most comprehensive exploration of the sea in its biological and physical features that has ever been attempted by one agency, was that of the British "Challenger Deep-Sea Exploring Expedition." Appropriately enough it was from the "Challenger Expedition," as it is commonly called, that the term "oceanography" was born. With the "Challenger" are associated a number of great names, more particularly those of Thomson and Murray, later to be known as Sir Wyville Thomson and Sir John Murray. There is a peculiar linkage between Forbes, Thomson, and Murray. Thomson, like Forbes, studied in the Medical School at Edinburgh; also like Forbes, he left without a degree but later became professor of natural history in the University. In Thomson's case, ill health caused him to leave the University just four years before Forbes returned to it. Doubtless he derived inspiration from Forbes's distinguished work. At least he had a somewhat similar interest and was an early and enthusiastic addict to the use of the dredge in collection of animals from the bottom. Murray, with the greatest name of all in the general field of oceanography, was also a student of medicine in the University of Edinburgh a few years after Forbes's death and, like the other two, preferred to go his own way; he had no interest whatever in obtaining a degree and, according to Herdman, expressed a contempt for all examinations. He early became an associate and assistant to Wyville Thomson and succeeded Thomson, not in the professorship of natural history, but in the office of the Challenger Expedition Commission located in Edinburgh and associated with the University. The directorship of that commission had, by the time of Thomson's death, become a full-time career.

Notwithstanding the lack of a doctorate, Wyville Thomson soon won distinction as a naturalist, and came to occupy successively such positions as lecturer on botany in the University at Aberdeen (1851), professor of natural history in Queen's College, Cork

(1853), professor of geology in Belfast (1854), and, a few years later (1860), professor of zoology and botany in the same college. As with Forbes, Thomson's interest and competence extended over several fields of natural science.

With the aid of an older friend, Dr. W. B. Carpenter, and the Council of the Royal Society, Thomson succeeded in inducing the British admiralty to provide for exploration of eastern Atlantic waters from the Faroes in the north to Gibraltar in the south. The cruises of the "Lightning" in 1868 and the "Porcupine" in 1869 and 1870, although overshadowed by subsequent and more extensive explorations of the sea, were of great significance at the time. They prepared the way for the "Challenger" and they led to the publication of Wyville Thomson's book, *The Depths of the Sea* (1873), which is another claimant to the title of "first textbook in oceanography." Again, through Thomson, Carpenter, and the Royal Society, the British government was led to organize and equip a deep-sea expedition on a unique scale. H.M.S. "Challenger," a spar-deck corvette of a little over 2,000 tons displacement, propelled by sail power and auxiliary engines, sailed in December, 1872, and returned three and one-half years later, in May, 1876, after voyaging 69,000 miles in the Atlantic, Antarctic, and Pacific oceans. Thomson was director of the scientific staff. He had a corps of assistants including young John Murray (1841-1914), who, as was previously mentioned, was to become his successor as director of the Challenger Expedition Commission.

It is difficult now to form a clear conception of what the Challenger Expedition meant to knowledge of the sea in all its aspects and to biological and geological sciences, because it is hard to realize what was unknown before that expedition. The "Challenger," through its observations and records, furnished data for a general map of the ocean basins with their main contour lines. It gave knowledge of the low and constant bottom temperatures over the great areas that exceed 2,000 fathoms in depth, where the temperature of the water stands always at but a little above the freezing point, with some differences characteristic of different oceans.[13] The "Challenger" located the exact position of many islands and

13. Murray mentioned that the ooze dredged from the bottom in the tropics was too cold to be handled comfortably; and he is quoted as telling friends that the officers of the "Challenger" used it to ice their champagne.—Herdman.

rocks. It determined currents at the surface and at various depths. It showed that there was no great azoic area, but rather that animal life existed at the greatest depths. It exploded the idea of an organic jelly, "Bathybius," presumed to cover the bottom as a primitive protoplasmic slime. It defined the chief classes of strictly marine deep-sea sediment, such as globigerina ooze, radiolarian ooze, diatom ooze, and red clay. It obtained innumerable new kinds of animals including a new protozoan radiolarian group, named in its honor the Challengerida, living at great depths but not on the bottom. It gathered materials to show that the fauna of the deep sea is not, generally speaking, a fossil survival but rather the derivative of shallow-water fauna. Its scientific results were published during a period of fifteen years in fifty large quarto volumes; these were edited under the direction of the Challenger Office, headed first by Thomson and later by Murray, but they were written by the leading biologists of the world regardless of nationality. That great series of books, based upon one cruise, will not go on a "five-foot book shelf"; it requires several such shelves!

Sir John Murray, 1841-1914

In a certain sense John Murray, who might be described as a Canadian-born Scotsman, may be designated as the "father of modern oceanography." He came to Scotland early in life to live with a maternal grandfather and complete his education. He began with an interest in electricity and the physical sciences in general but, to a considerable extent, shifted into biology and geology. When he was twenty-seven years old and an ex-medical student without a degree, he managed to qualify as "surgeon" on board a whaler cruising in Arctic waters. It happened that he was working in a laboratory at the University of Edinburgh while Thomson was making up the staff of the Challenger Expedition. At the last moment a vacancy among the assistant naturalists had to be filled and Murray entered upon a career which he was never to leave completely and in which he was to become a leader. Chance plays a great part in the making of careers and in the advancement of knowledge. Murray was most active and productive in his work for the Challenger Expedition and he published important works on deposits, plankton, and coral reefs. In fact he was author or part author of five of the fifty large volumes of Challenger Reports.

It was fortunate for oceanographic science that Murray could stay with the Challenger work long after the actual cruise to follow through with publication of the results, that he lived a long life without loss of interest in his first distinct calling, that he was canny Scotsman enough to acquire considerable financial independence, and, finally, that he was willing to apply his personal financial resources to the advancement of oceanography. His acquirement of financial independence makes a good story in itself and one pertinent to the science of oceanography. Herdman, who enjoyed close association with Murray, tells us how Murray, in the examination of materials from all sorts of sources for comparison with the sediments obtained by the "Challenger," and, on the basis of a sample of rock supplied him by a naval officer, became impressed with the possibilities of mineral wealth in a neglected, uninhabited, and unclaimed island in the Indian Ocean. He induced the British government to annex "Christmas Island," organized a company to work its phosphate deposits, sent out scientific expeditions to study and report, and laid out a model community which was occupied by about 1,500 colonists. He subsequently estimated that the share of the British government in the returns from the mining operations more than equalled the cost of the Challenger Expedition.

Murray's own share enabled him to do much for the promotion of oceanographic research. We may cite a single but significant instance of Murray's financial aid to oceanography. Over in Norway was a comparatively young oceanographer, Dr. Johan Hjort, upon whom was later to fall the mantle of oceanographic leadership. Sir John Murray invited Hjort to visit him and proposed that, if the Norwegian government would furnish a vessel and Dr. Hjort direct the expedition, Sir John would pay the full scientific expenses.[14] This generous offer was promptly accepted by the Norwegian government and by Dr. Hjort. Thus was organized the cruise of the "Michael Sars" in the North Atlantic in 1910. The scientific results of that expedition were published in a series of volumes by the Bergen Museum. One notable result was the general work, entitled *The Depths of the Ocean*, by Murray and Hjort with distinguished collaborators (1912). An authoritative and generally readable book, covering the whole field of oceanography with reports on the latest

14. From personal conversation with Dr. Hjort.

discoveries up to the time of publication, this excellently printed and beautifully illustrated work of over eight hundred pages has long served for the general run of students of the ocean as a sort of Bible of oceanography. A year later Murray published a small book entitled *The Ocean: A General Account of the Science of the Sea,* "undoubtedly the most concise and accurate and, so far as is possible within its small compass, complete account that has yet appeared of all that pertains to the scientific investigation of the sea. It is written in simple language for the general reader, and is probably the best introduction to oceanography that can be recommended to the junior student or the intelligent non-specialist inquirer who desires information merely as a matter of general culture."[15]

A notable instance of the interrelations of the different sciences in the field of oceanography is afforded by the discovery, at first indirect and then direct, of the Wyville Thomson Ridge extending from the northwest extremity of Scotland toward the Faroe Islands. During the cruises of the "Lightning" and the "Porcupine" it was found that, in crossing over this general line, the temperature in the upper layers, something like a quarter of a mile in depth, remained essentially unchanged; nearer the bottom, however, water to the southeast was found to be warmer, by 12 °F. or more, than it was a little northeastward, where it was actually 2 degrees colder than fresh water at the freezing point. The inference was that, while the upper waters of the relatively warm Atlantic moved freely to the northeast, the deeper waters of that ocean were stopped by a barrier that prevented their mixing with the deep Arctic water on the northeast. A subsequent sounding expedition, originated by Thomson and participated in by Murray, revealed the actual existence of such a ridge rising to within 300 fathoms of the surface. Still later, a dredging expedition brought to light a striking difference in the bottom fauna on the two sides of the ridge, with Arctic forms to the north and Atlantic forms to the south.[16] Thus the study of temperature conditions (physical oceanography), zoological exploration (hydrobiology), and deep-sea sounding (hydrography) proved mutually supplementary.

15. Herdman, *op. cit.,* p. 96.
16. Forbes, by the way, had long before suggested that dredgings in this region would throw much light on marine biology.—Murray and Hjort, *The Depths of the Ocean,* p. 7.

We are reminded of how effectively Alfred Russell Wallace, in his study of animal life in the Malay Archipelago, made biology an adjunct to geology. Here are innumerable islands disposed over an area of truly continental dimensions. Many are small; some are only tiny dots of land; others (Borneo, New Guinea, Sumatra) are immense for islands. Hundreds of miles or only a few miles may separate them; but it was not the distance between the islands, nor even the physical features of the several land masses, that primarily determined the nearness or remoteness of relationship between the animals of all kinds which inhabited the islands. Consideration of the animal life alone justified the division of the archipelago into two great sub-archipelagos: the Indo-Malayan to the northwest, related faunally to Asia, and the Austro-Malayan to the southeast, related to Australia. The two groups were presumed to have been far longer separated from each other than had the several islands of either group, regardless of present distances. The line between them would pass through the Macassar Strait; in the southern chain of islands, running in a long line from Java toward New Guinea, it would cut through the tight fifteen-mile passage between Bali and Lombock, just east of Java. Here there should be the deepest water; subsequent soundings are understood to have shown that Wallace's surmise, for which he had no adequate direct knowledge regarding depths, was not too wide of the mark although not precisely correct.

Palumbo and the Closing Net

We have seen that Forbes's idea of a lifeless or azoic area of sea bottom below 300 fathoms was shown, particularly by the Challenger Expedition, to be quite erroneous; but a new concept of an azoic region developed, that of a great zone of open water beginning at a level about 200 fathoms beneath the surface and ending a short distance above the bottom. It was true that freely drifting organisms had been brought up in nets hauled at intermediate and great depths. But it was claimed by champions of the doctrine of a watery desert that this proved nothing: the organisms in the net were not necessarily brought from the deep; they could have been captured as the net was hauled up through the upper inhabited strata. Alexander Agassiz in this country was a leading advocate of the idea of an azoic zone, believing that his own observations tended to establish

Pl. 1. Woods Hole Oceanographic Institution, showing two main laboratory buildings, long shed for machine shop, and the following research vessels (from left): ARIES, ATLANTIC, BEAR (against dock), and CRAWFORD. Dock at right is for seaplane landing; a hangar will be built there for the helicopter.

Above, Pl. 2. Aerial view of The University of California's Scripps Institution of Oceanography. The large building at the lower left is a laboratory-and-office building. Attached to it by an arcade is the wedge-shaped, 250-seat auditorium. The largest building at the rear is Ritter Hall, completed in 1931, and its two wings, one occupied in 1955, the other in 1960. Ritter Hall encloses the Library building on three sides. Near the head of the pier is the Thomas Wayland Vaughn Aquarium-Museum. *Below,* Pl. 3. The research vessel ARGO, 213-foot, 2,000 ton former Navy auxiliary rescue and salvage vessel, part of the oceanographic research fleet of The University of California's Scripps Institution of Oceanography. She carries a crew of 31, and a scientific crew of 24.(The University of California, La Jolla)

Pl. 4. Aerial view of U.S. Fish and Wildlife Service Biological Station, Beaufort, N.C. (foreground), and of Pier and Buildings of Duke University Biological Station (mid-background).

Pl. 5. ATLANTIS under sail.

the absence of life in the deeper off-shore waters, above the bottom-most layers.[17]

Obviously what was needed was a method of collecting that would insure against the mixing of collections taken at different levels and so would bring to the surface only such animals as were actually taken into the net while it was at the depth being tested. The first solution of the problem on the mechanical side was the devising of what is now known as the "closing net." This was a net that could be lowered in closed condition to any desired depth, opened at will, hauled as long as was desired, and then closed before being raised. An Italian commander, Palumbo, has been credited with the first design of such a net, which was used during the three-year cruise of the "Vettor Pisani" around the world. It was first employed in 1884 in the Pacific Ocean, where one of the early hauls was made between the Galapagos and the Hawaiian Islands at a depth of 4,000 meters (nearly two and one-half miles.) The Palumbo net was much improved by the engineer Eugen von Peterson and Professor Carl Chun of Breslau, and later by Victor Hensen and by Fridtjof Nansen, the polar explorer.

There are now various types of "closing net." Opening and subsequent closing are accomplished by sending metal "messengers" down the line by which the net is hauled. The impact of the messenger trips a catch which causes the net to open, or another to cause the net to close. Closing may be effected by a weighted cord which "purses" or constricts the net, or by a canvas cone which falls across the mouth of the net, or in other ways.

The closing net has settled for all time the question of the occurrence of microscopic drifting life (plankton) at all depths: there is no azoic zone on or above the bottom. This is not to say, however, that there may not be regions where, because of paucity of materials for subsistence, life is extremely scanty; there may be areas of bottom sparsely inhabited and there are open waters remote from the chief sources of food materials and virtually desert—areas where the water is bluest, for reasons that will be mentioned later in connection with the subject of light and color.

17. Agassiz's observations in the Pacific, and especially his work with the Tanner self-closing net, "led him to believe that pelagic life did not extend to a depth below 200 fathoms, and that the abyssal forms did not rise far above the bottom, thus leaving a relatively lifeless zone between."—Charles A. Kofoid, "Contributions of Alexander Agassiz to Marine Biology," *Internationale Revue der gesamten Hydrobiologie und Hydrographie,* IV. (1911), 42.

Victor Hensen, Carl Chun, and the Prince of Monaco

For the progress of biological oceanography, much credit should be given to Victor Hensen and Hans Lohmann, of Kiel, Germany. Hensen proposed the collective term "plankton" for the small drifting organisms, the basic life of the open sea. It is to him that we owe distinct improvements in the Müller net and the introduction of quantitative methods in the collection and study of plankton. What is more important, we are indebted to Hensen for the concept of systematic study of the plankton as a subject in itself and as necessary for a general understanding of the biological productivity of the sea. Perhaps Hensen exaggerated the simplicity of quantitative studies, the uniformity of populations of plankton, and the possibilities of quantitative appraisals of productivity. Nevertheless, his studies, his methods, and his ideas have had a profound and beneficent influence in the field of hydrobiology. The critics of his ideas, among whom the great Ernst Haeckel was foremost, must in the end rely upon quantitative methods such as were inaugurated by Hensen if they are to prove the limitations (and incidentally the utility) of quantitative appraisals. It was Haeckel, by the way, who popularized the term "plankton" while he added a number of new terms differentiating the several types of relations between aquatic animals and the environmental conditions.

Hensen is also known as the organizer and scientific director of the German North Atlantic cruise of the S.S. "National" in 1889, when collections of plankton by quantitative methods were first extensively made; its published reports are designated as reports of the "Plankton Expedition." Another notable voyage of oceanographic exploration by the same nation was the German deep-sea expedition of the "Valvivia" of 1898-99, directed by Carl Chun, which has yielded a great series of scientific memoirs; investigations were conducted in the Atlantic and Indian oceans and partly in the Antarctic.

A most active participant in oceanographic research, and noteworthy both for his own personal cruises and his unique benefactions, was Albert Honoré Charles (1848-1922), Prince of Monaco, who pursued oceanographic studies in the Mediterranean and the North Atlantic with his yachts "Hirondelle," "Hirondelle II," "Princesse Alice," and "Princesse Alice II." He was founder of the great Oceanographic Museum and laboratory at Monaco and the Oceanographic Institute in Paris, both of which institutions, with several professorships in oceanography, were subsequently presented to the French nation.

Of the thousands of tourists who have visited the great aquarium and museum on the rocks overlooking the Mediterranean at Monaco, probably few have had any thought that the royal founder was himself personally distinguished in scientific research. Besides publishing in scientific journals, the Prince of Monaco financed several important series of elegantly printed memoirs of oceanographic results issued from his own press: *Resultats des Campagnes Scientifiques*, and *Bulletins* and *Annales de l'Institute Oceanographique*. The International Hydrographic Bureau, shared by various nations, including the United States, was established at Monaco in 1919.

Among the important oceanographic researches of the Prince of Monaco, perhaps the following are most notable: his extensive investigations of the food of whales, in which he discovered parts of hitherto unknown animals, such as the gigantic squid, a *part* of the arm of which measured 27 feet in length; his discovery of the great outflow of deep Mediterranean water into the Atlantic and of a partially enclosed basin of relatively warm water, the "Monaco Deep," on the floor of the Atlantic in the general vicinity of the Azores; his studies, by the use of drift bottles, of surface currents in the North Atlantic, making him at the time of his death in 1922, undoubtedly the leading authority on circulation of the Atlantic water.[18]

"By his researches the Prince of Monaco has won for himself a place in the foremost rank of men of science, and by enshrining the results in the monumental buildings at Monaco and Paris he has invested his labours with permanent value for all time."[19]

Hans Lohmann and the Centrifuge

The plankton nets of Müller, Hensen, and Palumbo led to the discovery of virtually a new world in biology while making possible the exploration of the greatest in extent of all animal and plant habitats, the open waters of seas and lakes. Nevertheless, the net still

18. Herdman, *op. cit.*, p. 126.
19. *Ibid.*, p. 132.

left undiscovered, or, at least, inadequately explored, a yet greater world of life: the minute organisms, chiefly those classifiable as plants, which will pass through the meshes of the finest devisable net. It was Hans Lohmann who first made extensive use of the centrifuge for separating out the finest forms of microscopic life; for these, in 1911, he introduced the term *nannoplankton*, meaning dwarf plankton. With the old-time laboratory centrifuges, only a few cubic centimeters of water could be tested at one time. Working on lakes in America, Birge and Juday of Wisconsin greatly improved the efficiency of this method by introducing the use of a continuously operating centrifuge, designed in their laboratories by H. M. Foerst, and basically like a cream separator. The organisms thrown out for study are mainly the most minute animals and plants (protozoa, algae, and bacteria). It is enough to say now that the nannoplankton, or "centrifuge plankton," greatly exceeds in volume the "net plankton." These groups are discussed below (p. 210).

Recent European Oceanographic Expeditions

Comparatively recent cruises, exclusive of American, are those of the Norwegian "Michael Sars" (1910) directed by Murray and Hjort; the German "Deutschland" (1911-12) partly in the Atlantic and Antarctic; the Norwegian "Armauer Hansen" of Helland-Hansen (from 1913); the Danish "Dana" (1921-22) in all oceans and, again, in circumnavigation of the globe (1928-29); the British "Discovery" and "Discovery II" (1925-39) in Atlantic, Indian, and Antarctic; the German "Meteor" (1925-39); the British "William Scoresby" (1926-31) in the Antarctic and South Pacific; the Dutch "Willebrord Snellius" (1929-30) in the Indian Ocean and East Indian Archipelago; and the British "Mabahis," better known as the "John Murray Expedition" (1933-34) in the Indian Ocean.

Merely as suggestive of the part played in the advancement of oceanography by other European countries than those mentioned, there may be cited the dredgings by Michael Sars and his son, G. O. Sars, off Norway in 1850 and afterward, studies by the Swedish investigators Otto Pettersson and Gustav Ekman in 1890, and such expeditions as the following: the French ships "Travailleur" and "Talisman" in the eastern Atlantic from 1880 to 1883; the Italian ship "Washington" working in the Mediterranean, and the "Vettor

Pisani" in its round-the-world cruise of 1881-85, when the closing plankton net was first used; the Russian "Vitiaz" cruising around the world in 1886-89; the investigations of the Austrian steamer "Pola" in the Mediterranean and Red seas, 1890-98; the celebrated drift of the Norwegian "Fram" with the ice in the North Polar Sea, under the direction of Nansen, 1893-96; the Danish "Ingolf" in the northern part of the North Atlantic, 1895-96; the Belgian Antarctic Expedition of the "Belgic," the first vessel to winter in the Antarctic region, 1887-88; the Dutch "Siboga" Expedition of 1899-1900 in the Dutch East Indies under the leadership of Max Weber.

The Hydrographic Department of the Imperial Japanese Navy, established in 1871, has been active in oceanographic research and, especially since 1926, has employed several vessels in exploration of the western Pacific. The Imperial Marine Observatory at Kobe (1919) and the Institute of Physical Oceanography (1921) at Kyoto have engaged in oceanographic research.

China has had a Department of Oceanography in the Tsingtao Observatory since 1936. Russia, as would be expected, has given special attention to hydrobiologic and hydrographic surveys of the Caspian, Black, and Azov seas and Arctic waters. Particularly to be cited in this place are the All-Union Scientific Research Institution of Marine Fisheries and Oceanography (1933) and the Polar Scientific Research Institute of Marine Fisheries and Oceanography, which began in 1930 as the Murman Branch of the State Oceanographic Institution.

Ships that have engaged in oceanographic exploration and institutions of research on the ocean are listed extensively in the monograph by Thomas Wayland Vaughan and others, *International Aspects of Oceanography*, published by the National Academy of Science, Washington, D. C., 1937.

Shore Stations Across the Atlantic

Little has been said of important European and British stations on land, other than brief reference to the Oceanographic Museum at Monaco (where also is located the International Hydrographic Bureau), the Oceanographic Institute in Paris, and a few others. Since the founding in 1872 of Dohrn's laboratory at Naples and the establishment of Agassiz's highly significant but short-lived summer station at Penekese in Massachusetts, laboratories by the sea have developed all around the world and have played a principal part in the advancement of biological science. In direct or indirect ways, many of these have contributed greatly to the development of oceanography. Marine biological stations have been described as seaside workshops in which are brought together the well-equipped laboratory, competent specialists of diverse interests and qualifications, and the marine organisms in their native homes. Such a station may have a small permanent staff of investigators, but usually the greater part of the research is done by specialists from various universities who come for a few months during the year.

Perhaps most notable of all is the Stazioni Zoologica di Napoli of which the great Anton Dohrn was "founder, benefactor, director and center of activities." At Naples, as at Monte Carlo, one aspect of the great scientific station is familiar to many tourists who visit the popular aquarium associated with the laboratories. The first building was completed in 1874, at a cost of 400,000 francs, three-fourths of which was contributed by the founder himself. Afterwards, the institution was greatly enlarged as it received support from many countries: until the beginning of the Second World War, several institutions in America made annual contributions. A continuing income from fees paid by visitors admitted to the aquarium has aided substantially in maintenance of the station.

Indebted to the station are not only the specialists from all countries who have made use of the excellent facilities it affords, but also all students of marine animals and plants, who find in libraries the several series of scientific contributions and memoirs issued by the station. Oceanographers anywhere value highly the thirty-nine large, elegantly printed, and finely illustrated *Fauna e Flora del Golfo di Napoli*. It is most fortunate that the "Naples Station," as it is so widely known, passed through the bombardment of Naples with little damage. This great laboratory has continued to be most active under the successive leaderships of a son and a grandson of the original founder, Drs. Richard and Peter Dohrn, respectively.

One of the most active and significant of all marine stations is the laboratory of the Marine Biological Association of the United Kingdom at Plymouth, England, begun in 1879 under the sponsorship of T. H. Huxley and E. Ray Lankester. Supported by the Association, the British government, private donations, entrance fees to the aquarium, and the sales of specimens, it has been concerned chiefly with hydrography, the chemistry of sea water, and plankton. In various places in this volume we draw upon the distinguished work of Harvey, Russell, Atkins, and others associated with the Plymouth station.

Great Britain has many other useful marine stations and agencies for study of the seas. We can mention briefly only a few. The station of the Liverpool Biological Committee at Port Erin on the Isle of Man in the Irish Sea, founded in 1885 by Sir William Herdman, is devoted particularly to fisheries research. The marine laboratory of the Fishery Board for Scotland at Aberdeen was established in 1882 and pursues fishery and oceanography research in the northern area. On the Firth of Clyde is the Marine Biological Station at Millport which was established in 1885 by Sir John Murray, to whom oceanography owes so much in so many ways. The government-operated Fisheries Laboratory at Lowestoft, Suffolk, founded in 1920, engages in the investigation of fisheries problems, both national and international. The Department of Zoology and Oceanography at University College, Hull, with oceanographic laboratories, opened in 1931, has been active in studies of the North Sea area. Last to be mentioned for Great Britain, but first in origin and in world-wide importance, is the Hydrographic Department of the Admiralty, established in 1795, and maintaining, just before the war, eight or nine surveying vessels. For a century and a half it has engaged in hydrographic surveys, the preparation of charts, sailing directions, and tide tables, and in many other services to mariners and to science.

As might be expected, Germany long had prominence in studies of the basic problems of oceanography. The great Naples Station (1872) was born in great part from German initiative and support. "The venerable Institution at Kiel (1871) has always been a leader in marine exploration as related to the fundamental problems of marine biology and the fisheries."[20] This station and the Royal Prussian Biological Station on Helgoland in 1892 worked in cooperation with each other and with the German Fisheries Society and the International Commission for the Investigation of the Seas

20. Charles Atwood Kofoid, *The Biological Stations of Europe*, United States Bureau of Education, Bulletin, 1910, No. 4. Whole number, 1940. The institution referred to is the University of Kiel, with several laboratories and commissions associated with it for the study of the seas.

(1902). The laboratories at Kiel were the land base of the "Plankton Expedition," whose importance we have already mentioned (p. 32, above). From the laboratory came the quantitative methods of Hensen and Lohmann's conception of the minute drifting life to be taken by the use of centrifuges. No mention of agencies for marine investigations would be complete without reference to the Institut und Museum für Meereskunde at Berlin, which was established in 1900, and which, before the war, pursued studies in oceanography and economic geography in the widest sense. References will occur on other pages to the work of Defant and Wüst, of the staff of the Institut.

France pioneered with seaside stations. Let us cite those at Concarneau (established in 1859), Arcachon (1863), Roscoff (1871), Wimereau (1874), and the laboratory Arago at Banyuls sur Mer (1881). Banyuls, attached to the University of Paris, engages in marine biological studies and is a seat for oceanography conferences.

Russia was forehanded with a station at Sebastopol (1871), and Italy with one at Catania (1870). Dohrn's temporary laboratory at Messina (1867) was a forerunner of the great internationally supported station at Naples (1874).

The smaller countries of northern Europe have had great roles in the theatre of oceanographic operations, as might be expected in view of the importance to them of fisheries and navigation. Hardly any country has ranked above Norway, with its University Biological Station at Drøbak near Oslo, and the Geophysical Institute at Bergen. The former is associated with the University of Oslo and has been the base of operations for such leaders as Hjort and Gran, whom we mention and quote several times on other pages. The Geophysics Institute has operated the research vessel "Armauer Hansen," previously mentioned; with it are associated the names of such top specialists as B. Helland-Hansen in oceanography, J. A. Bjerknes in meteorology, and H. Mosby in physics.

In Sweden, we have among other agencies the Hydrographic Biological Commission, organized about fifty years ago by Otto Pettersson, Gustav Ekman, and others. Associated with it is the Börno Research Station, recently directed by Professor Hans Pettersson.

The Danish Committee for Fisheries Investigations and the Study of the Sea, with its laboratories in the old castle on Charlottenlund Slot, near Copenhagen, deserves special mention if only because in other pages of this volume mention must be made of contributions to oceanographic science by the first chairman, Dr. C. G. J. Johannes Petersen, and by Dr. Johannes Schmidt, who found the oceanic spawning area of the fresh-water eels (cf. p. 263).

The same castle near Copenhagen is the home of the Permanent International Council for the Exploration of the Sea (Conseil Permanent International pour l'Exploration de la Mer.), an organization established in 1899 and participated in by twelve European countries and Great Britain and Iceland. With the Conseil have been associated most of the leading oceanographers of Europe. Its work is done through special committees, individuals, and cooperative commissions in the several countries. Its publications, in half a dozen series, comprise many more than a hundred volumes.

We could not begin to do justice to all such institutions. Dr. Vaughan's volume entitled *International Aspects of Oceanography* and published in 1937 listed for the world 247 institutions engaged in oceanographic work.

CHAPTER 4

Oceanography in America

Early American Oceanographic Research other than that of Maury

SO FAR WE HAVE CONCERNED OURSELVES CHIEFLY WITH OCEANO-
graphic developments on the eastern side of the Atlantic.
On the western side, the United States has not been inactive.
We have already alluded to the first map of the Gulf Stream published by Benjamin Franklin in 1770, and we have considered the
pioneering work of Maury. As early as 1839 to 1842 the U. S.
Exploring Expedition under Captain Wilkes, with J. D. Dana as
naturalist, made deep-sea soundings and some dredgings. More
systematic research was undertaken by the U. S. Coast and Geodetic
Survey, beginning in 1844 when Director Bache arranged for the
taking of bottom samples in connection with soundings and for
competent study of the materials obtained. Soundings were also
made by the "Dolphin" and the "Arctic" in the North Atlantic
from 1851 to 1856; bottom samples were taken and studied.

Marine biology, particularly in America, owes much to the great
Swiss naturalist Louis Agassiz, who spent the latter and most productive part of his life in the United States as a professor at Harvard.
Agassiz more than anyone else stimulated interest in marine biology.
He was not primarily an oceanographer but he took part in a cruise
arranged by the U. S. Coast and Geodetic Survey in 1867, along
with Louis François de Pourtales, who was another Swiss naturalist
adopted by America. Louis Agassiz concluded that the continental
area and the deep oceanic areas had undergone little change in position since the earliest times.

Other oceanographic data was gained by the U. S. S. "Tuscarora" (about 1875) under the direction of Rear Admiral G. E. Belknap in the Pacific where piano wire was first used for sounding line instead of the bulkier and heavier rope or cable. The U. S. S. "Gettysburg" made deep-sea soundings in the North Atlantic in 1876. The U. S. Coast Survey steamer "Blake" explored the Caribbean and the Gulf of Mexico from 1877 to 1880, making the Caribbean "one of the best mapped parts of the deep sea." The name of Lieutenant Commander C. D. Sigsbee, commanding officer of the "Blake," is associated with several kinds of oceanographic apparatus —the Sigsbee trawl, Sigsbee sounding machine, water bottle, etc. It was the younger Agassiz, Alexander, son of Louis, who gave scientific direction to the work of the "Blake" and also to that of the U. S. Fish Commission steamer "Albatross," cruising along the Atlantic coast of the United States, and a few years later exploring the Pacific waters in the region of Panama. Agassiz directed a later cruise of the "Albatross" in 1889-1900 in the tropical Pacific. The results were published by the Museum of Comparative Zoology in a notable series of volumes.

In 1885-86 the U. S. S. "Enterprise" cruised in all the great oceans, making important collections of bottom samples. The U. S. S. "Nero," surveying a cable route between the Hawaiian and Philippine Islands in 1899, made the deepest soundings up to that time, 5,269 fathoms, in the vicinity of Guam.

Alexander Agassiz, 1835-1910

Alexander Agassiz has undoubtedly been overshadowed in reputation by his great father; but the younger Agassiz was great in his own name and rendered notable services in the fields of zoology, geology, mining development, and particularly, in oceanography. Lacking the buoyant spirit of his father, he was quiet and reserved but exceptionally able. A capacity for organization, determination, and clear judgment were qualities that he possessed in high degree. As mining engineer and businessman he developed, against great obstacles, the remarkable Calumet and Hecla copper mines and he remained head of the operating system. He attained considerable wealth, a substantial part of which he devoted to the advancement of the Museum of Comparative Zoology at Harvard and to the promotion of oceanographic research. He was, however, much more than a promoter of industry and science: while successful in constructive business operations, he was an active and productive zoologist and oceanographer. His personal achievements in the field of oceanography were not of the kind that is easily pictured to the general public; but oceanographers of the highest rank appreciated his unique service. Perhaps, then, Alexander Agassiz's significance may best be characterized by quotations from Kofoid, Herdman, and Murray.

"He was the first to use steel cables for deep-sea dredging, on the 'Blake' in 1877. This and all his subsequent expeditions on the 'Albatross' and other vessels were noted for the foresight with which they were planned with reference to all possible contingencies at sea, the perfection with which the plan was carried out, and the success with which the results were secured."[1]

As the greatest explorer of the sea, says Kofoid, his explorations in the Caribbean and in the Indian Ocean, and especially in the tropical Pacific, carried him over 100,000 miles. "It is safe to say that his expeditions mapped more lines across deep sea basins and made more deep-sea soundings than all other scientific expeditions combined."[2]

"Agassiz's knowledge and experience as a mining engineer were of the greatest value on board the 'Blake' in devising improvements in the apparatus for deep-sea work. He substituted steel-wire rope for dredging in place of hemp, and invented mechanical contrivances for equalizing the strain and facilitating the hoisting-in of the apparatus. He and Captain Sigsbee together devised a new form of double-edged dredge, generally known as the 'Agassiz' or the 'Blake' dredge or trawl, which will work equally well whichever way it falls on the bottom; and also a very ingenious closing tow-net (called the 'gravitating trap'), which could be lowered to any depth, opened and towed, and then closed again, so that it was possible to strain the plankton or minute organisms from a column of water of any given length at a particular depth."[3]

His explorations were made chiefly on the U. S. Coast Survey steamer "Blake" (1877-80) and on the U. S. Fish Commission

1. Kofoid, "Contributions of Alexander Agassiz to Marine Biology," *Internationale Rev. der geo. Hydrobiologie u. Hydrographie*, IV (1911), 40.

2. *Ibid.*, p. 41.

3. Herdman, *Founders of Oceanography*, pp. 107-8.

steamer "Albatross" in the South Seas (1899-1900), in the eastern Pacific (1891), and in the eastern tropical Pacific (1904-1905); but he often used smaller vessels.

The appraisal of Alexander Agassiz by Sir John Murray carries particular weight:

"If we can say that we now know the physical and biological conditions of the great ocean basins in their broad general outlines—and I believe we can do so—the present state of our knowledge is due to the combined work and observations of a great many men belonging to many nationalities, but most probably more to the work and inspiration of Alexander Agassiz than to any other single man."[4]

The "Albatross," 1882-1924, and "The Fish Commission"

We have had more than one occasion to mention the "Albatross," which, it should be noted, was the first large vessel ever designed particularly for oceanographic research; until her last years, at least, she was employed exclusively in such work. She was a twin-screw steamer of a little over 1,000 tons displacement, 200 feet long at the twelve-foot water line and rigged with sail as a brigantine. Like many other notable developments in the fields of fisheries, marine biology, and oceanography, the "Albatross" owed her origin to the vision and constructive imagination of Spencer F. Baird, who could properly be called "founder" of the United States Commission of Fish and Fisheries, and who was its first commissioner (without pay), 1871-87. In the early eighties Commissioner Baird called upon Z. L. Tanner, commanding officer of the Fish Commission vessel "Fish Hawk," to outline general plans and estimates for the construction and equipping of "a thoroughly sea-worthy steamer capable of making extensive cruises and working with dredge and trawls in all depths to 3,000 fathoms." From Tanner's sketches the final designs were made by Charles W. Copeland, marine architect and engineer. Tanner superintended construction, became its first commanding officer, and served in such capacity for nearly twelve years.

Commissioned on November 11, 1882, the "Albatross" was manned and officered by the United States Navy while its scientific work was guided by the Fish Commission under such distinguished directors as Alexander Agassiz and Charles S. Townsend. Tanner's

4. Murray, quoted by Herdman, *op. cit.*, p. 111.

"Report on the Construction and Outfit of the United States Steamer 'Albatross' " (1883) and his "Deep-sea Exploration: a General Description of the Steamer 'Albatross,' her Appliances and Methods," with many illustrations as figures and plates, are highly valuable for their details of description of the plan of the vessel and of her technical apparatus. Tanner has also left his name significantly in oceanographic literature by the invention of apparatus for oceanographic research, such as the Tanner beam trawl, intermediate tow net, sounding machine, etc.

The "Albatross" has a distinguished record of achievement giving ample testimony to the care and planning which went into her construction and which prompted Agassiz to write: "While of course I knew in a general way the great facilities the ship afforded, I did not fully realize the capacity of the equipment until I came to make use of it myself."[5] It is interesting to note that in one haul of the dredge, from 1,760 fathoms, the "Albatross" brought up more specimens of deep-sea fishes than were collected by the famed "Challenger" throughout her service. Late in the second decade of this century, the vessel became inactive, and in 1924 it was sold and converted to other uses.

Townsend, in an epitaph for the "Albatross,"[6] has well appraised her service to oceanographic science:

"The 'Challenger' was a pioneer ship in oceanographic work and must remain the leader in the literature of the science. The 'Albatross' entered the field much later, but, thanks to her more modern equipment and longer service, her collections were naturally much more extensive and the bulk of her published results was perhaps also greater."

"If ever the American people received the fullest possible value from a government ship, they received it from this one. The benefits to science, the fisheries, and commerce springing from her almost continuous investigations—the results of which have all been published and widely distributed throughout the world—are incalculable."

5. Quoted by C. H. Townsend, "The Passing of the 'Albatross,' " *Natural History*, XXIV (1925).

6. Townsend, *op. cit.* p. 619-20. An excellent history of the "Albatross", with listing of all its voyages has been given by Hedgpeth and Schmitt. Hedgpeth, Joel W. and Waldo L. Schmitt. "The United States Fish Commission Steamer Albatross." *The American Neptune*, 5(1), Salem, Massachusetts, 1945.

In the broad field of biological oceanography the old United States Fish Commission, the Smithsonian Institution (mainly through the United States National Museum), and the Museum of Comparative Zoology at Harvard have undoubtedly played leading parts. The vision of Spencer F. Baird, Assistant Secretary of the Smithsonian and first Commissioner of Fish and Fisheries, put everything connected with the knowledge of the sea and its organization in possible relation to the development of fishery resources. The Commission (and Bureau) acquired high distinction in oceanography, not only through its unique contribution in the design of the "Albatross" for oceanographic explorations and through its use of other smaller vessels, such as the "Grampus" and the "Halcyon," but also through its collaboration with other "sea-going" agencies of the government (the Hydrographic Office, the Coast Survey, the Coast Guard, and the International Ice Patrol), and with the National Museum and the Museum of Comparative Zoology for care and study of materials and publication of results. Among government agencies, it was the Fisheries service and the National Museum that were primarily qualified to deal with the biological aspects of oceanography.

Hydrographic Office, United States Navy, 1830—

No consideration of oceanography in the United States could omit mention of the long and distinguished service of the Hydrographic Office, United States Navy. Although it has borne that name officially only since 1866, the Office appropriately celebrated its one hundredth anniversary in 1930, dating from its establishment in 1830 as the "Depot of Charts and Instruments." An excellent resumé of the history of the Depot and Office was published on the occasion of the anniversary,[7] and I shall draw upon that paper in this brief appraisal.

The Depot has already been mentioned in connection with the pioneer work of Maury. It was established December 6, 1830, on the suggestion of Lieutenant L. M. Goldsborough, who became its first head, to be succeeded after two years by Lieutenant Charles Wilkes, whose name has already been mentioned. It soon began the

7. Naval Hydrographic Office. *Special Notice to Mariners, One Hundredth Anniversary Number, 1830–1930.* This is finely printed and illustrated with reproductions of photographs, colored charts, etc.

publication of lithographic charts, the first ones being based upon surveys off the northeast coast. Then came the United States Exploring Expedition, 1838-42, our first great government scientific expedition, carried on by a small fleet of five vessels, headed by Wilkes on the sloop-of-war "Vincennes." The Act of Congress in 1836, which provided for this expedition, was explicitly prompted by the very "important interests of our commerce, embarked in the whale fisheries and other adventures in the great Southern Ocean." Its explorations covered extensive areas in the Atlantic, Antarctic, and Pacific, touching the regions of the Philippine, Samoan, Fiji, and Hawaiian Islands, China, Japan, Alaska, the Columbia River, etc. The charts that resulted from the surveys "have continued to serve up to the present time as the basis of charts issued by all the maritime nations." Wilkes, by the way, was the first to recognize the Antarctic continent. More than 50,000 specimens were collected during the five-year cruise and there were several published volumes of scientific results.[8] The living land plants collected formed the basis for the National Botanical Garden, 1852.

The Naval Observatory grew out of the Depot in the decade of the 'forties to become a distinct agency in 1866. The historic Perry Expedition to Japan with eleven vessels (1852-54) was primarily diplomatic in purpose, but it engaged also in survey work for the Office, especially in the Gulf of Yedo (Tokyo). There were very limited biological collections, for which a bibliography is given by Meisel.[9]

Lieutenant Maury, the fourth head, assumed charge in 1842, but we have already told how his creative imagination, personal energy and enthusiasm, brought world fame to himself and to the Depot. During his incumbency the North Pacific Exploring Expedition, 1853-59, was organized and conducted with five steam vessels under the command first of Commander Ringgold and then of Lieutenant Rodgers. Extensive surveys by this expedition led to the publication of detailed coasting charts of the entire coast of Japan, the Bering Sea and Straits, a part of the Atlantic Ocean, and other regions. We

8. A full bibliography of the United States Exploring Expedition is given by Max Meisel in *Bibliography of American Natural History. The Pioneer Century, 1769–1865*, II (1926), 650–73. There are listed monographs and papers by Charles Wilkes and such noted biologists and geologists as Louis Agassiz, S. F. Baird, James Dwight Dana, Charles Girard, A. A. Gould, and Asa Gray.

9. *Ibid.*, III (1929), 145–48.

are grateful now for the work of both the Wilkes and the Ringgold-Rodgers expeditions in mapping critical areas of the Pacific so long ago. Rich biological collections were made by the North Pacific Expedition and assigned to distinguished American scientists. Reports upon them might have been forerunners to those of the "Challenger," but nearly all the collections, manuscripts, and drawings were destroyed in the Chicago fire of 1871.[10]

On suggestion of the Hydrographic Office, the patrol of iceberg-ridden regions of the North Atlantic was started by the United States Navy in the month following the loss of the "Titanic" in 1912, and the Office plays a major part in the International Ice Patrol, which was organized cooperatively a couple of years later and for which vessels and personnel have been supplied by the United States Coast Guard. The Office shares in the direction of the International Hydrographic Bureau at Monaco, or did so until interrupted by the war. Under the guidance of the Hydrographic Office, naval vessels have made surveys in virtually all seas and in the Great Lakes, and such explorations by naval vessels, with auxiliary aircraft for air-mapping, in which the Hydrographic Office pioneered, were in progress up to the beginning of World War II. Dynamic oceanographic surveys were then being carried out by vessels of the Hydrographic Office in cooperation with the Woods Hole Oceanographic Institution, the Scripps Institution of Oceanography, and the Oceanographic Laboratories of the University of Washington.

The Office has pioneered in many respects, but notably in improved charting, in better methods of depth-finding, and in "air-mapping." We can use the last term in two senses, referring to the mapping of land and water by photographs from planes and to actual mapping of air masses and air currents. A recent function is the publication of monthly charts of the upper air for the North Atlantic and the North Pacific Ocean.

We have already (p. 23) cited one of the most notable of early improvements in sounding the apparatus devised by Midshipman Brooke. The greatest recent contribution to oceanography was the

10. For neither the Wilkes nor the Ringgold-Rodgers expeditions was the program of publication well handled, according to the best accounts. Otherwise, these expeditions might have been more widely known and given greater stimulus to oceanography. The limited bibliography of the latter expedition is given by Meisel, *op. cit.*, III, 221–28.

development by the United States Navy of *sonic sounding*, the fruit of the researches of a number of persons. Credit is given, however, to the Navy and to Professor H. C. Hayes for developing the first practical instrument for sonic sounding at all depths (see p. 70 below). The early experiments of Dr. Hayes during the First World War were directed not at depth-finding but at locating submarines and other solid objects through the rebound of horizontal sound waves. Somewhat accidentally, it was discovered that, with appropriate adjustments, the method was equally applicable for the determination of depth. By 1929 practically all Naval vessels had been equipped with sonic sounding gear, the Fessenden type having superseded the original Hayes apparatus. It was reported by the Office in 1940[11] that it was receiving annually around 100,000 sonic soundings. In the realm of oceanography, the value of such a contribution to the mapping of the bottom of the seas can hardly be overrated.

United States Coast and Geodetic Survey, 1816—

Much is due to the Coast Survey for knowledge of hydrographic features of coastal waters and for an understanding of tides and currents. On many pages of this volume are references to the steamers "Blake" and "Bache" and to such Coast Survey leaders and specialists as Bache, Sigsbee, Pillsbury, and Marmer. Notwithstanding that, by virtue of its official responsibilities, the work of the Survey has been mostly in coastal waters, its charts, its researches on theory of tides and its prediction of tides have high significance to general oceanography, as well as to navigation, fisheries, and safety of life at sea.

Recent American Oceanographic Research

We have seen that, in the last century and the early decades of the twentieth century, the United States has contributed significantly to the study of the oceans—through Maury and Agassiz, and through the explorations of the Naval Hydrographic Office, the Coast and Geodetic Survey (generally called "Coast Survey"), and the Fish Commission, which later became the Bureau of Fisheries in the Department of Commerce and is now a part of the Fish and Wildlife Service in the Department of the Interior. The Naval

11. Thomas H. Whitecroft, "Sonic Sounding," U. S. Naval Institute *Proceedings* 69(2), No. 480: 216–23. Annapolis, 1943.

Hydrographic Office and the Coast Survey have continued to be somewhat active, but the pursuit of general oceanographic research by agencies of the United States government undoubtedly declined as the "Albatross" went out of commission. It may have been only a coincidence, but diminishing governmental activity in general oceanographic study, particularly in its biological phases, seems to have gone along with the growth of a sentiment for isolationism and a feeling among those who controlled public expenditures that the United States could live independently of the rest of the world.

Doubtless, the most notable explorations of the seas conducted or participated in by our government in the second and third decades of this century were the explorations by the Coast Survey in co-operation with the Bureau of Fisheries employing the Coast Survey steamer "Bache" in West Indian waters in 1914 and after; the intensive investigation of the Gulf of Maine by the Bureau of Fisheries in cooperation with the Museum of Comparative Zoology of Harvard and under the direction of Professor Henry B. Bigelow (from 1912); and the International Ice Patrol in the North Atlantic, guided by the United States Coast Guard.[12]

Even more significant for oceanographic research in America in recent times have been the studies made by institutions financed primarily through private endowments.

Although the Scripps Institution of Oceanography at La Jolla, California, assumed this name just twenty years ago, it has a long and productive career in studies relating to the sea. The beginning was a small seaside station at San Pedro, California, established in the closing years of the past century by Dr. William E. Ritter of the University of California. Professor C. A. Kofoid joined it in 1900. Soon the laboratory was moved to the vicinity of San Diego, where it settled at La Jolla in 1905 and was operated by the Marine Biological Association of San Diego. Drawing support from the Scripps family, its laboratory studies were supplemented by extensive field work. In 1912 it became the Scripps Institution for Biological Research of the University of California, and began to receive aid from the state as well as from private sources.

By 1924 when Dr. Ritter resigned and was succeeded by Dr.

12. The formation of this patrol was prompted by the loss of the British steamer "Titanic" with its loss of more than 1,500 lives after collision with an iceberg, April 14, 1912.

T. Wayland Vaughan, a research geologist, the Institution was well embarked on a broad program with a full-time staff of scientists qualified in diverse fields of oceanographic research. Its investigations, with specialist leaders in each field, embrace the physics of the ocean and marine meteorology, the chemistry of sea water and of marine organisms, marine biology and physiology of marine organisms, and the sea in relation to geology. More recently, on the retirement of Dr. Vaughan in 1936, the Institution secured as its director, Dr. H. U. Sverdrup, who had already in Norway attained international distinction in theoretical meteorology and oceanography.

At all seasons, but particularly in the summer, the productiveness of the station is greatly extended through the use of its unique facilities by many visiting investigators. Although the actual field operations are generally in waters at no great distance from the coast of California, the contributions of the Scripps Institution to science have world-wide significance to oceanography, because of their bearing on basic principles of marine dynamics and biology, fisheries science, and marine meteorology. Perhaps no other agency has contributed more to an understanding of vertical movements of the water off western coasts (cf. p. 140 below), the stratification of Pacific waters, and the influence of such great streams as the California current of the northern Pacific and the Humboldt current of the South Pacific.

The "Carnegie," a non-magnetic vessel of the Carnegie Institution of Washington, cruising the Atlantic and Pacific oceans, has associated physical and biological oceanography with its primary study of terrestrial magnetism, particularly during the last years before her tragic loss by fire at Apia, November 29, 1929.

The Bingham Oceanographic Laboratory was established at the Peabody Museum of Natural History, Yale University, in 1928 by Harry Payne Bingham. Under the direction of Professor Albert E. Parr, the laboratory at first devoted itself chiefly to descriptive marine biology, preparing detailed reports of the invertebrate and vertebrate material in the Bingham Oceanographic Collection which had accumulated from a number of private expeditions preceding 1928. Within a few years its staff was increased and its activities were expanded to include the dynamic aspects of oceanography, with research on physical and chemical as well as biological problems. Cooperative investigations with the former U. S. Bureau of Fisheries and the Woods Hole Oceanographic Institution were also undertaken. The results of this and subsequent work have been published in the *Bulletin* of the Bingham Oceanographic Collection, Volumes I to IX (1927 to the present), and other scientific journals.

In 1942 Professor Parr was succeeded in the directorship by Dr. Daniel Merriman. While continuing much of its previous work, the laboratory in 1943 also undertook a program in which a large share of its energies are directed toward the solution of practical problems relating particularly to the conservation and development of the food resources of the ocean and to the better utilization of waste products of the fisheries and other unused organic resources.

Associated with the Bingham Laboratory is the Sears Foundation, which publishes the *Journal of Marine Research*.

After exhaustive study of needs made by a committee of the National Academy of Sciences, the Woods Hole Oceanographic Institution, at Woods Hole, Mass., was established in 1930.[13] Its first director was Professor Henry B. Bigelow, student of plankton and general oceanographer, who was succeeded by Dr. Columbus Iselin, physical oceanographer, and professor of oceanography at Harvard. Its present director (1954) is Rear Admiral Edward H. Smith, U.S.C.G. (ret.). The Institution encourages and carries on the study of oceanography in all its branches, having a large and modernly equipped laboratory on the water front and several sea-going vessels. The smaller vessels are intended for operations within the borders of the continental shelf and within a few days' run of Woods Hole. The larger vessel, the "Atlantis," a steel ketch, built to order in Copenhagen, was especially designed for oceanographic work. Its cruising radius of 3,000 miles under Diesel-engine power can be indefinitely extended by the use of sail. With two laboratories on the ship, living quarters for crew and scientists, and the most modern apparatus for oceanographic studies, including 30,000 feet of dredging wire and a sonic sounding machine, the "Atlantis" is well-equipped for hydrological, hydrographical, and meteorological observations, for chemical and physical analyses, and for biological

13. Resulting in part from the survey made by this committee were the volumes by Bigelow entitled *Oceanography, Its Scope, Problems and Economic Importance* (1931), and the monograph of Vaughan and others, previously cited (pp. 35, 39), *International Aspects of Oceanography*.

collecting. So far its operations have been chiefly in the North Atlantic.

Although independent in endowment and organization, the Woods Hole Oceanographic Institution maintains, through its trustees and its staff, close association with many educational institutions and government agencies. Originally, it had a small permanent scientific staff, the greater part of its work being carried on through visiting investigators, research associates and fellows, appointed from other research agencies for definite terms of service on the staff of the institution. Now it has a very large staff and more vessels. The results of research are published in various scientific journals and bulletins, but reprints are collected and bound into volumes issued periodically as *Collected Reprints from the Woods Hole Oceanographic Institution.* The Institution also issues a series of *Papers in Physical Oceanography and Meteorology* (with the Massachusetts Institute of Technology). Most recently, a new Laboratory of Oceanography has been founded at Woods Hole, by the United States Office of Naval Research, to be operated in conjunction with the Woods Hole Oceanographic Institution.

The University of Washington Oceanographic Laboratories were organized in 1930 under the directorship of Dr. Thomas G. Thompson, professor of chemistry in the University of Washington.[14] At the present time, Professor Richard H. Fleming, oceanographer, directs the laboratories. The base of operations and study is a large and well equipped four-story laboratory building located on the University campus in Seattle, and facing on the Lake Washington Ship Canal at its entrance to Portage Bay. Especially designed for oceanographic research and built by aid of the Rockefeller Foundation, it was completed in 1932. The field laboratories, where there is most activity in summer, are those of the former Puget Sound Biological Station, known as the Friday Harbor Laboratories, on San Juan Island. The principal vessel for oceanographic explorations is the "Catalyst," seventy feet long and of heavy construction with a cruising range of 3,500 miles. Recently the "Catalyst" is in the service of the United States.

Field operations have been conducted in waters off the coasts of

14. L. D. Phifer, "University of Washington Oceanographic Laboratories," *The Biologist*, XIII (1932) 141-50; Thomas G. Thompson, "Oceanographic Laboratories of the University of Washington," *The Collecting Net*, X (1935) 281, 285-88.

Washington, British Columbia, and Alaska, in the Northeast Pacific, the Gulf of Alaska, and sometimes in the Bering Sea and the Arctic Ocean, with research in the fields of physics, chemistry, biology, and geology. Special studies have been made of the physical and biological effects of upwelling off the continental shelf, where, because of upwelling, the surface waters are colder and much richer in nutrient salts than waters of the same latitude beyond the continental shelf.

Oceanography in Canada

With its extended shores bathed by three of the five great oceans of the world, Atlantic, Arctic, and Pacific, the Dominion of Canada has vital concern with the seas. The greater part of her periphery is deeply dissected by gulfs, bays and straits, semi-enclosed, but saline, and most of her principal ports are approached through tortuous arms of the sea. As is natural in the conditions, much of the Canadian research relating to the ocean has been applied to waters in general proximity to the coasts, principally in the broad lower reaches of the St. Lawrence River and the Gulf of St. Lawrence, in the Bay of Fundy, in Hudson Bay, in waters, both semi-enclosed and open, off the coast of British Columbia, and to a less extent in Arctic waters. Biological stations maintained by the Dominion on both Atlantic and Pacific coasts include the adjacent oceanic waters within the scope of their biological and physical studies. A recently formed Committee on Oceanography, sponsored by the Fisheries Research Board and the National Research Council of Canada has been temporarily checked in activity by conditions of war.

More than a century ago, oceanographic exploration in the Gulf of St. Lawrence was undertaken with studies in the eighteen-thirties by Captain Bayfield and Dr. Kelly; the result appeared in scientific journals, as well as in *Sailing Directions for the Gulf and River St. Lawrence*. The reports of more recent studies are found in *Report of Tides and Currents in Canadian Waters*, published by the Department of Marine and Fisheries, in a series of *Contributions to Canadian Biology*, from the Biological Board of Canada, in the *Journal of the Fisheries Research Board of Canada*, in the *Canadian Arctic Expedition, 1914-18* (the Stefansson Expedition), and elsewhere.

In 1914 the Biological Board of Canada engaged the eminent oceanographer, Dr. Johan Hjort of Norway, to whom references have already been made, for a comprehensive investigation of Atlantic waters off the outer coast of Nova Scotia. The results appeared in 1919 as *Report of the Canadian Fisheries Expedition of 1914-15.* A general study of the same region, resumed in 1932, was necessarily suspended at the outbreak of war. Investigation was being extended over that broad continental shelf, or shoulder of the continent, from which Newfoundland emerges and on which, farther out, the Grand Bank approaches the surface. As is well known, this is an area prolific in food fishes and the locus of important commercial fisheries for several nations. That richness in organic life, so significant to the food supply of the world, is not just accidental. The general area is, indeed, one of the critical regions for the waters of the world. It is where warm subtropical waters flowing northeastward as part of the Gulf Stream system meet cold Arctic waters flowing southward As a region of convergence it is a place where surface waters sink into the deep to be conveyed in leisurely drifts to remote parts of the world. We shall have occasion later (p. 61) to cite this general locality as one of the chief sources of that vast volume of water which passes across the Equator from North to South Atlantic in compensation for the contributions at upper levels from the southern ocean to the Gulf Stream system of the North Atlantic. The phenomenal vertical circulations and mixing that prevail are too complex for analysis here.

The results of investigations for the International Passamaquoddy Fisheries Commission, sponsored by the North American Council on Fisheries Investigations, as published in the *Journal of the Biological Board*, are notable "as a thorough attempt to relate oceanography to fish production."[15] Indeed, no country has been more effective than Canada in showing the applicability of oceanographic research, in both its biological and physical phases, to the economic pursuit of fisheries industries and to the conservation of fishery resources.

Summary of Historical Review

It is to Forbes primarily that we owe the concept of organic communities in the sea and their relations to the environment. Maury conceived of the sea as a great dynamic system of waters in circulation and saw it, with the atmosphere above and the bottom beneath,

15. Personal communication from Dr. A. G. Huntsman, Consulting Director, Fisheries Research Board of Canada.

as an object for diversified scientific study. Thomson had the imagination and the initiative to plan and direct the greatest single worldwide oceanographic exploration ever undertaken. Murray played a great part in Thomson's Challenger Expedition, and followed through the publication of the greatest single series of publications embodying the results of oceanography; as compared with any one up to his time, he had probably the most complete grasp of the whole field of oceanography and doubtless he provided the greatest stimulus to general oceanographic research after Maury and Thomson. The expeditions guided by Alexander Agassiz covered the greatest number of miles and made the largest quantity of collections: he was notable as an organizer, as a designer and stimulator of design for oceanographic apparatus, as a zoologist, and as a practical and theoretical oceanographer. Certainly, these names stand out among those of the pioneers in oceanography. Nevertheless, we should not overlook the special services rendered by Johannes Müller in popularization of the straining net, by Louis Agassiz in the stimulation of marine biology, by Victor Hensen in the organization of planktology with the use of quantitative methods, by Carl Chun in the improvement of apparatus and in the organization and direction of a great oceanographic expedition, or by Hans Lohmann, who, with the centrifuge, brought quantitative knowledge of the bulk of marine life which the net cannot reveal. There are many others, whose names we have barely mentioned or have entirely omitted in a survey altogether too brief to do general justice, but whose value may rank above some of those already cited. Of such are Björn Helland-Hansen of Bergen, Sven Ekman of the University of Upsala, A. Defant and Georg Wüst of Berlin, Otto Krümmel, author of the classic handbook of oceanography, Gerhard Schott, the oceanographic geographer, Fridtjof Nansen of Norway, Hans Pettersson of Sweden, Johan Hjort and H. H. Gran of Oslo, Johannes Schmitt of the Danish Commission for investigation of the sea, and others. There are equally notable oceanographers now in harness, as it were, but it would be inappropriate and invidious to attempt here to appraise the special services of those whose work is in active progress.

In this abbreviated review, it has not been the purpose to give an even measurably complete account of the history of oceanography. Rather, we have tried to suggest in rough outlines the great story of scientific endeavor, by many persons, agencies, and nations throughout a long period of time. The cumulative results of so many and such widely distributed efforts have led to the development of oceanography as a coordinated and cooperative system of study applied to the long-neglected but dominant part of the surface of the earth. We say "dominant" part, having in mind two sets of admissible facts: In the first place, the area of the sea is nearly three times that of the land, and, as we shall see later, the volume of the habitable zones for living organisms is many times greater in the sea than on land; in the second place, and equally important, is the basic fact that the solar energy, which is the source of all action on the earth, must fall *predominantly upon the face of the sea* rather than upon the face of the land.

It is appropriate, indeed, that the study of the continuous seas covering three-fourths of the surface of the globe, bathing the shores of almost every important nation, serving as the highway of general commerce and offering a common field for fishery exploitation, should have been an area of internationally cooperative, or, at least, supplementary and harmonious, rather than competitive, study. It is evident that no one country has monopolized the study of the sea and that important oceanographic explorations have not even been the private preserve of the larger nations. Norway, Sweden, Denmark, and Holland have been in the front rank along with Great Britain, the United States, Germany, Russia, and Japan.

It is natural, too, that the great expeditions and institutions mentioned have not ordinarily concentrated upon any one scientific aspect of oceanography, but have usually concerned themselves with the acquisition of physical and biological data by all practicable methods consistent with the general purposes of the cruise.

Finally, it must be evident that the Atlantic, and particularly the North Atlantic, has been much more thoroughly studied than the other seas and that much remains to be done, in all oceans, but particularly in the Pacific.

CHAPTER 5

Sea and Land

Some Gross Features of the Oceans

L IVING AS WE DO UPON LAND WE ARE INCLINED TO BE MORE interested and concerned with areas of land than with areas of water. It takes, however, only a moment's examination of a globe to reveal the facts not only that much the greater part of the surface of the earth is water (the proportion of land to water being about 29 to 71) but also that the seas, taken together, form one continuous body out of which emerge separately the small and large land masses that we call islands or continents. The great continents and the larger groups of islands tend partially to divide a continuous sea into more or less separate masses to which we assign special names, such as the Pacific Ocean, the Atlantic Ocean, the Mediterranean Sea, the South China Sea, the Gulf of Mexico, the Bay of Bengal, etc. It is impossible to set more than arbitrary boundaries for most of these, and it is equally impossible to draw sharp and inevitable lines between the great oceans, the Atlantic, the Pacific, the Antarctic, the Indian, and the Arctic. Of these five principal seas, the Arctic is the most nearly surrounded by natural land barriers and the Antarctic the least well defined in its relations to Atlantic, Pacific, and Indian oceans. (See Fig. 2, p. 64.)

Another glance at the globe shows that the emergent lands are neither uniformly placed nor randomly distributed; consequently, the oceans have distinctive sizes and forms. In the first place, the surface of the earth is very conveniently divided, of course by arbitrary lines, into eastern and western hemispheres. The eastern

57

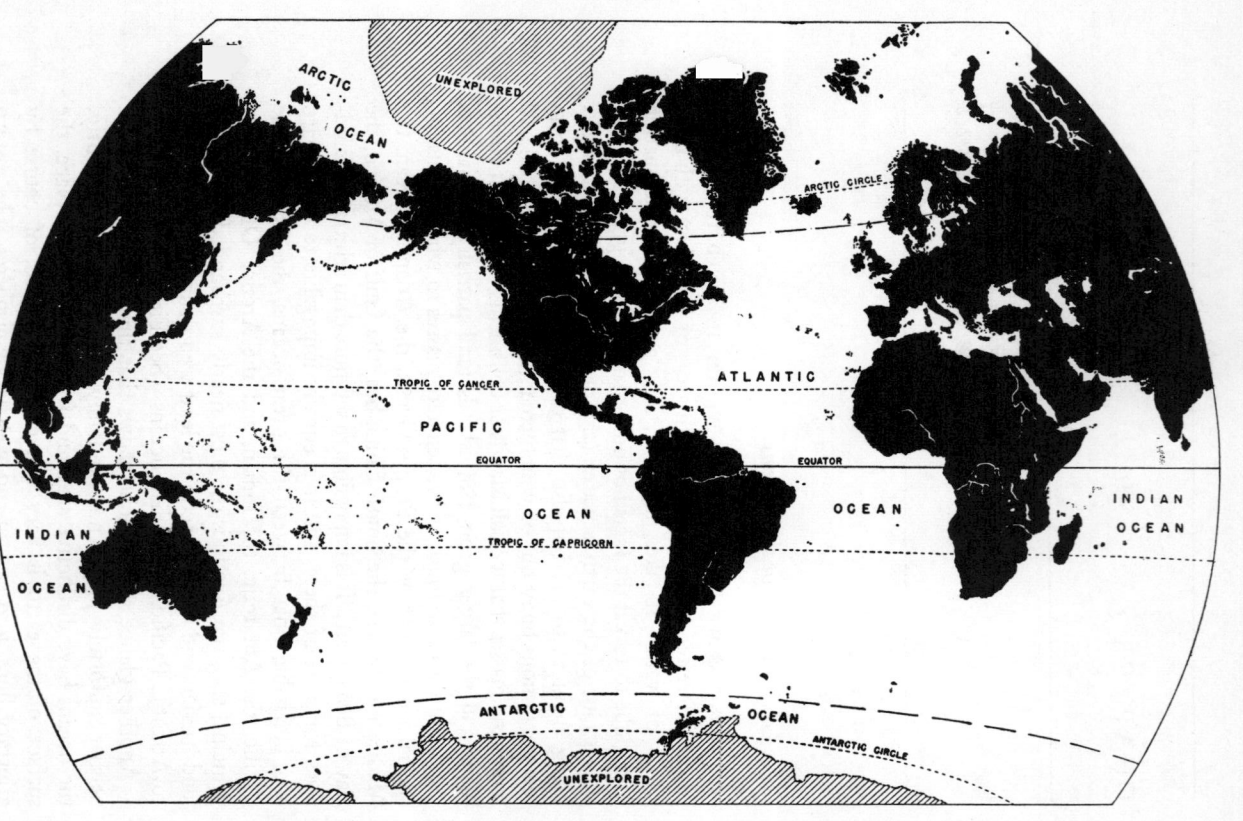

FIGURE 1. Map of the world, showing all oceans (with inevitable distortion).

hemisphere has by far the greater bulk of land, including Europe, Asia, Africa, Australia, and a large number of islands, many of which are of substantial size. The western hemisphere includes North and South America, Greenland, and a much less extensive body of islands. The Antarctic lands may be divided between the two hemispheres, but its larger part would undoubtedly lie in the hemisphere of the great land masses, the eastern hemisphere.

In the second place, if we divide the earth into northern and southern hemispheres, as we may do in a very natural way by following the line of the Equator, we find that the northern hemisphere includes by far the greater part of the land. Eurasia and the greater part of Africa, North America, Greenland, and a small part of South America are all comprised within the northern hemisphere. In the southern hemisphere we have the greater part of South America, but only a small part of Africa, with Australia and Antarctica and about half of the islands. It has been calculated that in the southern hemisphere something less than one-fifth of the total area is land; in the northern hemisphere there is more than twice as much land, but, even there, the proportions of land and sea are something less than two to three. Marmer[1] has pointed out that if consideration is restricted to the temperate zones, which are best adapted for the productive energies of man, we find in the northern hemisphere the proportion of land and water to be approximately 50 to 50, whereas in the southern hemisphere the proportions are approximately one of land to eight of water. There is much more room for people in the north temperate than in the south temperate zone.

If we compare the several great oceans, as they are commonly delimited, each is found to have its characteristic features. The Atlantic and Indian oceans are not greatly different in size, each being one-third or less the size of the Pacific; but their forms offer marked contrasts. The Atlantic is long in the north-south direction and shows extreme irregularity of form; it is almost cut in two by the prominent bulges of South America and Africa which offer such convenient termini for intercontinental airways. North Atlantic and South Atlantic are almost distinct oceans with characteristic forms: the South Atlantic has relatively smooth contours; the North Atlantic intrudes intricately into the land masses to form such partially

1. H. A. Marmer, *The Sea.*

enclosed bodies of water as the Caribbean Sea, the Gulf of Mexico, the Gulf of St. Lawrence, the Labrador Sea, the North and Baltic seas, the Bay of Biscay, the Mediterranean, and many other bodies; perhaps, we should include also the Gulf of Guinea and the Gulf of Maine, to say nothing of such smaller indentations as Long Island Sound and Chesapeake Bay. The Chesapeake Bay alone is said to have, with "Tidewater" Virginia and Maryland, a shoreline of 5,000 miles, equal in mileage to one-fifth of the circumference of the earth.

The Indian Ocean, which is at least as broad as it is long, has little irregularity of form except on its northern and eastern boundaries. The Pacific Ocean, too, has a relatively smooth outline except on its western side. Contrast again the Atlantic, which extends into the land masses in so many places and so deeply that, although it has only about one-fifth the combined area of the Pacific and Indian oceans, it has a longer coast line than those two oceans taken together.[2] Furthermore, the coastal indentations of the Atlantic are chiefly in the northern hemisphere and in the temperate zone, where there are offered a far greater number of harbors and other conditions favorable for the development of navigation and trade. It is not by accident alone that the great populations and the great developments of agriculture, industry, navigation, and trade have been realized in the north temperate zone, around the North Atlantic, and, originally, on the western side of the North Pacific.

Some Interrelations of the Oceans

For our purposes it is important to keep in mind that the oceans are interrelated, not merely spatially, but also functionally, or dynamically, in that more or less interchange of water occurs across the imaginary lines of division. One ocean affects another and all are organically connected. The phenomena of the Atlantic cannot be understood without considering what takes place in the Antarctic, nor those of the Antarctic without reference to its relations with the Pacific and Indian oceans. Thus, the deep and bottom water of all oceans is held to be derived chiefly from Arctic and Antarctic regions. "From the Indian Ocean the Antarctic circumpolar water with its components of Atlantic and Indian Ocean

2. *Ibid.*, p. 88.

origin, enters the Pacific Ocean"; "The Pacific deep water is, therefore, Deep Water of Atlantic and Indian origin"; "the influence of the Red Sea can probably be traced to the Antarctic."[3] These few brief statements of fact by a leading oceanographer indicate how definitely the five great seas are one.

Furthermore, South Atlantic water enters the Gulf of Mexico to continue on far into the North Atlantic and some of this water that crossed the Equator was of Antarctic origin. A corresponding amount of North Atlantic water must, of course, flow into the South Atlantic. The interchange between the North and the South Atlantic is not insignificant; it has been calculated to be of the order of six million cubic meters per second each way. The North Atlantic water passing into the South Atlantic is supposed to have its origin, in approximately equal quantities, in three general and widely remote regions: in the Labrador Sea, off the southeast of Greenland, and off the straits of Gibraltar. North Atlantic deep water crosses the Equator to flow south " 'sandwiched' between the Antarctic Intermediate Water and the Antarctic Bottom Water, both of which are of low salinity."[4] The Mediterranean element of this water can be traced through the North and South Atlantic, crossing the Equator beneath a mass of Antarctic water and continuing on around the southern extremity of Africa and to some extent through to the Antarctic. There is little interchange of water across the Equator in the Pacific; such interchange occurs chiefly in the Atlantic.

It is an interesting thought that a particular particle of water moistening one's toe on a Carolina or New Jersey beach may have engaged in considerable global travel: it may have also dampened the toe of a South Sea Islander, and that of a penguin in Antarctica; that same particle, earlier in its travels, may even have contributed to the drowning of Pharaoh's Army in its disastrous attempt to follow the Children of Israel across the Red Sea. We need not forget either that the same water may sometimes engage in aerial travel in the form of water vapor taken into the atmosphere by evaporation.

3. H. U. Sverdrup, *Oceanography for Meteorologists*, p. 215.
4. *Ibid.*, pp. 213, 214.

Continuity and Contrasts

In contrast to the continuity of the bodies of sea water is the isolation of the bodies of land. Furthermore, if we turn attention to bodies of fresh water in the form of lakes and streams, we find still greater degrees of isolation, where lakes and ponds and rivers are separated from each other by the greater areas of land. Within a continent or an island there is continuity of land, but continuity of fresh waters is limited to those of a single system or basin, several or many of which are found on any given land mass.

The contrasting aspects of continuity and isolation have noteworthy biological significance. For an animal or a plant, different systems of fresh water, even though comparatively close together geographically, may be widely separated the one from the other by almost insuperable barriers of land, salt water, or atmosphere. In the State of New York, for example, the passage from Lake Chautauqua of the Mississippi drainage to Lake Seneca of the North Atlantic drainage involves a journey of about 125 miles by land or air, but one of several thousand miles by water, fresh and salt, down the Mississippi, across the Gulf of Mexico, through the Atlantic Ocean and up the St. Lawrence River. The journey from Lake Chautauqua to Lake Erie, only about eight miles by land or air, once represented (before the construction of the Chicago drainage canal) a similar path by water equal in length to nearly a fourth of the distance around the earth at the Equator.

Notwithstanding the continuity of the oceans, there still exist effective barriers to the free migration of animals and plants—barriers of temperature, of depth and pressure, of character of bottom or of food supply. Perhaps there are also less prominent barriers of salinity, but chemical barriers in the seas are based on degrees of concentration rather than on different combinations of mineral substances such as distinguish different fresh waters or soils. The barriers that exist within the ocean are, then, of the sort that we should call "intangible," as contrasted with the more prominent and abrupt barriers that may bar the free movement of fresh-water or terrestrial animals and plants. Assuming, however, that an animal was broadly tolerant of temperature conditions, as some of the whales may be, it could wander at will over the greater part of the surface of the globe. Assuming, again, that an animal was capable of adapting itself to great extremes of pressure and to foregoing the presence of

sunlight, as may be the case with some copepods and other invertebrates, it could find practically uniform conditions of temperature
(at some depth) in travel from the Arctic across the Equator to the
Antarctic in either ocean. (See Fig. 7, p. 97.) We need not, however, overstrain the imagination by assuming that any invertebrate
animal could accomplish such a journey in its lifetime.

The oceans are not alike, of course. It is not only that Arctic and
Antarctic waters are extremely different in temperature and dissolved gases from tropical waters of Atlantic, Pacific, and Indian
oceans, but that the several oceans are different in corresponding
latitudes. Geologic events and the distribution of continents and
islands, as they influence the movements of currents, must have profound effects on the physical and biological conditions in the several
oceans and in their various parts. The coastal contacts of Atlantic
and Pacific are markedly different, as a glance at the map will show.
"The Pacific is bounded everywhere by steep slopes, rising abruptly
from profound ocean depths to lofty lands crowned with mountain
ranges parallel to its shores and surrounding its whole area. . . ."
" 'This mountain ring,' as Charles Lapworth said, 'is ablaze with
volcanoes and creeping with earthquakes, testifying that it has been
recently formed and is still unfinished.' "[5] Almost everywhere the
continents present a very different sort of front to the Atlantic,
with, generally, a broader continental slope. It has been interestingly
suggested that the Atlantic was originally formed by the splitting
of a greater continent and the slow drifting apart of the Americas
on the one side and Europe and Africa on the other—a highly theoretical assumption, of course, if it does look well on the map.

The oceans differ among themselves and in their several parts.
The nearly isolated Arctic ocean covers the polar region and is sur-
rounded tropicward by lands. The Antarctic Ocean, on the con-
trary, surrounds polar lands and merges tropicward into Atlantic,
Pacific, and Indian oceans; its northern boundary can be set only
arbitrarily (at 60° south latitude). In a sense there is no Antarctic
Ocean. The Atlantic, Pacific, and Indian oceans merge south of
Africa, Australia, and South America, and a part of their undivided
circumpolar body of water is commonly called the Antarctic Ocean.
The Indian Ocean is largely in the southern hemisphere, although its

5. W. W. Watts, "Form, Drift and Rhythm of the Continents," *Science,*
LXXXII (1936), 203–13.

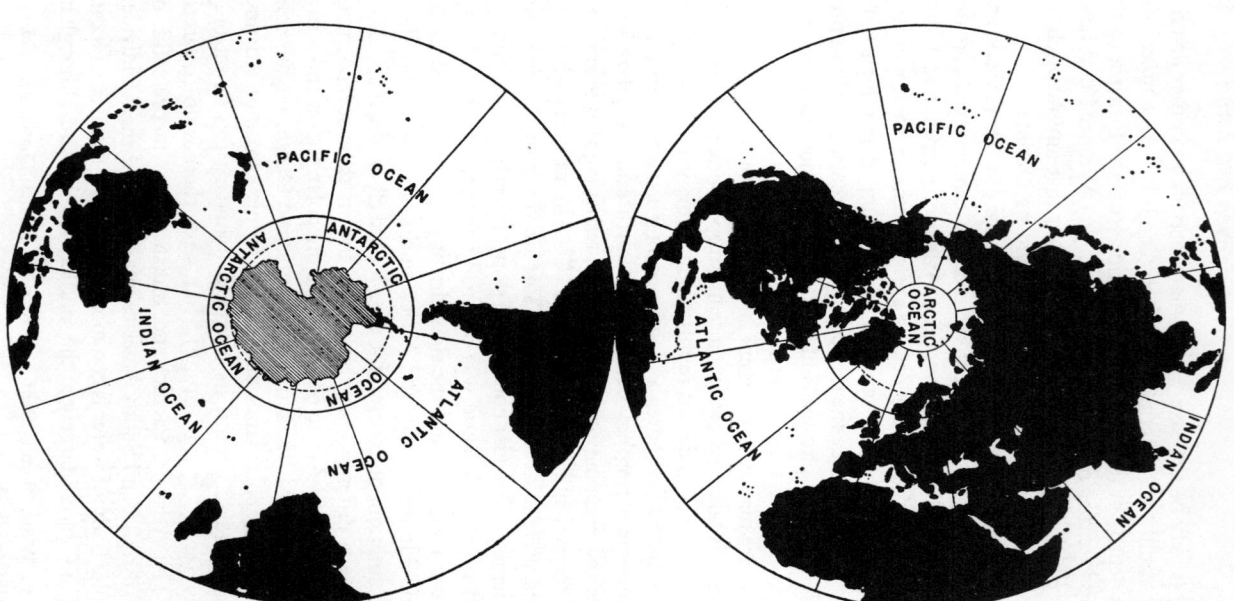

FIGURE 2. Maps of northern and southern hemispheres showing the relative proportion of land and water areas.

southern boundary can be fixed only by agreement among geographers. The Atlantic Ocean, as contrasted with the Pacific, has a much greater proportion of its area in temperate zones. It is noteworthy, also, that by far the major portion of the fresh water draining the lands through great rivers finds its way into the Atlantic Ocean. The Atlantic and the Pacific are different oceans biologically as well as geographically. Without going more into details, it is adequate for the present purpose to give warning, as it were, that the conditions of life and the compositions of the organic communities are different in the several oceans and in the several parts of each ocean. In consequence of these and other conditions, the constitution of organic deposits on the bottom are distinctive of different regions.

The distinctiveness of different regions of the sea, whether viewed horizontally or vertically, is well reflected in the fact that knowledge of currents and drifts is generally found, not so much by the use of current meters as by study of the salinities, temperatures, dissolved gas contents, or the drifting micro-organisms (the plankton). Whence comes the water of a particular place and time and whither it goes are often discoverable by chemical and biological analyses rather than by direct physical observation of water movement. Deep-lying Mediterranean water, for example, is traced for thousands of miles westward and southward to round the Cape of Good Hope; and it is so traced, not by the use of current meters or drift bottles, but by precise observations of temperatures, salinity, and oxygen content.

Depth and Topography

The combined area of the oceans, as has been mentioned, is more than twice that of the lands (71 to 29) and their mean depth (about 3,800 meters or roughly 2 1/3 miles),[6] more than five times the mean elevation of the land (700 meters or 2,300 feet); hence, if all the land were submerged in the sea, such a cataclysm would, after all, cause the displacement of only a relatively small part, about one-eighth, of the total volume of the seas.

The greater part of the sea is below two thousand fathoms, or 4,000 meters, roughly speaking, but only a very small part, some 6 per cent, is below three thousand fathoms (about 3 1/2 miles, or

6. Marmer, *op. cit.*, p. 95.

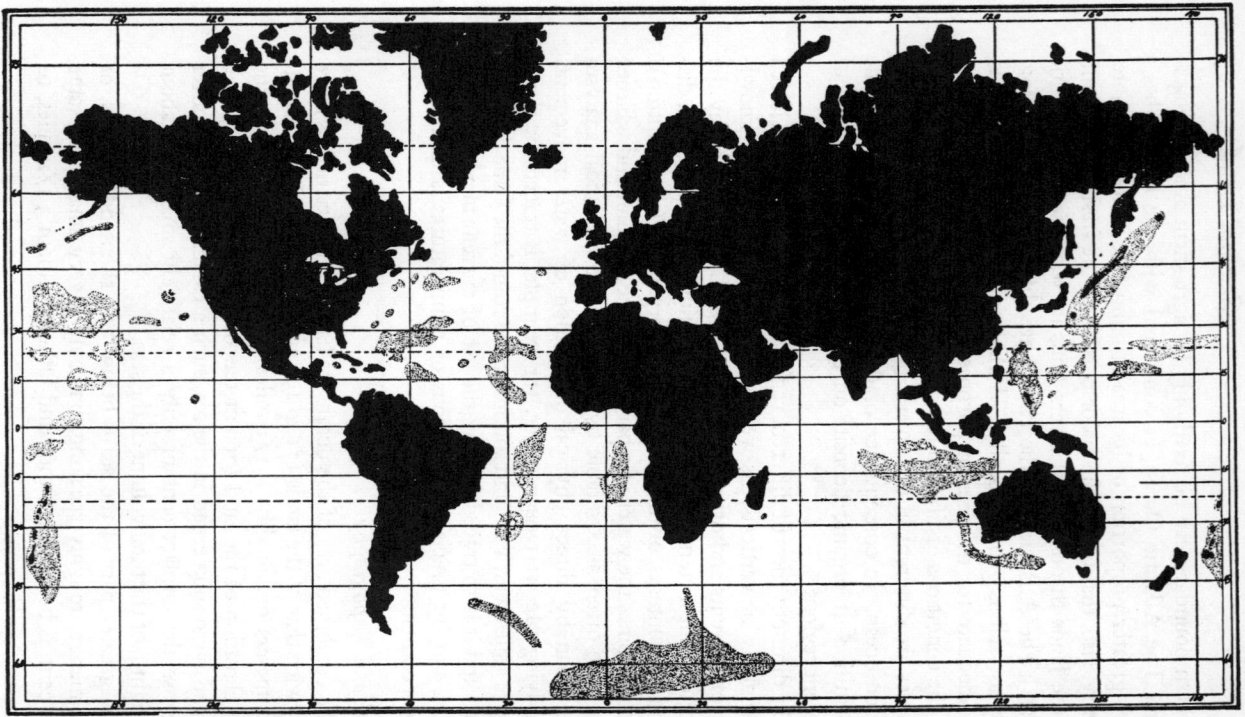

FIGURE 3. Distribution of the "deeps" (indicated by stippling), or areas exceeding 3,000 fathoms in depth. (After Murray and Hjort)

some 6,000 meters). Areas of greater depth than three thousand fathoms are known as "deeps." Greatest height of land (Mt. Everest, 29,002 feet) is more than a mile less than the greatest sounded depth of the sea (35,400 feet, or about 6 1/2 miles) in the Emden Deep off Mindanao in the Philippines. Deepest known in the Atlantic is the "Milwaukee Depth" (30,246 feet, in the Puerto Rico trough, 95 miles northwest of Puerto Rico). Nearly sixty deeps have been mapped (fig. 3). The bottom of the sea lying between two and three thousand fathoms is described as generally an undulating plain with slopes that are usually, but not invariably, gentle. There are high cone-like elevations rising from the deep, with slopes of about 35 degrees—comparable in inclination to a steep mountain side; these, with narrow tops, which may be only some 50 meters below the surface of the ocean, are thought to represent submarine volcanic peaks. The Hawaiian Islands are good examples. If continents and islands are great solid masses rising above the level of the sea, so are there other rock masses, in form like islands or ridges hundreds or thousands of miles in length, which do not reach to the surface and, therefore, constitute shoals, banks, plateaus, or ridges more or less deep beneath the water. The "Mid-Atlantic Swell," extending through North and South Atlantic, is some 2,000 fathoms down, but it still separates broad eastern and western basins.

Proceeding from the shores of the continents toward the central parts of the oceans, there are commonly distinguishable (fig. 4): a *continental shelf,* having generally very gentle inclination, but with many deep and surprisingly precipitous gorges, and extending for a greater or less distance to the *continental edge* at about one hundred fathoms; beyond this, the much steeper *continental slope,* notched by the mouths of the gorges and leading down to the *floor* of the ocean. On some coasts the continental shelf is virtually wanting, as on the western coast of Peru, where the steep slope from the high peaks of the Andes continues almost unbrokenly down to the floor of the ocean below 20,000 feet, giving a roughly continuous incline of some 40,000 feet from peak to deep.

Continental shelf and continental slope together constitute the *continental terrace,* the flank of the continent. Its width may vary between, say, zero and 800 miles, with an average of about 30 miles.[7]

7. H. U. Sverdrup, Martin W. Johnson, and Richard H. Fleming, *The Oceans, Their Physics, Chemistry and General Biology.*

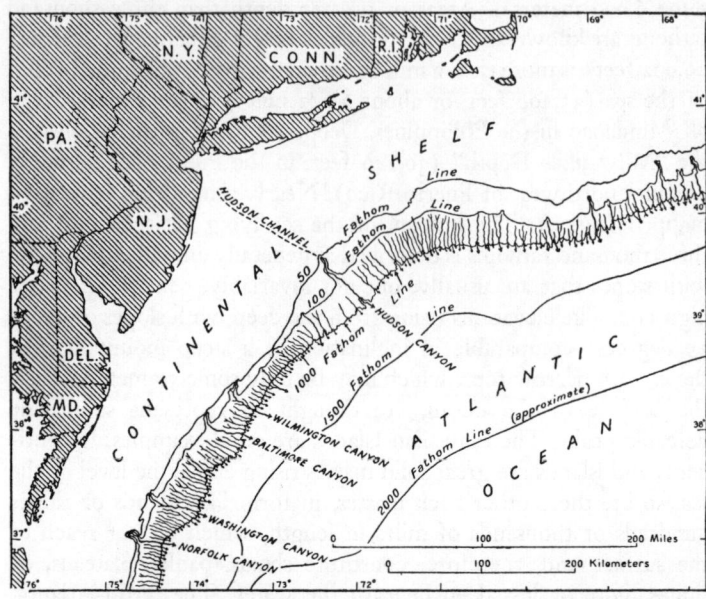

FIGURE 4. Map showing the location of canyons and principal furrows off the Mid-Atlantic states; also the extent of the continental shelf and the location of the continental slope. (After R. A. Daly, *The Floor of the Ocean*)

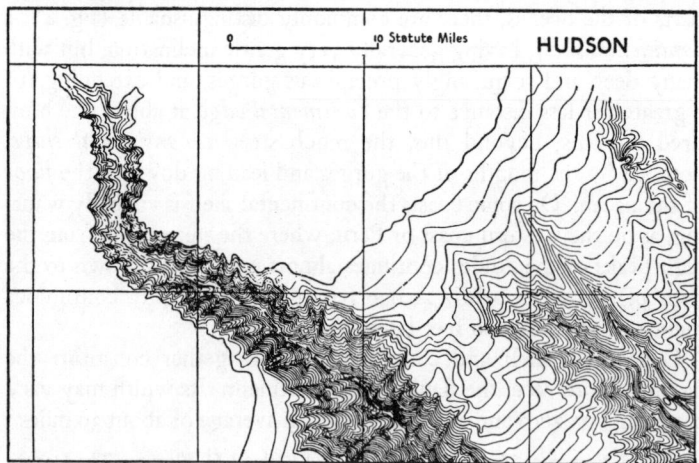

FIGURE 5. Map of the Hudson canyon and vicinity. (After R. A. Daly, *The Floor of the Ocean*)

The slope, which begins at a depth of 50 to 100 fathoms, is actually steep. Its average fall off the eastern United States is said to be about one mile vertically in ten horizontal miles, but actually it is much steeper toward the top.[8] Once thought to be a relatively smooth bank, the shelf and the slope are now known to be extremely rugged and deeply cut with gullies, gorges, and great canyons. The explanation of the sharp sculpturing is not certain, but it is one view that the cuts were made during certain stages of the glacial period by the rush of heavy silt-laden submarine currents. If they are thus attributable to the action of moving water, they have an origin very similar to that of terrestrial gullies and canyons. The Grand Canyon of the Colorado River, pre-eminent example of a continental water-worn gorge, has its measurable rivals on the continental terrace.

It may be asked: How have we learned about the great depths in the ocean? The simplest sounding apparatus is, of course, a piece of lead on the end of a line marked in fathoms or meters. The lower end of the lead may be hollowed out and filled with soft soap to bring up a slight sample of the bottom, whether sand, mud, or shell fragments. For great depths, where the length of line must run into thousands of fathoms, or miles, the bulk and weight of a line made of rope is very great; furthermore, a heavy sinker is necessary to carry the line to the bottom within a reasonable period of time and at a rate such that the slackening of the line is apparent when the lead reaches bottom.

Strabo is said to have sounded the Mediterranean to a depth of more than a mile, but we do not know how he did it. Magellan is said to have sounded to a depth of some thousands of fathoms, but without reaching bottom. As early as 1840, Sir James Ross made soundings at a depth of more than 3 miles, but not all of his soundings were correct. The "Challenger" used a fine hemp line and recorded accurately the time when each hundred-fathom mark went over. When the rate at which the line ran out suddenly changed, the bottom was presumed to have been reached.

It is a difficult and time-consuming task to haul in the line with the heavy lead; many hours are required for a single sounding, and, during the whole period, the ship must be kept as nearly as is possible in the same place. Another improvement, that of Midshipman Brooke, working with Maury, was the use of a detachable weight

8. Daly, *The Floor of the Ocean: New Light on Old Mysteries*, p. 101.

released when it touches the bottom. Twine could then be substituted for the heavier and bulkier rope. When the sounding is made at a great depth, the value of the lost weight is much less than the cost involved in raising it through miles of water. The vessel must, of course, be provided with at least as many heavy shot as the number of deep soundings it proposes to make. The Sigsbee and the Tanner sounding machine and necessary accessories are well described in Tanner's report of 1897, previously cited (p. 44).

It was a further improvement when Lord Kelvin in England and Belknap of the U. S. S. "Tuscarora" substituted piano wire for the rope or twine. Not only does the fine wire, of a diameter of about one-twentieth of an inch, require less space for storage, but, when properly protected, it is more durable and more economically manipulated. The line, whether of rope or wire, may be coiled on a drum from which it runs out over a revolving wheel; each turn of the wheel corresponds to a known length of line. If the number of turns is automatically recorded, the amount of line paid out and the depth of the sinker at any moment is readily determinable, provided one can tell, by the slowing of the wheel, when the sinker has stopped on the bottom some miles below.

It can readily be understood that deep-sea soundings taken by the use of a line and weight are expensive in many ways. The miles of line required and the many heavy weights which must be discarded represent considerable initial expenditure and occupy substantial space on the vessel. The time, in hours, consumed in letting out and hauling in miles of line while the boat is kept in one place means expensive delay. Even with the most modern motor-driven sounding machines, a sounding in the greatest depths requires about three hours. It is obvious that only a limited number of deep-sea observations requiring the use of long lines are practicable from a vessel engaged in oceanographic exploration of general purpose.

An ideal sounding apparatus would be one that determined depth in a few seconds or minutes and virtually continuously while the boat was in motion. The answer to this need was the sonic depthfinder developed in the early 1920's by Dr. Harvey C. Hayes, a research physicist in the United States Navy.[9] The apparatus con-

9. Harvey C. Hayes, "Measuring Ocean Depths by Acoustical Methods," *Journal of the Franklin Institute*, CXCVII (1924), 323–54. A very instructive and interesting but concise account of the development of sonic sounding is given by Thomas H. Whitecroft, "Sonic Sounding," *loc. cit.*, pp. 216, 223.

sists chiefly of a means of making a sound on the ship, with the sound waves directed toward the bottom of the ocean, a delicate receiving apparatus to catch the echo from the bottom, and a highly accurate and delicate clock mechanism to measure the time interval in small fractions of a second. Knowing the velocity of sound in water, the depth can be calculated very closely. The "sound" is not necessarily audible to the ears: supersonic waves may be more effective.

Obviously "sonic sounding" presumes exact knowledge of the velocity of sound in sea water and this has been found to vary with temperature, salinity, and pressure, but to be generally a little over 800 fathoms per second. An intensive investigation of this subject was made by the Coast Survey steamer "Guide,"[10] cruising from New London, Connecticut, by way of Porto Rico and Panama to San Diego in 1923. The determinations of depth with the sonic sounder were checked against repeated wire soundings while temperatures were determined at several depths and water samples taken for later determination of salinity; bottom samples were taken also. The cruise extended over 6,500 miles, and the conditions encountered covered wide ranges: the temperature range of the water 0° to 28° C., the salinity 31 to 36.5 o/oo, the depth 185 to 4,617 fathoms. The computed velocities varied between 810 and 841 fathoms per second. The depths recorded by the sonic sounder, with corrections for the several variables, seem to be accurate within a very few fathoms and without appreciable error even where the bottom is steeply sloping.

Given the necessary equipment, which occupies little space, and a qualified operator, a practically unlimited number of soundings can be made from any vessel on a continuous cruise. Consequently, the sonic sounder has been of great significance to oceanography and knowledge of the topography of the bottom of the ocean has been much advanced in recent years. Curiously enough, we have only recently begun to use "sound" in "sounding" the depths. In another place (p. 279) we shall refer to the use of the echo-sounder in locating schools of fish.

Now, although there is relatively little difference between the greatest' height of land and the greatest depth of the sea, there is a

10. N. H. Heck and Jerry H. Service, *Velocity of Sound in Sea Water.* U. S. Coast and Geodetic Survey, Publication No. 108, 1924.

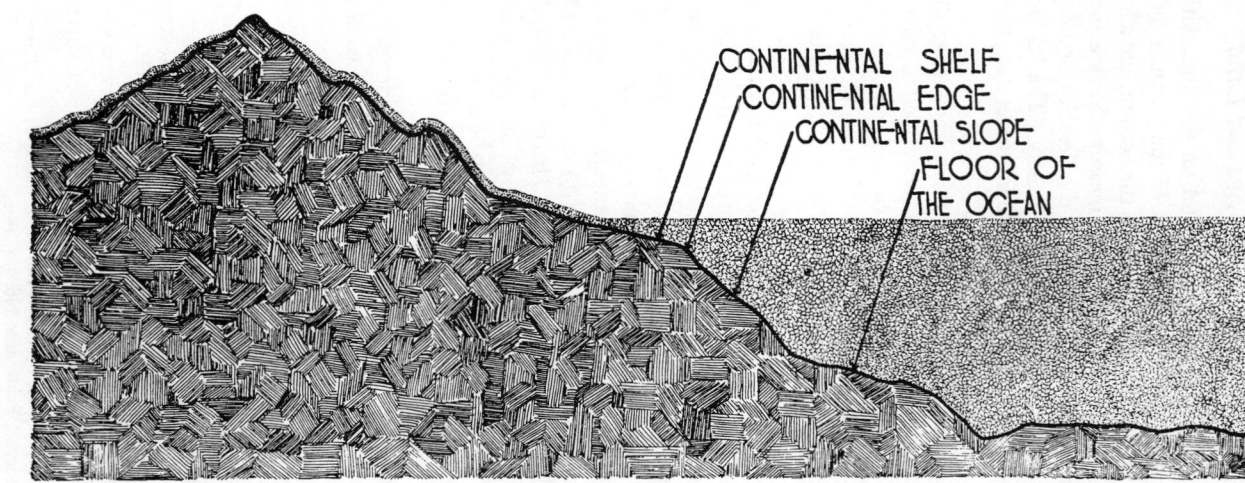

FIGURE 6. Schematic representation of the disparity of the respective depths of the biosphere on land and in the sea. Habitable regions (the biosphere) are indicated by stippling. The scale is unavoidably misleading, since the stippled area over land represents a zone with depth of about 30 meters, while the sea has a mean depth of some 4,000 meters. Some prominent topographical features are also shown.

vast difference between the thickness of the zones of life on land and in the ocean, respectively. Terrestrial life everywhere occupies a very thin stratum that follows roughly the contours of the land, except at the greatest elevations, while oceanic life extends throughout the space from the surface of the ocean to the bottom, however deep it may be (fig. 6). The thickness of the stratum of life on land, which may roughly be said to extend from the tops of the crowns of the trees to the greatest depths to which their roots penetrate, will not ordinarily exceed 100 feet, or some 30 meters, and the mean thickness would certainly be much less; but if, with some exaggeration, we assume this to be the mean and take the mean depth of the habitable regions of the sea as about 12,000 feet (about 4,000 meters), and if we remember that the area of the sea is more than twice the area of the land, we find the volume of space available for organic life in the ocean to be some three hundred times the space available over the continents and islands. This is a very rough sort of calculation, but it indicates at least the order of relative magnitude of the terrestrial and the oceanic communities as a whole.

Interrelations of Sea and Land

Not only are the continents and islands completely surrounded by the continuous sea, but almost all lands everywhere, as a result of weathering processes, are being worn down and washed or blown into the sea. It is estimated that nearly three billion metric tons of material from the land are annually being dumped into the sea. Indeed, were there no compensating returns to the land, a few geologic ages might have sufficed to cause the complete disappearance of all dry land. There have been, however, and there must always be such compensating movements, so long as the equilibrium of the crust of the earth is maintained by the gradual elevation, in continental regions at least, of great areas of sea bottom to become dry land. Enormous terrestrial areas, even the very tops of some of our mountains, are known by their geologic formation and fossils to have been former sea bottoms and, thus, to represent the repayment of long-term loans from land to sea. The highest point of land, the peak of Mount Everest, was once at the bottom of the sea.[11]

In other ways than through geologic upheavals does the sea reg-

11. Daly, *op. cit.* p. 93.

ularly contribute to the land. The interrelations are too complex to be analyzed briefly. It may only be suggested that the source of our rain and snow and of rivers, lakes, springs, and ground waters everywhere is, in part, the surface of the sea, where the heat energy of the sun enables the atmosphere to pick up by evaporation the topmost layer of water, some of which may fall later upon mountain or plain. Then, too, the climates on land are regulated from the sea in various ways. The winds from the sea are well-known tempering influences, but it is not so generally understood that the great amount of heat energy absorbed by evaporation of the sea water is, to a notable extent, released by the precipitation that occurs when the warm water-laden breezes are cooled over sea or land. It is hardly relevant to our purpose to recall that the water powers which operate our lights and engines are giving us merely the energy of the sun that was stored through evaporation and that this capture and storage occurred in some part at the surface of the sea. In comparison with these contributions from sea to land, the gift to man, bird, and other terrestrial animals of a few billion pounds of food and salt seems relatively insignificant, however important, and perhaps absolutely essential, these materials are to man and to terrestrial life in general.

II

CHEMISTRY AND PHYSICS

CHAPTER 6

The Sea As a Solution

Chemical Nature of Sea Water

ALLUSIONS TO "THE BRINY DEEP" NEVER NEED EXPLANATION; everyone knows the sea is salty. What is not a matter of such general information is the great array of other substances that go along with the common salt in solution: the minerals, organic substances, and gases. It is easy to learn that sea water is an elaborate chemical mixture; but without special study and consideration one does not readily conceive what it means for plants and animals, unlike those on land, to live completely immersed within a nutrient chemical medium and what it means that this medium is kept always in circulation. What is even less generally understood is that the very saltiness of the sea has much to do with the mechanics of world-wide circulation of ocean waters.

Without wishing to become too much concerned with the technicalities of ocean chemistry and physics, one has to recognize that there can be no satisfactory understanding of conditions of life in the sea without considering several special aspects of the sea as a solution of so many substances. In this chapter the attempt is made to treat in as simple language as is practicable the composition of sea water, the distribution of the constituents by area and by depth (geographic and bathymetric), the changes that may occur here and there, some features of utilization of the chemicals and the effect of changes in concentration on movements of water masses. There will be attempted also a brief exposition of the means by which we learn about the composition of sea water at all depths. It is convenient to deal first with the inorganic constituents of sea water, ignoring for a while, the organisms and their wastes in solution.

Inorganic Substances in Solution

Barring, of course, a few relatively small isolated basins, such as those of the Great Salt Lake, the Caspian Sea, Lake Poopo in South America, and the Dead Sea, all land drainage is toward the oceans. The seas taken together, constitute a great catch-basin for all that leaches from the land or is washed from its surface. To the surface and soil drainage entering the sea, there are added the air-borne materials originating on land or coming from interplanetary space. Obviously the ocean water must be a great chemical potpourri: doubtless it has in solution the salts of every one of the chemical elements, although many occur in traces so slight as not to be detected by ordinary methods of chemical analysis. Indeed, until recently, elements that had never been detected in the water were, nevertheless, found in marine organisms.[1] Since the animals or plants could only have gotten the chemicals by extraction from the water, it might be inferred that, at least in the extraction of some of the rarest elements, the protoplasm of the organism was more efficient than the most expert chemist. Chemical laboratory techniques have undergone great refinements in recent years, but, as every chemist and biologist recognizes, the protoplasm of plants and animals has always led the field in organic chemistry. Only a limited number of the materials in solution have presently known biological significance; yet some of these, such as iodine, an important component of some seaweeds, and copper in the blood of crabs, will show only as traces in the records of chemical analyses. The cell membranes have selective capacities, so that the concentration of substances in the surrounding medium gives no indication of the concentration within the plant or animal.

The accompanying Table I reproduces a rather old-fashioned report of the analysis of sea water. It serves merely to give a rough idea of the relative abundance of the several inorganic materials that occur in greatest quantities. One notes the absence in this record

1. Vanadium in the blood of ascidians and holothurians, cobalt in lobsters and mussels, nickel in mollusks, and lead in the ash of various marine organisms.—Henry B. Bigelow, *Oceanography*, pp. 109-10. Sverdrup, Johnson, and Fleming (*The Oceans*, pp. 175 ff.) list 49 elements now known to occur in sea water.

of such known essentials as phosphates and nitrates or of silica, iodine, copper, and other chemicals. It must not be understood, either, that the materials listed occur in just the combinations indicated, for the salts in sea water are largely in ionized form and consequently are susceptible of diverse and changing combinations. The sodium ion, for example, may occur in combination with chlorine,

TABLE I

ANALYSIS OF UNEVAPORATED RESIDUE OF SEA WATER*

(From Helland-Hensen in Murray and Hjort, after Dittmar in Challenger Reports)

		gms.	per cent
Sodium chloride	NaCl	27.213	77.76
Magnesium chloride	MgCl$_2$	3.807	10.88
Magnesium sulphate	MgSO$_4$	1.658	4.74
Calcium sulphate	CaSO$_4$	1.260	3.60
Potassium sulphate	K$_2$SO$_4$	0.863	2.46
Calcium carbonate	CaCO$_3$	0.123	0.34
Magnesium bromide	MgBr$_2$	0.076	0.22
Total.............................		35.000	100.00

* For the expression of Dittmar's values in the units now in common use, see Sverdrup, Johnson, and Fleming, *The Oceans*, Table 33, p. 166.

carbonate, sulfate, or bromine ions or with organic negative ions; this has its advantages for the grasping organisms with their diverse needs.

Collection of Samples and Analysis

It may be asked how the water for chemical or gas analysis can be sampled at different depths. Given the proper equipment, this can readily be done by the use of what is termed a "water-bottle." Water-bottles may be attached in series to a line lowered from the ship to any depth, even to thousands of fathoms. Each bottle usually consists of a metal cylinder, open as it goes down so that the water passes freely through it, but capable of being closed at will when a small cylindrical weight or "messenger" is allowed to slide down the line and trip the catch of the uppermost bottle, as shown in pl. 25. The closing of this bottle releases a similar messenger previously suspended below the uppermost bottle, and this, sliding on down the line, effects the closing of the next bottle, and so on, until the lowermost bottle is closed. The closing mechanism may be a rotating valve, caused to rotate by the weight of the metal bottle when it has been released, or it may be some form of top and bottom "stoppers," so placed that the cylinder, which was previously open at top and bottom, falls upon the bottom stopper while the weighted upper stopper falls into the top of the bottle.

By whatever type of mechanism the water samples are taken, they may be titrated in the ship's laboratory at once or they may be transferred to glass bottles which are then sealed for later precise analysis of the contents. Needless to say, analyses for salinity or oxygen content must be done with extreme precision where a particular mass of water, distinguishable by a small difference in salinity or oxygen content, is to be traced over considerable distances as it lies above and below masses of different characteristics, and perhaps of different directions of movement. Salinity can also be computed from the accurate determination of density, from measurement of the electrical conductivity or from the refractive index at a given temperature. For determinations by measurements of electrical conductivity it is not always necessary to take actual samples of water and bring them to the surface.

Throughout the oceans there is general *uniformity* in the proportions of the several inorganic salts with chloride ions constituting about 55 per cent of the dissolved solids. Except, then, near continental shores, where land drainage affects the constitution of the sea water or where special conditions may prevail, the differences in the composition of sea water from place to place and from time to time are differences of *concentration*. Consequently, to ascertain the composition of any particular mass of sea water it is sufficient to determine only the amount of chlorine, or the *chlorinity*, which is readily and accurately determined by titration with silver nitrate, employing potassium chromate as the indicator. The salinity is then recorded by multiplying the chlorinity, stated in grams per kilogram, by 1.805 and adding 0.03; it is expressed in parts per thousand using the symbol o/oo. Actually the determinations are not nearly so simple as this brief account may seem to imply: for one reason, because they involve the use of a standard "normal water" which was formerly prepared and distributed from the hydrographical laboratories of the International Commission for the Exploration of the Sea in Copenhagen, and now from the Woods Hole Oceanographic Institution.[2]

Since density, salinity, and chlorinity are closely interrelated and indirectly determinable from specific gravity, and since these terms are sometimes confused, it is well to keep in mind their respective meanings. *Density* is the mass of matter per unit volume; we might say that its measure, with respect to gravity, is the weight of a given volume, stated generally in grams per cubic centimeter at some specified temperature, which, in the case of water, is 4°C. Pure water at either a higher or lower temperature than 4°C., because of expansion, has a density somewhat less than one. Water with salts in solution has greater density than pure water at the same temperature. The measure of density of a solution relative to that of distilled water at 4°C. is called *specific gravity*. When we speak of the densities of different masses of sea water we are usually treating of specific gravities, which vary with salinity, with temperature, and, to a less extent, with pressure. Now, although the specific gravity of sea water is proportionate to its salinity, or to the amount of salts in solution, the measures of the two qualities are not identical. Thus, the presence of 35 parts of salts per 1,000 parts of sea water gives a salinity of 35 o/oo, but a specific gravity of only about 1.028, a little more or less, according to temperature. It will be somewhat higher under the conditions of great pressure in the depths of the sea, and the pressure will, in turn, have some effect on temperature (cf. p. 111, below). The relations of *salinity* and *chlorinity* have already been mentioned.

Distribution of Salinity

Generally the salinity in the oceans is between 34 and 37 and, since the range in all oceans is small, the average salinity is usually given as 35; actually it is a little less. In regions of high rainfall or of dilution by rivers or melting ice the surface salinity may be considerably less, as in certain semi-enclosed areas, such as the Baltic, where it may be less than 10, or, the Gulf of Bothnia, below 5. On the other hand, in isolated seas in intermediate latitudes where evaporation is excessive, the Red Sea being an outstanding sample, salinities

2. See Sverdrup, Johnson, and Fleming, *op. cit.*, p. 51.

may reach 40 or more, even up to 46.5.[3] There are oceanic areas of relatively high surface salinity. Probably the greatest of these is the central part of the great North Atlantic eddy, known as the Sargasso Sea, with salinity as high as 38; a somewhat similar area is found in the South Atlantic. The Indian Ocean has two such areas, one large and extending southward from the Persian Gulf to the equator, and another west of Australia with salinity of about 36. The North Pacific presents no large area of surface waters with salinity above 36, but in the South Pacific there is found off the coast of Peru an area with salinity of 36.5.[4]

On the average, the surface water of the sea as a whole is saltier in the southern hemisphere (salinity about 35) than in the northern (about 34). This is not surprising in view of the fact that there is less sea water in the northern hemisphere (p. 59, above) to receive the fresh water of rainfall upon land and sea.

In regions of low temperature and little evaporation, the surface waters may be notably low in salinity, as in the Arctic where it is 30 or less. In general, the salinity is low in high latitudes and high in low latitudes; yet the maximum mean salinity is found not just at the Equator but, rather, approximately in the regions of the Tropics of Cancer and Capricorn, or some 1,500 miles north and south of the Equator. From causes that are not yet fully understood the waters of the North Pacific are, in general, substantially less saline than are those of the Atlantic, and this is surprising considering that "about half of the world drains into the Atlantic Ocean, and most of this into the North Atlantic."[5]

The salinity of deep and bottom water varies within narrower limits than does that of the surface water, which is more directly affected by rainfall and evaporation.[6] The range for deep water is generally 34.5 to 35, but exceptions are found in the Mediterranean and Red seas, where waters of high salinity and high temperatures are found at great depths. The outflows into the great oceans from these nearly enclosed seas form distinctive deep waters of unexpect-

3. Richard Hesse, W. C. Allee, and Karl P. Schmidt, *Ecological Animal Geography*, p. 164.

4. Marmer, *op. cit.*, p. 135.

5. Herdman, *Founders of Oceanography*, p. 182.

6. "It has been estimated that the surface waters of the sea have a salinity of about 34½ while the waters of the sea as a whole have a salinity of about 34¾."— Marmer, *op. cit.*, p. 150.

edly high salinity which can be traced for thousands of miles.

It may be added finally that there is as yet no adequate explanation for the great disproportion in which chlorine and sodium occur in the sea, as compared with other chemical substances currently contributed by the rivers. The whole question of the disparity between relative abundance of the elements in sea water and in the total drainage from lands into the ocean is too complex for proper examination here. Living organisms undoubtedly play and have long played a significant part in affecting concentrations of the several elements in sea water and in contributing to the permanent removal of some materials through deposition on the bottom of the sea.

Effect of Salt on Circulation

As is often the case, the capacity to change is more important than is the condition at any given time. The concentration of salts in sea water is subject to change almost anywhere, because of dilution by fresh water that comes from the lands, directly from the atmosphere, or from the melting of drifting icebergs. Such changes occur chiefly in continental regions; but everywhere over the whole expanse of the oceans, changes in concentration are regularly taking place because of *evaporation* at the surface. The increased specific gravity that goes along with increase in concentration leads to vertical movements; that is to say, to the transport of surface waters to the depths and the lifting of deeper and lighter waters toward the surface. Because of various complicating factors horizontal movements are superadded to vertical shifts. If the waters of the oceans were not a solution of many salts there would still be changes of density due to rising or falling temperatures, but one of the great factors in the general scheme of oceanic circulation would be missing.

If, as the physical oceanographers tell us, water from the Mediterranean Sea, flowing out over the sill at the bottom of the Straits of Gibralter, can be traced through the South Atlantic and around the Cape of Good Hope (see p. 128 below), this great movement could have originated only because the water exposed to the Mediterranean sun was salty to begin with and became more so through evaporation. The salts of the earth are important to plants and animals of land and fresh water, but nowhere else than in the ocean could they play such a great part in causing *movements of environments*.

The general scheme of circulation that makes the oceans one great dynamic mechanism will be a subject for later discussion. Let us keep in mind, now, as we consider the saltiness of the sea, only that one *key to the dynamics of the sea* is found in the fact that sea water is not pure water but a chemical mixture of evaporable water and heavier non-evaporable mineral substances. Furthermore, as we shall see later, we may have in any region, between the surface and the bottom, a series of identifiable strata of water distinguished in part by degrees of concentration of salts in the waters of the several strata. Of course there is slow mixing along boundary surfaces, but, with the great masses of water involved, the recognizable stratification is long persistent.

Organic Substances in Solution and Their Distribution

The comparative uniformity in proportions of dissolved materials in offshore waters is generally accepted. It is a near approximation to the truth and one that may easily be overemphasized. Most substances in solution become, directly or indirectly, nutriment to organisms that live in the waters, and the abundance of the plants that chiefly appropriate them is very variable with the season and with other conditions. It may well be, then, that materials which occur in minimal quantities relative to demand are at times removed from solution, either entirely or to such an extent as to place a limit on the development of the organisms that require such substances. W. R. G. Atkins and H. W. Harvey, at the Plymouth Laboratory, England, and some others, have investigated this subject extensively. Nitrogenous compounds and phosphates, particularly, and perhaps silica, sometimes become so depleted as to check the growth of drifting microscopic plants and the animals that feed upon the plants. Then, too, some of the dying plants and animals may sink into deeper layers of water, there to become decomposed and dissolved, yielding the chemical materials in a region where, for lack of light, they can not again be immediately utilized.

On land, leaves, twigs and other parts of plants, and the wastes of animals, fall a distance of a few feet to the ground to decay and become the nutrients of other plants or to furnish food for small animals or for bacteria of decomposition, which in turn are eaten by animals. In ponds and lakes the organic wastes likewise accumulate on the bottom and there harbor a luxuriant community of scavenger animals and bacteria. In the great open sea, however, the fall extends through a long distance and, since the bodies of the predominant populations of the sea are minute, the rate of sinking is exceedingly slow. Even a large copepod falling at a rate of about one centimeter per second (or about 2 feet a minute) would require a couple of days to reach a depth of a mile; protozoa, diatoms, and coccolithophores must sink at vastly slower rates, except, perhaps, as the streamline form of some diatoms may facilitate sedimentation. Meanwhile, the living animals of intermediate depths are all to be supported, and what other source of food than the down-falling bodies is available for such animals? There is also ample time for the dissolution of the small bodies, so that in areas of great depth even calcareous and silicious skeletons may be completely dissolved before the bottom is reached. It appears that, barring the extensive deposits of skeletons in regions of appropriate depth, there is no great accumulation of *solid* organic wastes in the depths of the sea.

On the other hand, there is a considerable accumulation of organic matter in solution, which, although in dilute form, is substantial in amount. Krogh estimated that the dissolved organic substance was equivalent to some three hundred times the amount of living organic material in the sea at any one time. He calculated that the Atlantic Ocean had dissolved organic matter equal to 20,000 times the world's wheat harvest for one year; he suggested the possibility that this material had "in the main gone out of organic circulation," that it was unrecoverable and was possibly accumulating. There is, however, increasing knowledge of the capacity of bacteria and other organisms of the depths of the sea to utilize the dissolved organic matter.

Clearly, with the slow but continuous subsidence of organic material from the upper into the deeper waters, questions arise as to its ultimate fate or the fate of its component substances. Does the drainage from surface to deep represent in considerable part an irretrievable loss to the organic world? Rates of diffusion are so slow, and the distance so great, that the return by diffusion of dissolved nutrient matter from the bottom to the upper waters has been thought to be insignificant. A quotation from Krogh will suffice here:

"If no mixing took place the depletion would go on to exhaustion and life would die out except along the coasts, but in certain areas, mainly at fairly high latitudes, but also for instance in the huge Gulf of Guinea, waters from the deep rise to the surface and become the seat of a large outburst of planktonic life which imparts a distinct tint of green to the water. From these areas of fertility and abundance the waters spread by the currents become progressively poorer in the salts necessary for plant growth, and the large areas of the ocean where the water is of a pure blue can only be compared to deserts supporting a minimum of life."[7]

Gases in Solution[8]

There can be no life in water or on land without two simple substances which, almost invariably, at least, can be used only in the gaseous form. Reference, of course, is to oxygen and carbon dioxide. The production of organic matter of all kinds is based ultimately on the synthesis of sugar from water and carbon dioxide in sunlight. To the best of our knowledge, the activities and functions of both plants and animals, including growth, reproduction, and the various mental functions of such organisms as have them, are generally associated in some way with oxidation; the anaerobic bacteria and some other anaerobes may get their oxygen second hand.

The chief gases dissolved in the sea are nitrogen, oxygen, and carbon dioxide. *Nitrogen* occurs in sea water in a ratio to other gases somewhat smaller (64 per cent) than in the air (78 per cent), but in approximately saturated solution. The elemental nitrogen in the sea, so far as is now known, has little or no biological significance, except in so far as nitrogen-fixing bacteria may use it for the production of ammonium salts and nitrates. Such are found to be active on or near the bottom, and more abundant on some bottoms than on others. There is now no reason to suppose that such bacteria play any considerable part in the economy of the open ocean.[9]

Oxygen is about one-fifth less soluble in sea water than in fresh water, but it is absorbed in sea water in a proportion to other gases

7. Krogh, August. "Conditions of life in the ocean." *Ecological Monographs, 4:* 1934, pp. 423-4.
8. As they are found by plants and animals, the relations of these gases to water is a physical rather than a chemical one, but we consider them in this chapter because we are concerned with them only as they play their parts in chemical reactions involving the use of water and the chemicals in solution.
9. H. W. Harvey, 1928, p. 14 (quoting Krogh), and 1945, p. 112.

(34 per cent) substantially greater than in the air (21 per cent)—percentages applicable to sea water at the surface with salinity of 35 and temperature of 10°C. The figures indicating the ratio of oxygen relative to other gases in dissolved, as compared with atmospheric, air are of less practical significance than are those indicating the volumes of oxygen in a liter of sea water at the point of saturation—and this varies with the temperature, the pressure, and the salinity. At any given temperature and pressure, sea water can hold in solution less oxygen (about one-fifth less) than can fresh water, as is indicated by Table II.[10]

TABLE II

SOLUBILITY OF OXYGEN IN FRESH AND SEA WATER AT DIFFERENT TEMPERATURES UNDER CONDITIONS OF ATMOSPHERIC MIXTURE AND UNDER A PRESSURE OF ONE ATMOSPHERE

Temperature	Fresh Water (Salinity 0 per M.) Oxygen in cc. per liter	Sea Water (Salinity 35 per M.) Oxygen in cc. per liter
0°	10.29	8.03
10°	8.02	6.40
20°	6.57	5.35
30°	5.57	4.50

The free oxygen in sea water is derived partly from the atmosphere by absorption at the surface and partly from the photosynthetic activities of plants. The photosynthetic zone, as we shall see later, is a superficial stratum some hundreds of meters in depth; but it does not follow that the plants throughout all the depths at which they may live are *net* contributors to the supply of free oxygen available for animals. In the deeper zones inhabited by plants they may consume as much oxygen as they produce, or more, so that the net contribution is nil or a minus quantity. The level at which oxygen consumed and oxygen produced are in balance is called the *compensation depth;* in the Gulf of Maine in June, 1934, this was at 24-30 meters.[11]

10. After Fox, from Murray and Hjort, *The Depths of the Ocean*, p. 254.
11. G. L. Clarke and R. H. Oster, "The Penetration of the Blue and Red Components of Daylight into Atlantic Coastal Waters and its Relation to Phytoplankton Metabolism," *Biological Bulletin*, LXVII (1934), 71.

The solubility of *carbon dioxide* in sea water is such that it has about fifty times the ratio to other gases which it has in the atmosphere, but even that is a very small proportion—approximately 1.6 per cent of all gases by weight in sea water, as compared with 0.03 per cent in atmosphere. But carbon dioxide in the sea is present in several forms: (1) as CO_2 in true solution; (2) as the undissociated carbonic acid, H_2CO_3, in minute quantity; (3) as dissociated carbonic acid, $'HCO_3^-$; (4) as the slightly soluble carbonates; and (5) as the more soluble bicarbonates. The carbonates and bicarbonates are possible because the bases, calcium, magnesium, etc., in sea water are present in amounts greater than the equivalent of stable acid radicals. This excess base constitutes the "alkali reserve" which, in changing combination with carbonic acid, is of considerable significance in maintaing a reserve of CO_2 for the use of plants. The capacity of carbon dioxide to form loose or stable combinations with bases helps to maintain the acid-base equilibrium in sea water and to preserve a more favorable environment for all forms of life. Although the amount of carbon dioxide in true solution in a liter of sea water must be measured in tenths of a cubic centimeter, there is usually available, free or in combination, something like 45-50 cc., as compared with 5-10 cc. of free oxygen. About two-thirds of the excess base is present as the bicarbonate, which, being unstable, readily yields carbon dioxide to plants in time of need. Consequently, the changing combinations of CO_2 and the bases present in sea water, act as a sort of bank-account for plants, the all-important CO_2 being subject to regular "deposit" and "withdrawal."

Sea water is a little on the alkaline side of neutrality, but the degree of alkalinity varies with hour of the day and season of the year. When the minute green (or yellow) plants are most active in bright sunlight, as at midday, and particularly in summer, the supply of CO_2 is diminished, the carbonic acid is less, and the shift is toward greater alkalinity. At night or in midwinter, when the release of CO_2 in respiration exceeds its withdrawal for photosynthesis, the supply of CO_2 and acid is greater and the water shows somewhat less alkalinity. So far as animals and plants are concerned, the small changes in alkalinity or in hydrogen ion concentration, in off-

12. See Harvey, 1928, *op. cit.*, pp. 64, 67.

shore waters, probably have no significant effect on their movements or welfare. More extreme changes of this kind, artificially induced in the laboratory, may have decided effects. Changes such as may occur in coastal waters, from the inflow of drainage waters or from the extreme utilization of CO_2 in prolific plant growth, may also have biological significance.

The relatively high solubility of carbon dioxide in sea water is of great biological significance. After all, the synthesis involving union of carbon dioxide and water in sunlight is the basis of all life. Terestrial plants are surrounded by an atmosphere having only about three one-hundredths of one percent of the essential carbon dioxide and they must generally find their water through extensive root systems. Pure water can hold in solution a somewhat greater amount of carbon dioxide than is present in an equal volume of atmosphere. Sea water is not pure but alkaline, and the alkalinity enables it to hold in true solution and in loose combination something like one hundred times as much carbon dioxide as does an equal volume of ordinary atmosphere. Consequently, where sunlight is available, the minute marine plants have at hand a larger store of this necessity along with an unlimited supply of water that does not have to be "pulled up" from a soil through roots and stems.

Carbon dioxide moves very slowly from atmosphere to sea, and vice versa, but it has been said[13] that the sea generally absorbs CO_2 from the atmosphere. If that is broadly true, the atmosphere is a reservoir of CO_2 for the sea, and it might be presumed that photosynthesis in the sea exceeded that on land. To the speculative mind this would tie in with the fact that the drift of raw materials for the production of organic life is toward the sea. At any rate, the greater the photosynthesis in the sea, the less is the permanent loss from the organic cycle of materials caught in this great catch basin of terrestrial wastes.

The conditions of life of all animals and plants in the sea and in other waters, as compared with those of terrestrial organisms, are marked by this important distinction—that the gaseous oxygen essential for respiration, occurs in relatively extreme degree of dilution. A liter of air contains twenty-five or more times the amount of oxygen that can be dissolved in a liter of sea water. The reverse

13. *Ibid.*, p. 64.

(with different proportions) is true of carbon dioxide, as we have seen.

Since the solubility of gases in water varies inversely with temperature, the cold waters of the Arctic are much richer than tropical waters, in both dissolved carbon dioxide, necessary for photosynthesis, and dissolved oxygen, required for respiration. Cold waters, being heavier than warmer waters of like salinity, tend to seek the bottom, and abyssal waters of all oceans are presumed to be derived in considerable part from the polar regions, particularly from the Antarctic, and to have been especially rich in oxygen at the start. Surface waters generally have an overabundance of oxygen. Deep waters might be supposed to be generally poor in oxygen, since the dissolved gas is used both in the respiration of abyssal animals and in the decomposition of organic materials which have settled to the bottom from the waters above, while, in the absence of photosynthesis in the darkness, no free oxygen is being liberated there. Mixing ("overturn") occurs in high latitudes, as we shall see later, and especially during the end of winter, when the colder heavier waters of the surface, laden with oxygen, sink to a lower level to replace the somewhat lighter waters which rise to the top to become reoxygenated. Unfortunately for a happy answer to the problem of the sources of oxygen in the depths, too many of the known vertical movements seem to affect only the relatively thin upper strata of sea water.

The actual conditions do not conform to any rules that may be simply stated. Bottom waters, especially in the Atlantic, where they may be 75 per cent saturated, may contain more oxygen than layers far above them. Seiwell[14] observes that the minimum concentration of oxygen in the western North Atlantic is generally between depths of 200 and 900 meters, with values ranging from 1.7 to more than 5.0 cc. per liter. Vaughan[15] says that there is in the eastern Pacific, usually between 600 and 1,200 meters, a layer where the water is only 5 per cent saturated with oxygen, while, below that, the maximum saturation may range between 30 and 40 per cent.

14. H. R. Seiwell, "The Minimum Oxygen Concentration in the Western Basin of the North Atlantic," *Papers in Physical Oceanography and Meteorology,* V (1937).

15. T. Wayland Vaughan, "Present Trends in the Investigation of the Relatioi of Marine Organisms to their Environment," *Ecological Monographs,* IV (1934), 501–22.

Carbon dioxide is certainly not consumed by green plants below some 1,000 meters, and doubtless rarely at that depth, although it must be produced there in quantity both by the respiration of animals and by the decomposition of organic material. What then becomes of that part of it in the depths which may not enter into permanent chemical combination with dissolved minerals? Are the vertical movements of water sufficient to maintain the proper equilibrium of dissolved gases in the depths? We do not seem to have the complete answers to these highly important questions.

Utilization of Material in Solution

At best sea water is a very dilute solution of many of the materials, such as phosphates and compounds of nitrogen, required for the growth and multiplication of plants; and, of course, the animals are dependent upon plants for protein food, for the energy stored by plants, and for a continuing supply of oxygen. Concentration of some of the food substances in sea water is many times less than in good soil. Correspondingly, marine plants must be adapted to derive nutriment from an extremely weak solution, to take oxygen where it is relatively scant, and to absorb radiation where the light is comparatively dim. Put in another way, they must have *greatly extended surfaces relative to size of body* to permit of maximum efficiency in absorption through the surface. In short, they must generally be of *minute* size, since the smaller the body the greater the ratio of surface to volume.

As Brooks pointed out long ago, it is advantageous for the new plant cells formed by cell multiplication to separate from each other as soon as possible in order to expose the whole of their surface to the water. Cell aggregation and specialization in form have not taken place among marine plants in any way comparable to what has occurred with terrestrial vegetation. Hence we find in the sea no direct counterparts to the grassy meadows and prairies or the true forests and jungles of the land. The coastal "forests" and "gardens" of dense populations of relatively simple seaweeds and the so-called "floating islands" of sargassum are only apparent exceptions to the rule.

Of course, marine life requires no protection against desiccation, such as is requisite for terrestrial animals, except where the home of the marine organism is between tide lines or where there may be occasional emergence at extreme low water.

In further consequence of its chemical surroundings, the marine organism, in comparison with its relatives in fresh water or on land, has a much simpler task in preserving its own internal chemical stability. Living continuously immersed in a solution not differing widely in salt content from its body fluids, the minute plant, the protozoan, the soft-bodied larva or the adult of higher groups requires relatively little protection against unfavorable or fatal chemical interchanges between body and environment. Even for them, however, the problem is not entirely wanting and protective devices may be needed.[16]

Perhaps the most notable distinctive feature of the conditions of life in the sea (or life in a chemical medium) as contrasted with the conditions of life on land is the promptness and completeness of the effects of fertilization of upper water by the upwelling of the relatively rich deep-lying waters, wherever that may occur. This is discussed further in connection with "upwelling" (p. 140, below). Only certain features of contrast need be mentioned now. When soils are fertilized by man or by nature with the formation of humus, the growing plants have to search for the nutrients through elaborate root systems. In contrast, when surface waters are naturally fertilized by upward movement of deeper waters, the bodies of one-celled plants are all in immediate contact with the pre-dissolved fertilizers. Ultimately the materials may be lost from upper water through the falling of solid wastes, but this occurs only *after* utilization of nutrients in solution to form plant and animal bodies.

We have passed over an important group of organic products in solution. Living or decomposing organisms may give out into the water "metabolites," wastes that may have diverse effects. They could be beneficial, as are vitamins, harmful to one or another species as "antibiotics," or actually toxic. Mortalities of fishes and other animals in the so-called "red tides" are attributed to wastes released by dinoflagellates (pp. 172 and 204) when from unknown causes they develop extraordinary populations. On the other hand, animals often do better in company of others of their own or another kind. A substance that helps one kind may be harmful to another.[16a]

16. For an example, with respect to fish, see p. 182, below.
16a. I need refer here only to W. C. Allee, "Recent Studies in Mass Physiology," Biol. Rev., *9*, 1934, and C. E. Lucas, "The Biological Effects of External Metabolites," *ibid.*, *22*, 1947.

Finally it is worth while to stress, not only the availability of the nutrients in sea water, but also the completeness of the menu, so to speak, for plants. The agriculturist now knows the importance of what are called "trace elements"—which are not necessarily found in ordinary commercial fertilizers and are irregularly present in soils. If deficient in the soils, they will be deficient in the plants growing on the soils and in the animals that subsist on the plants. Accordingly, the diet of whole communities of people may be sub-standard in respect to this or that element essential for proper body functions. Who does not know of goitre-ridden communities where soils are deficient in iodine and sea food is not readily available? But iodine is only one of the trace elements. The story has been told concisely and vividly by Taylor.[17]

"For ages the rains have been falling on the land, washing out the soluble nutrients and carrying them down the rivers to enrich the sea. By this process the sea has become an inexhaustible reservoir of nearly all the soluble nutrients of the world—not only of the familiar fertilizers, fixed nitrogen, phosphorus and potash, but of the indispensable array of trace elements such as iodine, fluorine, boron, manganese, copper, zinc, and indeed whatever additional elements may yet be found necessary to life; for they are all there, and in such quantities that if the whole of mankind took all of its chemical supply from the ocean, or dumped into it all of the chemicals it possesses, not the slightest detectable change would be made in the composition of the sea. The plants and animals at sea are collectors and concentrators of these elements, and when we bring them ashore we return to the land a tiny fraction of what has been taken from the land. The ocean is not only quantitatively the biggest, but qualitatively the most perfect source of nutriment in the world."

17. Harden F. Taylor, "Research in the Fisheries for the Betterment of the South," in *Research and Regional Welfare*, Chapel Hill: The University of North Carolina Press, 1946.

CHAPTER 7

Some Physical Properties of Sea Water

Temperature

THE OCEANS CONSTITUTE AN ENORMOUS RESERVOIR OF HEAT. This is not only because by far the greater part of the radiation coming to the earth from the sun falls upon the surface of the sea but also because, of all liquids and solids except ammonia, water has the highest "specific heat," or the greatest capacity to absorb heat with minimum rise in temperature; to raise the temperature one degree requires the application of more heat for water than for any other ordinary substance except ammonia. Raising the temperature of the surface of the sea at any spot by only a few degrees represents a tremendous storage of heat, which can be given off in winter or at some distant place to which the water may be transported by currents, if the air above the water at the second place is cooler than the sea. Obviously, too, great volumes of air can be heated with little reduction in temperature of the water.

Furthermore, the sea contributes greatly to the reservoir of heat in water vapor of the atmosphere. Water has by far the highest heat of evaporation of all known substances that are liquid at ordinary temperatures; in change from the liquid state to vapor it absorbs and holds more heat than does any other such substance in making a corresponding change, and sea water is not essentially different from pure water in this respect. Therefore, it is through evaporation of the surface of the ocean that great quantities of heat are stored in the form of water vapor, to be released again over other parts of the ocean or over the land. Since, as it has been estimated, some 90 per cent of the heat surplus of the oceans is used for evaporation, "evaporation is of much greater importance to the heat balance of the ocean than is the transfer of sensible heat."[1]

Water is peculiar also in the amount of heat absorbed in the melting of ice, and conversely, in the amount of heat that has to be removed from water to permit freezing.[2] In this respect, again, it is exceeded among common substances only by ammonia. It is not by chance that we use water or water vapor (steam) for the distribution of heat throughout our buildings or that we use ice or ammonia in refrigeration. So the seas serve in the great terrestrial heating and cooling system, playing a leading part in the world-wide distribution of heat, and giving a sort of thermostatic control to regional temperatures.

The source of heat is the sun, but the sunshine falls unevenly on the earth, being greatest in tropical regions and least at the poles. The absorption of solar radiation by the sea, its influence on movements of sea water, and the part the sea plays in the general distribution of heat over the earth are proper subjects for consideration in a later chapter. At present we are concerned merely with the general conditions of temperature in the seas as compared with temperatures on land.

In the first place, it is to be noted that the range of temperature in the sea is far less than that on land, and this is true whether we consider daily or seasonal changes at a particular place, or the extreme range over the whole world. Apparently, sea water is never more than two or three degrees below the freezing point of fresh water, the formation of ice checking a further fall; and it is rarely higher than about 80°F. (27°C.). Evaporation serves as some check on the rise. Air temperatures over the open sea are never far different from those of the water. Over land, on the other hand, the air temperatures may be 60° or 70°F. below zero or more than 120°F. (about 50°C.) above; they vary widely, not only with the season, but also with the hours of the day. Nowhere in the sea, in contrast, is the surface temperature likely to vary more than 10° with the season or more than about one degree between day and night.[3] The

---

1. H. U. Sverdrup, *Oceanography for Meteorologists*, p. 62.
2. But see footnote 4,.p. 98, below.
3. There are, however, some geographic areas where at certain times warm currents displace cold water, and vice versa, so that seasonal differences as great as 40°F. may be found. (See Marmer, *The Sea*, p. 132, and below, p. 132.)

highest temperatures in the oceans are found to come about two o'clock in the afternoon and the lowest about five in the morning. In the northern hemisphere surface waters are coolest in February and warmest in August; in the southern hemisphere, the reverse is the case. The temperature of the surface water in the ocean does vary to some extent with season and with longitude, but much more notably with latitude and with depth. At any given place deep water is virtually unchanging in temperature, and it is always cold; bottom water varies between $4\,^{\circ}C$. and $-1.5\,^{\circ}C$. Consequently, the range of temperature between surface and bottom may be nearly as great as between any two points on the surface.

Because of currents, to be discussed later, which convey great masses of equatorial water toward the poles or bring waters from Arctic and Antarctic regions toward the tropics, and, in part also, because of sinking and upwelling movements of water in different regions, the seas are generally warmest in their western parts. At the most, the seasonal variations in temperature are relatively small as compared with those that prevail on land in temperate and subpolar regions and as compared with those of most fresh waters in the same regions. Indeed, beyond a depth of about 200 meters, seasonal variations do not occur at all. Differences between summer and winter temperatures of the surface of the Atlantic Ocean are least in polar and in tropical regions, greatest in the north temperate zone. Variations with latitude are notably modified by ocean currents; so that, while comparatively warm water in the course of the Gulf Stream prevails far up in the northern Atlantic, surprisingly cold water is encountered in the path of the Humboldt, or Peru, Current very close to the Equator in the eastern part of the Pacific Ocean. The drift of icebergs also has observable effects on the temperature of the North Atlantic, effects that vary with the year and with the shifts of currents.

Sea water has no definite freezing point. There is a point on the temperature scale for sea water of any given condition of salinity when ice crystals begin to form; but the "freezing out" of pure water leaves the remaining unfrozen water with higher salt content and, therefore, with lower freezing point. Further cooling causes formation of more ice crystals with still further increased salt concentration and lowered freezing point in the remaining water, until finally there is formed a solid block of mixed ice and salt crystals.

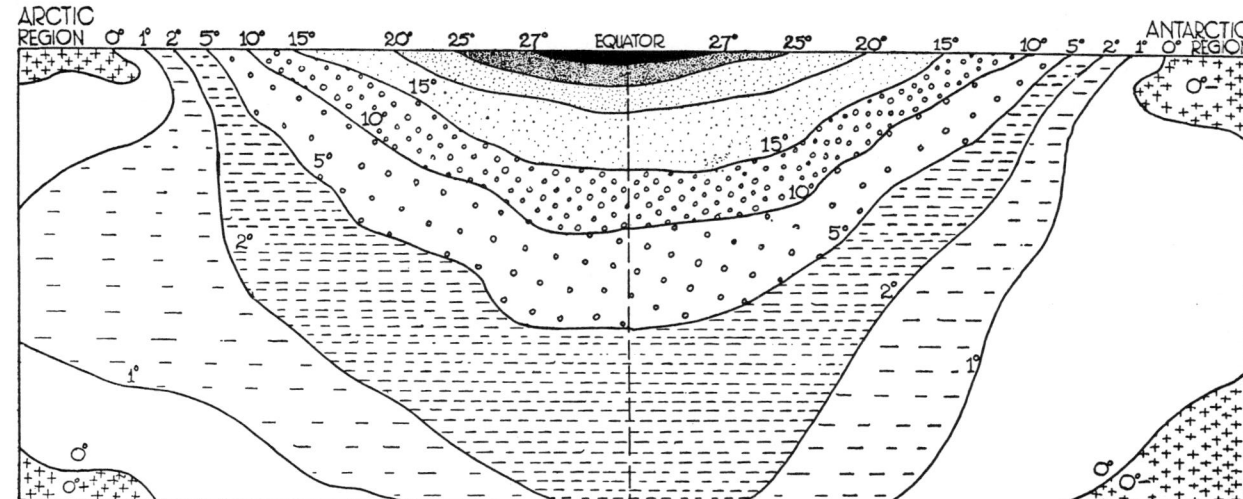

FIGURE 7. Schematic representation of the distribution of temperatures by depth and latitude, showing the possible continuity of zones of low temperatures through all latitudes. The depth scale is greatly exaggerated relative to the latitude scale. (Suggested by a chart of Chun for a restricted region). Actually, there is more asymmetry with latitude than is shown here.

The sketch is crude and makes no pretence of offering a reliable picture of the actual conditions of temperature in any latitude. For a more informative and accurate but more complex representation of the distribution of temperatures in the deeper waters of the Atlantic, see the charts of Georg Wüst in one of the Meteor reports: *Schichtung und Zirkulation des Atlantic Ozeans, erste Lieferung: Das Bodenwasser und die Gliederung der Atlantischen Tiefsee* (Berlin and Leipzig, 1933).

With rising temperatures the process is reversed: the first thawing liquefies a part of the ice, and takes up heat; further heating is necessary to cause further melting. It is a fact well known to polar explorers that, where sponge ice has been forced into heaps in such a way that the concentrated salt water may seep out, the solid sea ice, when melted, may give good drinking water.[4]

Unlike fresh water, sea water becomes heavier as it is cooled until its freezing point is reached,[5] so that the limitation of 4°C. for temperatures at the bottom of lakes does not apply in the sea, and bottom temperatures of $-1°$, or lower, may occur in polar currents; but, although the temperature at which freezing begins ($-1.9°$ for water with salinity of 35 o/oo) is substantially lowered under high pressure, bottom temperatures below the freezing point of fresh water seem to be rare; nevertheless, they do prevail in some places, as in the Norwegian Sea. Generally the temperature of abyssal waters is a little above zero, owing no doubt in great part to what Helland-Hansen has called "adiabatic warming"—warming resulting from the effect of pressure (see p. 111, below.) In the North Atlantic generally the bottom temperature is around 2°C. The bottom water is cold in equatorial as well as in polar regions; even at the Equator one can find sea water close to the freezing point, if one only goes deep enough. It may be recalled (p. 26, above, footnote 13) that ooze from the bottom in tropical seas served well in lieu of ice for the cooling of champagne! "Over 4/5 of the ocean floor exceeds one mile in depth and has a temperature colder than 3°C."[6] The barriers of temperature and pressure that exist between the bottom and the surface (separated by a distance of 4 or 5 miles) at the equator are much more effective than those that exist between two points 10,000 miles apart on the bottom.

With respect to surface temperatures, latitude is the principal

4. Often sea ice contains air bubbles, since air may creep in where brine has trickled out. Consequently the density of sea ice varies; it may be a little more or a little less than that of pure ice. Sea ice is said to be highly transparent for visible radiation. We speak of the *heat of fusion* of ice which is approximately 80 cal/g. With sea ice, in contrast to ice from pure water, melting occurs whenever the temperature rises, no matter how low it may be, so that no specific value for the heat of fusion of sea ice can be stated. It does, however, require a substantial amount of heat to melt a given amount of sea ice. See Sverdrup, 1942, pp. 33, 34.

5. This applies to water with a salinity of 24.7 o/oo or higher.

6. Claude E. ZoBell, "Microbiological Activities at Low Temperatures with Particular Reference to Marine Bacteria," *Quarterly Review of Biology*, IX (1934), 460–66.

factor determining differences between different regions. There is on the whole a decrease in average temperature from about 81°F. (27°C.) near the Equator to about 29°F., or 3° below the freezing point of fresh water, in Arctic and Antarctic regions. As a rough rule, it may be said that the average surface temperature decreases about one-half a degree C. for each degree of increase in latitude.[7]

The average surface temperature for the sea as a whole is about 63°F., but it is higher in the northern hemisphere (67°F.) and lower in the southern (61°F.). For the Atlantic and the Indian oceans the average temperatures of surface waters are not greatly different, but for the Pacific it is some 4° higher (66½°F.). Obviously the principal reason for this difference is found in the forms of the two oceans. The Pacific is roughly oval in shape, with great breadth in equatorial regions where high temperatures prevail, but the Atlantic is somewhat hour-glass shaped, with a narrow waist in the low latitudes crossing the Equator obliquely.

Evaporation tends, of course, to increase the density and weight of surface water and might be expected to cause it always to sink, but *widespread* vertical movements from this cause are believed to be relatively insignificant—because, where evaporation is considerable, as in warmer regions, its effect in raising specific gravity may be more than counterbalanced by the decrease in density resulting from the warming of the surface water. The cooling effect of evaporation comes also into the picture. The lower salinity of surface water over the continental shelf, where runoff from land is felt, and the higher temperature of surface waters over the seas generally, both tend to keep top water on top. Nevertheless, "overturn" occurs in high latitudes, especially during or at the end of winter, whenever the surface-cooled waters become colder and heavier than those beneath them; but this overturn affects, perhaps, only the waters above the thermocline or zone of most rapid change of temperature.

How Temperature in the Deep Is Taken

From what has been said about the continuity of the seas and the constant movements of water masses, it may be understood that *generally* there are neither sharp differences nor continously progressive changes in temperature of sea water from place to place or from depth to depth. If we are to trace movements of masses of

7. Marmer, *op. cit.*, p. 143.

water on the partial basis of temperature differences, we must be prepared to measure very small differences and to do so with a high degree of accuracy. Surface thermometers should be accurate to 0.10 of a degree centigrade and they must be repeatedly standardized. For the depths, the thermometer must be accurate to a much smaller fraction of a degree, say to one one-hundredth of a degree. There is the further complication that precise recordings of deep temperatures have to be made at a great distance, often thousands of fathoms, from the observer.

At one time insulated water bottles were used to take samples of water at desired depths, and the temperature would be read an hour or several hours later when the bottle was hauled aboard ship. The insulation prevented great change of temperature between time of taking and time of observation. It is obvious that really accurate determinations were not insured. What was needed was a thermometer that would register the temperature at a particular depth and not change as it was brought up through the warmer, upper waters to be read later, perhaps hours later. This need was first met by the *reversing thermometer*, introduced by Negretti and Zambra of England in 1874. Subsequently, the instrument was greatly improved by the makers, and particularly, by a German instrument-maker named Richter. The technician who can make such a thermometer is rare indeed; it is only recently that they have been made in America.

The tube of a reversing thermometer is drawn exceedingly fine in one section, which is coiled in a complex way. At a particular point the fine bore is still more reduced to make a "breaking point" for the column of mercury. In the position of the thermometer as it is lowered, the bulb, or reservoir of mercury, is at the lower end, but the scale, to be read after reversal, has the zero mark near the upper end of the thermometer, which is quite empty of mercury. When the instrument has been lowered to the level at which the record of temperature is to be made, a metal "messenger," clasped around the line, is released to slide down and trip a catch that has held the thermometer in unbalanced position: the thermometer inverts itself immediately. The scale, which was upside down, is now right side up. In this process of violent upset, the column of mercury should part at the "breaking point"; so that all the mercury that was above this point at the time of inversion falls to the new bottom end, from which its length can be read on the scale at *any* later time of observation. It does not matter what happens later to the main mass of mercury, since the reading will be taken *from the mercury that was beyond the breaking point at the moment of reversal*. It is only this snapped-off mercury that counts. It is customary to have also a small thermometer alongside the stem and within an outer protective case. The reading of this "stem thermometer" gives the temperature at the time of reading and makes possible certain small corrections for expansion or contraction of the snapped-off mercury between the time of reversal and the time of record.

The reversing thermometer lowered to great depths is subjected to high pressures and it must, therefore, be protected by an outer *closed* tube of heavy glass with a lot of cushioning mercury around the reservoir. The protection is in part against the effect of extreme hydrostatic pressures on the mercury in the thermometer proper, and, therefore, on the reading of the thermometer. Obviously a thermometer mounted in an *open* glass tube would give a reading that would be dependent both upon the temperature and the pressure, and this would affect the apparent reading. Consequently, if an *unprotected* reversing thermometer is paired with a *protected* reversing thermometer the difference between the readings of the two thermometers will be an indication of the *pressure* and, therefore, of the *depth* at which the thermometers were reversed. Such a determination of depth is particularly desirable where the line by which the thermometers are suspended extends at an angle from the ship and may even be curved.

By means of *thermographs* continuous records of temperatures may be taken; but this type of instrument can be used only from fixed stations or for records near the surface of the sea. The thermograph is a mechanism by which a record of the temperature is made on a revolving paper-covered drum. In other types of instruments a pin moved by the thermometer draws a line on a smoked-glass slide, the position of which changes with the pressure, that is to say in this case, with the depth. One of the latest instruments is the *bathythermograph*. This contains a bellows that contracts with increase in pressure as the instrument descends and a Bourdon element that responds to temperature changes. This torpedo-shaped instrument at the end of a light cable can be lowered into the water from a vessel in movement. During its descent a record of temperature is plotted against depth on a small glass plate.

Temperature and Life in the Sea

Temperature apparently exerts in many ways an influence on the chemical activities in protoplasm that underlie growth, form, and multiplication. Rate of photosynthesis increases with temperature, while rates of most biological activities are more than doubled by a rise of 10°C. Temperature governs, to some extent, the distribution of animals and plants and, where a particular species has a range extending through low and high latitudes, its form or the character of its shell may differ with the latitude. As will be mentioned again in connection with the consideration of density, the form of an animal or plant in a given region may be notably different in summer from that which it has in winter. It is not, however, easily determined whether the differences that appear to go with temperature are governed actually by temperature or by other environmental conditions associated causally or incidentally with temperature. In many instances, and perhaps as a general rule, the size that an animal attains is greater when it is reared at a lower temperature.

It is true of some organisms, and perhaps generally true, that organisms grow faster, but attain smaller adult sizes in warmer waters; that they reproduce earlier and more frequently in warmer waters. If they grow more slowly and reproduce less frequently in colder waters, they may not only become larger but also live longer; so that colder waters may harbor much larger populations of some organisms, such as diatoms and copepods. Cold-bred organisms may also differ in form from warm-bred members of the same species, the latter tending, sometimes, at least, to develop spinous or plumose extensions of the body surface.

Gran says: "Temperature, more perhaps than any other factor, determines the growth and decrease of the various species and the character of the communities dominating the plankton. But some species are adapted even to the most extreme temperatures found in the sea, and a rich growth can take place as well at the lowest (−1.5°) as at the highest temperatures observed."[8] "Temperature," says Martin,[9] "is less directly important in the sea than on land since there is no great danger of injurious extremes being

8. H. H. Gran, "Phytoplankton, Methods and Problems," Cons. Perm. Intern. Explor. Mer., *Jour. Conseil.* VII (1932), 348.

9. George W. Martin, "The Food Resources of the Sea," *Scientific Monthly,* XV (1922), 457. (Of course, fish in the sea, subject to a narrow range of temperature, may be highly sensitive to small changes.)

reached. Indirectly, its importance lies in the fact that carbon dioxide is much more soluble in cold water than in warm, and it is probably this, rather than the direct influence of temperature, which accounts for the fact that the most luxuriant development of plant life is in the colder waters of the earth." Allen,[10] on the other hand. questions the certainty of a generally greater productivity of plankton in high as compared with low latitudes.

Viscosity

Water is a liquid, but liquids vary in respect to their fluidity, alcohol being more and glycerine less fluid than water. The same liquid is more or less fluid under different conditions: thus, as everyone knows, warm water flows more readily, or is "wetter," so to speak, than cold water. An animal expends more energy in moving the same distance through cold than through warm water. We are concerned, then, with the *viscosity* of sea water, meaning its resistance to change of form or to movement, so far as that is due to the combined effect of the qualities of adhesion and of cohesion among particles of water. The viscosity of fresh water is an environmental factor of substantial significance to both animals and plants. The viscosity of sea water is a little greater than that of fresh water and increases gradually with increasing salinity. It varies much more with temperature, being nearly doubled by a decrease in temperature from 25°C. (77°F.) to 0°C. (32°F.). The change in viscosity with falling temperature is not uniform, the increase per degree of lowering temperature being greater at the lower temperatures.

Under actual conditions, simple *laminar viscosity* is greatly complicated by what is called *eddy viscosity*. A body moving through a liquid sets in motion, through frictional stress, the liquid immediately in contact with it, and that in turn sets in motion the next adjacent layer of liquid and so on. Actually, however, we do not have thin uniform layers gliding smoothly over one another (*laminar* motion.) Not only does random movement of molecules cause interchange of molecules between adjacent layers, but also masses of water pass from layer to layer, introducing *turbulence* phenomena *and dynamic eddy viscosity*, which is effective in both horizontal and vertical directions. The analysis of turbulence phenomena or

10. Winfred E. Allen, "The Primary Food Supply of the Sea," *Quarterly Review of Biology*, IX, 175.

eddy viscosity now taxes the skill of the most expert physicists and mathematicians. We refer at all to these complex subjects only because it ought to be kept in mind that "coefficients of viscosity," as expressed in ordinary tables, touch only a small part of the problem of viscosity associated with the movements of animals and plants through water. Eddy viscosity is many times greater than laminar viscosity.

In consequence of the relation between viscosity and temperature, an incompressible object may sink much more rapidly at the surface than in the colder waters below; but any object will continue to sink so long as its specific gravity is higher than that of the water it meets. The old idea that sinking ships are arrested in their fall at some level of intermediate depth is, of course, without foundation. A wooden ship would, indeed, attain a greater sinking velocity as the pressure reduced its displacement by squeezing out the air from the wood cells. Contrary to what might be surmised, pressure does not materially effect viscosity; for pure water viscosity is even somewhat reduced by high pressure at temperatures below $32°C$.

Influence of Viscosity on Organisms in the Sea

The viscosity of the medium offers two of the marked contrasts between life in water and life in the atmosphere. As any swimmer or any designer of automotive craft well knows, it requires a very much greater expenditure of energy to propel a body through water than it does to drive it through the atmosphere. One might suppose, then, that aquatic animals were necessarily slow of movement as compared with terrestrial animals; but again we find such adaptations of form and of locomotive power that the swiftest animals of the sea, such as the bonitos and related fishes, and even bulky animals like porpoises and the larger whales, are capable of velocities of movement that compare well with those of the swiftest of terrestrial or aerial birds and mammals.

The viscosity of sea water has a further significance to organic life in water in that it retards sinking; but sinking velocity is also a function of form. Because of the inverse correlation of viscosity with temperature, the viscosity of water, unlike its salinity, varies materially with the season. A peculiar phenomenon that has engaged the attention of many students of the drifting life of sea and fresh waters is the seasonal change of form manifested by some

short-lived plants and animals, notably some diatoms, rotifers, cladocera, and copepods. The change occurs, not in the individual from
time to time, but in successive generations; thus at any given time the
animals (or the plants) may be quite different in appearance from
their ancestor or from their descendants living within the same
year but at other seasons. There seems clearly to be a variable adaptation between form and viscosity, but it is not so evident whether the
changes in form observed in these phenomena of "cyclomorphosis"
are actually induced by changing viscosity or by changing temperature or by other conditions that vary concomitantly with temperature.

In the discussion of temperature and life (p. 102 above), we mentioned the fact that warm-bred organisms of the open waters often
attain less size than those bred (and grown) in colder waters. It is
obvious that small bodies have greater surface area than do larger
ones of the same form. The smaller size, with greater proportionate
surface exposure to the surrounding medium is, then, thought of as
an adaptation to the reduced viscosity of the medium. Less energy
is required to prevent sinking (in the "more liquid" medium) below the favored or favoring level. We say more of this after considering density.

The "streamlining" of the bodies of aquatic animals is governed
largely by the phenomena of viscosity and density in the medium
through which the organism moves. Its importance varies with the
speed of movement characteristic of the organism; for the faster the
movement, the greater is the stress exerted on the surface of the animal, and the greater the volume of water that must be displaced in a
given time. In this connection it should be added that the filling-in
of the space left behind the moving animal is a large part of the problem. Anyone who has felt the backward and downward "drag" on
the stern of a speed boat when the power is suddenly cut off can ap-
preciate the fact that replacement of water behind is as much a feature of movement as displacement of water ahead. As Welch has well
said, the results of experiments show that the closer is the approach
of body shape to the streamline form the greater is the reduction of
resistance to progress in water; so that, contrary to popular impression, an object or an animal with short, rounded, blunt forward
portion followed by a longer, tapering after-portion meets less resistance to movement through water than does an object of the

reverse form. The sperm whale is a notable example of good streamline form.

Density

The density of sea water, or, practically speaking, its specific gravity, or weight relative to that of an equal volume of pure water at 4°C. and at atmospheric pressure, is correlated with salinity. Higher *specific gravity*, of course, reduces the effective weight of animals or plants in the sea. The specific gravity of sea water of salinity of 35 parts per 1,000 is close to 1.028 at 0°C., but it is greater at lower temperatures and less at higher, and slightly greater under high pressure (1 ¾ per cent greater at 400 atmospheres, as at a depth of 4,000 meters).[11]

The protoplasm of marine animals is not greatly different from that of terrestrial animals, but the former live in a medium of approximately the same specific gravity as the living parts of their bodies, while the latter are surrounded by a medium of far less density. The support of the body against the pull of gravitation presents a problem to the terrestrial animal that must be met by adaptation in form, appendages, skeleton, and muscles. This problem is less acutely felt by aquatic animals in fresh water, and much less so by those of marine habit. Even when, on occasion, the problem of support is not successfully met, the fall of an animal on the land is a much more violent occurrence than the fall of an animal in the water—within the range of depth to which it is adapted. In the plant world as well, the differences in form and structure of terrestrial and marine plants are probably related in no little measure to the differences in density of the respective media in which they have their being.

Doubtless all marine animals and most marine plants are somewhat heavier than the surrounding media except as they have special buoyancy organs. But any one who has witnessed the effects of an explosion of dynamite in the water knows that some of the dead bodies of fish rise to the surface while others sink to the bottom. The problem for marine animals that do not live on the bottom, and for plants as well, is generally that of keeping above the bottom rather than that of staying beneath the surface; falling to the bottom, it may be understood, is a serious matter when the bottom is several miles removed and marked by conditions of pressure, temperature,

11. Welch, Paul S., *Limnology*, New York and London, 1935 (McGraw-Hill).

and darkness that may not be tolerable to organisms of the upper strata. Keeping within a zone of tolerable pressure represents for animals in the sea a problem to which there is nothing comparable for animals on land—the problems of falling neither downward nor upward to levels of extremely different conditions of pressure. Gas bladders, accumulations of fat or oil droplets contribute to buoyancy, while in both animals and plants notable extensions of the body surface, the so-called "flotation processes" offer resistance to sinking or serve as keels and rudders to facilitate movement in a horizontal or upward direction.

The contrast in densities of sea water and fresh water is illustrated by the fact that many marine fishes have eggs that are "emersal"— float at the surface—or that remain suspended at intermediate depths; the eggs of fresh-water fishes sink to the bottom, or are "demersal." Floating eggs are almost unknown in fresh water, except for some Amphibia, some Cladocera, and a very few insects.

In this connection, as in others, references may be made to the minute size of the vast majority of organisms of the sea, a condition that seems not to prevail to the same degree with land and fresh-water organisms. Doubtless, also, a great number of small organisms quickly disintegrate after death into still smaller particles. Rate of sinking is a function both of weight and of the frictional resistance to movement through the water, and friction is a function both of the viscosity of the medium and of the surface area in contact with the medium.[12] The more viscous the medium and the greater the surface in proportion to mass, the slower the rate of falling. It is a

12. By Stokes's law the rate of sinking is inversely proportional to the viscosity but directly proportional to the difference in specific gravity between the body and the medium. Sinking rate also depends upon size, varying with the square of the radius, and upon form. Stokes's law holds only for a small sphere, whereas the bodies of plankton organisms, which are generally of more or less irregular *form*, offer special resistance derived from the increased area exposed to the medium. As the dead body sinks there is also the possibility of its taking up salts to change its specific gravity and its sinking velocity. There enters in, moreover, the influence of "eddy viscosity," previously alluded to, which retards sinking.

The formula for Stokes's law, expressing the velocity of fall of a spherical body through a liquid, is

$$V = \frac{2g(P_1 - P_2)r^2}{9\mu}$$

Where V stands for velocity of fall, g is the acceleration due to gravity (32.16 feet per sec.²), P_1 and P_2 are the respective densities of sphere and liquid; r is the radius of the sphere; and μ is the dynamic viscosity of the liquid.

well-known law that the smaller the object the greater is the surface relative to volume. As Krogh[13] has expressed it, "the rate of sinking of the minute plankton organisms is so low that they can remain in the upper strata of the water for the length of their natural lives." Yet this does not fully answer the question of how non-motile organisms continue to live in the upper layers of water; for, unless the rate of sinking were zero, each succeeding generation would begin falling where the preceding generation had left off; and, after a few generations, the bottom would be reached by all: the upper strata would have become entirely depopulated.

The rate of sinking can be zero only if the viscosity were infinitely great—that is to say, if the ocean were solid, which it is not; or if the ratio of surface to volume were infinitely great, which is impossible; or finally, if the organisms were of like weight with the water in which they live. Should the last condition prevail, there would be no need to invoke either viscosity of the medium or size and form of the organism as factors of retardation, since there would be no tendency to sink—nothing to be retarded. We may assume that sinking at a very slow rate does occur, but that either some compensatory capacity for upward movement is inherent in the smallest organisms, or upward currents in the water lift the organisms as much as they sink.

In short, the mechanics of flotation of non-motile or weakly motile organisms is not a fully solved problem. The phenomena of viscosity to be encountered are by no means so simple as might at first be thought. The sea is not static: there are movements of animals and of plants, even if only sinking movements, with accompanying disturbances of smaller or greater masses of water. Anywhere, too, there may be drifts or currents, as yet little known, but producing correlative viscosity effects which can now be but imperfectly analyzed by the most expert mathematician.

As a final word in this brief consideration of the subject of specific gravity, it may be remarked that the dead bodies of marine animals and plants must generally sink to the bottom except as they are devoured by scavengers or become dissolved in the water in the course of their long descent. Since sinking velocity varies directly with the size of the body, the smaller animals and plants are the more

13. *Op. cit.,* p. 423.

likely to be dissolved or to be devoured on the way down; their components may then reappear in part in new forms as the soluble metabolic wastes of the "consumer." Bodies of larger organisms, sinking much more rapidly and dissolving more slowly, have the greater relative chance of reaching the bottom. Nevertheless, we shall see later that the skeletons of myriads of minute plants and animals make up a large part of the deposits on the floor of the ocean. The remains of many large animals too are found at greater depths. Speaking of whales, Krogh says:[14] "A sinking velocity of 100 meters per hour will bring a body to the bottom in most places in less than two days. At one station in the Southern Pacific the 'Challenger' got up in the trawl from the red clay bottom at 4,300 meters (over 2½ miles) several thousand sharks' teeth and not less than fifty ear bones of whales, but of course it is not known how many thousands of years this accumulation required."

Pressure

Pressure in the ocean, increasing by one atmosphere for every 33 feet of depth, varies from one atmosphere (about 15 lbs. per square inch) at the surface to nearly 1,000 atmospheres at the greatest depth. It is obvious, of course, that the greatest difference in pressure to which a terrestrial animal may be subject in passing from the lowest level of exposed land to the top of the loftiest mountain peak or even to the greatest height to which a bird or a plane can soar, must be considerably less than one atmosphere. In the sea so great is the pressure even at the very moderate depth of 1,000 meters (a little over 100 atmospheres) that a block of ordinary wood, it is said, would be reduced to half its volume, through the squeezing out of air ordinarily imprisoned in the cell spaces; compressed to this extent, it would sink instead of float. A similar statement would apply to cork.

It is an old but, as we now see, a very irrational assumption that the conditions of pressure that prevail in the depths of the sea were inconsistent with the existence of life. As was mentioned in consideration of the pioneer work of Edward Forbes, an azoic area beyond the depth of some 1,800 feet (600 meters) was once conceived to exist. Not only have explorations with deep-sea trawls,

14. *Op. cit.*, p. 433.

dredges, and plankton nets revealed the falsity of such an assumption, but obviously there was no *a priori* reason for it. It is a quality of liquid, as of gas, that pressure at any level is uniformly distributed in all directions. Consequently, for an organism adapted to the pressure, it is no more to be supposed that the animal should suffer from it than that we should be overwhelmed by an atmospheric pressure of some fifteen pounds to the square inch—let us say, some tens of thousands of pounds of pressure per total area of body. Being adapted to it we endure it, without even being aware of it—except under conditions of *change* of pressure.

Nevertheless, the change in pressure with depth does interpose some barrier to the vertical migration of animals. If we suffer in undergoing the relatively slight modification of pressure within the limits of a single atmosphere when we ascend to an elevation of 10,000 or 15,000 feet or when we descend only a few meters into the water, what must be expected to be the physiological effect upon a marine organism that, in its daily or seasonal wanderings, may undergo changes of pressure to the amount of several atmospheres? One of the most noteworthy qualities of marine organisms is their capacity for rapid adaptation to great differences in pressure. To take only one conspicuous example, how does the whale escape damage from compression when it "sounds" to pass in a few minutes through ranges of pressure that would completely wreck a human system even if it were allowed an indefinite period for the transition? And why does it not suffer "caisson disease" from decompression when it re-emerges? (One difference: air is not pumped to the whale!)

If the whale, according to the best records, may dive rapidly to a depth of more than half a mile, not all marine animals are so adaptable. As Dr. Herdman has said, "If deep sea fishes accidentally get out of their accustomed depth and pressure, the expansion of air in their swim-bladders renders them so buoyant that they continue to tumble upwards to the surface, helpless, and are eventually killed by the distention of their bodies and the disorganization of their tissues due to the diminished pressure. They die a violent death from falling upwards."[15] Is death due sometimes to the extreme change of temperature suffered in rising from the cold depths to the relatively warm surface water?

15. *Founders of Oceanography*, p. 161.

Great pressures have certain secondary effects to which only allusions may be made here. Curiously enough, high pressure reduces slightly the viscosity of water, or what we might loosely describe as the cohesiveness of its particles (cf. p. 104). Under the great pressures prevailing in the depths the water is a little more fluid than is water of the same temperature and salinity at the surface. Presumably, however, we can find no particular biological significance in the slightly greater ease of movement for animals living in deep water of slightly decreased viscosity, especially since, at the same time that viscosity is reduced, density is increased.

Water is generally described as incompressible; but it is not entirely so. We are told that, if the compression of water in the sea under its own great weight could be miraculously eliminated, the general sea level would rise about 27 ½ meters, or nearly 93 feet.[16] It is only because of the compressibility of sea water, slight as it is, that our eastern Atlantic coast line is where it is, instead of a hundred or more miles to the west. Of some real significance, on the other hand, is the effect of pressure on temperature. Deep water has actually a higher temperature than it would have except for the pressure to which it is subjected. A sample of water having a temperature of 2 °C. at 8,000 meters, when brought to the surface, will, without addition or subtraction of heat, have a temperature nearly 1° lower.[17] For an animal of the deep, there must be some biological significance in such a difference, although, when we think of particular animals, the question is of theoretical interest alone: animals of the deep are almost exclusively such as have experienced no changes of conditions over great spaces and throughout their lives.

16. James Johnston, *An Introduction to Oceanography.*
17. Sverdrup, *Oceanography for Meteorologists*, p. 14.

CHAPTER 8

Deposits on the Bottom of the Sea

W E HAVE ALREADY CONSIDERED (P. 67, ABOVE) THE TOPOGraphy of the bottom, with its continental terrace (shelf and slope) and rolling floor marked with hills, ridges, furrows, and deeps. The continental shelf extends out some 100 miles, to where the water is something like 100 fathoms. We have also alluded (p. 85, above) to the general absence from the floor of the ocean of soft organic materials such as compose the familiar silt at the bottoms of ponds and pools. Most falling organic material is dissolved or decomposed in the course of a lingering descent from the prolific upper waters to the floor thousands of meters below. Where the depth is great, only the hard parts or skeletal materials arrive at the bottom. Even in the case of the skeleton of a minute organism, the chance of arriving at the bottom depends upon its solubility and the length of time required for the descent. The duration of the period of falling is conditioned, in turn, upon the size and form of the skeleton or skeletal part and upon the depth of the sea at the place of sedimentation. Because of the density and viscosity of the water, the tooth of a shark or the ear-bone of a whale will reach the bottom in a fraction of the period of time required by the skeleton of a protozoan and, because of this and of its size, it will be less affected by processes of dissolution during the period of sinking. A minute silicious skeleton of a radiolarian protozoan will arrive intact at the bottom in deeper water than will the calcareous skeleton of a foraminiferan of the same size, because it is more resistant to the corrosive agents in sea water. Where the depth is very great, no fine skeletal materials will reach the bottom and there one may find only the original rock supplemented by skeletal remains of larger animals and inorganic materials that have drifted into the sea through the atmosphere. It is evident, then, that the floor of the deeper parts of the sea is not padded with mire, or covered with a sludge, as may be the bottoms of ponds and bays, but, rather, that it is covered with a litter of hard remains of animals and plants and some inorganic "dust."

The bottom may be sampled by the use of the deep-sea dredge or of a bottom-sampling tube. Various forms of dredges are used. The ordinary dredge consists of a bag hung behind a rectangular or triangular frame of iron. Dredges are usually made so that they function equally well, whichever long side lies on the bottom, and the lips are beveled to scrape the upper layers. For special purposes, dredges may have teeth to plough the bottom and stir out the burrowing mollusks, worms, etc. There are also "bottom grabs" of the clam-shell bucket type, the Ekman and the Petersen dredges, which fall on the bottom in open positions; when a "messenger" of brass tubing is sent down the line and releases a catch, powerful springs close the mouth of the heavy bucket, causing it to bite into the bottom, taking whatever in the upper layer is between its jaws. In samples collected by such apparatus, the materials are mixed, and there is no indication of their natural vertical disposition.

To gain information as to subsurface material or as to the natural arrangement in layers, a steel tube may be driven into the bottom to bring up a core sample. If the tube is lined with a smaller cardboard tube, the latter can be withdrawn and stored for later study without disturbance of the original layering. The bottom-sampling tube may be driven into the bottom by allowing a heavy weight to drop automatically upon the head of the tube when its foot touches the bottom. A more recent and effective method of applying force to the tube is with the use of an explosive charge in a gun, such as the "Piggott gun," which is attached at the top of the tube: the tube is literally "shot" into the bottom.

For more than half a century cameras have been used for photographing the bottom, and this instrument has great possibilities in the future; the shutter may be operated from the boat, or shutter and flashlight may be set off automatically as the camera, or a trigger-like extension from it, touches the bottom.[1]

1. *Science*, C (Supplement), 10.

It was Sir John Murray who originally described the principal marine deposits, after extensive studies of the "Challenger" (and later) collections. His general classification is still followed. The conditions of sedimentation beneath the shallower waters of the continental shelf are naturally quite different from those below the deep waters of the open seas. Because of the conditions just described, deposits on the bottom of the ocean may be considered in three chief groups: (1) *terrigenous*, with quartz and other mineral matter brought from the land by rivers and wave action, and, on the average, some two-thirds silica; (2) *neritic*, farther out, consisting of materials from the land mixed with organic substances formed in the shallow coastal waters, such as the remains of mollusks, crustacea, echinoderms, worm tubes, etc.; and (3), beyond the direct influence of land, *pelagic*, comprising materials originating almost exclusively in the sea or coming through the atmosphere, from land or interplanetary space.

Terrigenous and neritic deposits are, of course, found chiefly on the continental shelf. The terrigenous deposits, mainly materials from the land, are the shallow-water sands and muds, in which quartz grains constitute a prominent part, and the deeper red, blue, and green muds, with colors due to predominance of different mineral substances, such as oxides of iron and manganese and glauconite (silicates of iron and potassium); volcanic muds and coral sands and muds may form a part. Terrigenous deposits shade into the neritic, in which materials formed by organisms in the sea play a greater part, along with the finer terrestrial materials.

The pelagic deposits comprise four chief "oozes" of organic origin and "red clay." Oozes, in the oceanographic sense, are not to be thought of as comparable in appearance or in character to the oozy mud of ponds or coastal regions. We shall describe their composition in a moment. Named for the type of materials most conspicuous in them, these are: diatom ooze, globigerina ooze, radiolarian ooze, and pteropod ooze.

Diatoms are minute plants, with outside coverings that are like fine glass boxes in pairs, one box fitting over the other. Diatoms and their silicious shells were known from bottom samples and water dippings long before anyone had an idea that the diatoms were minute plants. They occur in great numbers in the sea constituting a major source of food for the small animals, copepods, larvae, etc., which, in the ocean, play the same part in the organic cycle as do the vegetarian grazers, browsers, and gnawers of the land. Diatoms, with the still more minute coccolithophores, constitute the "grass" of the sea, but, unlike most of the land vegetation, they have indigestible cases which pass through the alimentary tracts of the animals that feed upon them to sink to the bottom and form a part of the permanent flooring of the sea. Diatoms are of microscopic size, although some may be large enough to catch the eye of the close observer. They occur all over the ocean but reach their greatest numbers in cold waters. Sometimes, indeed, they are present in almost inconceivable abundance to make the water "soupy" and give it a yellow tint. There are hundreds of different kinds. In form they may be needle-like, boat-shaped, or disc-shaped, and they may have slender extensions from the body of the shell.

Diatom ooze is found principally in cold regions of the Antarctic and in the southern and far northern Pacific at 600-2,000 fathoms. It is not that diatoms are restricted to waters above such areas or that other skeleton-bearing organisms do not occur there, but rather that in such regions the shells of diatoms are found on the bottom in such extraordinary numbers as to obscure the other skeletal remains.

Globigerina ooze is the designation for deposits where the calcareous shells of a particular kind of protozoan predominate. Globigerina is one of the divisions of Protozoa known as Foraminifera. Unlike many protozoa that paddle or scull themselves through the water, a foraminiferan effects its movement, such as it is, by the flowing of its living protoplasm in changing lobes or rays, to which are given the name *pseudopodia*, meaning "false feet." In this respect they are like the amoebas, from which they differ in having a calcareous shell with one or many chambers. The shell is porous and has larger openings through all of which the pseudopodia stream. When globigerina outgrows its tiny shell, it forms another and larger shell which remains attached to the first shell. Successively larger shells are formed until the whole is a tapering linear series of capsules or, more commonly, a chambered spiral suggestive of the nautilus on a minute scale. In some cases the shells eventually become large enough to be detectable by the unaided eye. Globigerina lives both on the bottom and freely in the open water as an important element of the plankton. One is shown in Fig. 14, p. 220.

About two-thirds of the floor of the Atlantic, and more than one-third of the total area of all sea bottom, is covered by globigerina ooze, composed in considerable part of the calcareous shells of

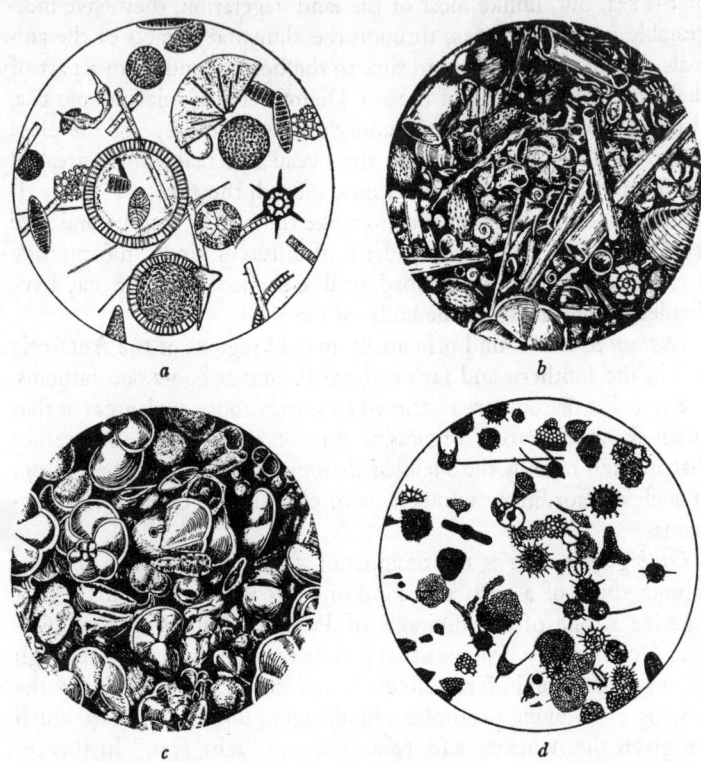

FIGURE 8. The pelagic oozes. (a) Diatom ooze (from Steuer, after Chun). (b) Pteropod ooze (after Murray and Hjort). (c) Globigerina ooze (after Murray). (d) Radiolarian ooze (from Steuer, after Krümmel).

Globigerina bulloides, mixed with coccoliths, or shell fragments of the coccolithophores, to be mentioned later (cf. p. 205); this deposit is about 65 per cent calcareous matter and is found at 1,000-2,500 fathoms. Although it was once supposed that globigerina ooze was the basis of chalk deposits, it is now believed that the chalk was formed in shallow seas and that such deposits do not, therefore, represent old deep-sea bottoms. Bigelow[2] refers to globigerina ooze

2. *Oceanography*, p. 35.

as reported to be accumulating over submarine telegraph cables at the apparent rate of a tenth of an inch a year, or a fathom in 720 years, but comments that the sea floor, over all the vast area occupied by the globigerina ooze, is certainly not generally building up at such a rate. Other estimates for deposition in the open seas approximate a millimeter, or one twenty-fifth of an inch, in a hundred years!

In contrast to the calcareous ooze just mentioned is the silicious *radiolarian ooze*, consisting of a foundation of red clay in which are mixed the remains of radiolarian shells; it occurs at 2,500-5,000 fathoms in isolated areas of the tropical Pacific and Indian Oceans. The radiolaria, like the foraminifera, are protozoa with flowing pseudopodia, but they differ from globigerina in that the shell is usually silicious rather than calcareous and is, therefore, less soluble. They differ also in the fact that the skeleton is internal: the body is divided into two regions, one within the membraneous capsule and one without, the capsule being elaborately perforated for continuity between the two portions of the body. The animals may be fairly large for protozoa, with a diameter of one-twelfth of an inch. The pseudopodia are fine and raylike. Shells and bodies may be extremely complex and beautiful.

It is a distinctly higher type of animal that gives rise to the fourth principal type of deep sea deposit of organic origin, *pteropod ooze*. Usually we think of mollusks in terms of creeping snails, burrowing clams, sedentary oysters or free-swimming squid; but there are small mollusks whose whole individual lives are passed in the open water, where they swim by means of fin-like structures on the head. The pteropods have thin shells which in different species may be snail-like in form, globular and spinous, or slender, conical, and straight or curved. They are generally large enough to be plainly visible to the eye, some of the slender ones having a length of approximately half an inch. (See Fig. 15, p. 226) Other free-swimming mollusks, not closely related to pteropods, are the heteropods, which may be described as minute conchs with transparent shells that are conical or spiral and disc-like. The bodies may have delicate and beautiful colors. Some of them are larger than the pteropods.

Like the organisms previously mentioned, pteropods, under favorable conditions, become extremely abundant, dominating large areas of the sea in such degree as to have attracted long ago the attention of whalers who call them "whale feed," and who know that they offer promise of the proximity of "right whales" (whales that bear whalebone). The whalebone whales, which include the largest of all animals, follow the pteropods, as well as copepods and small shrimplike crustacea, to strain bushels of tiny organisms from the sea through the whalebone sieves on their jaws. Calcareous pteropod ooze, comprising the shells of pteropods, principally, and heteropods, mixed with shells of Globigerina, occur principally in tropical regions at depths of 500 to 1,300 fathoms.[3] At greater depths their delicate shells may be dissolved to leave only the more durable remains of globigerina or other organisms.

Red clay is mostly inorganic material that has been deposited on the bottom anywhere but is notable more particularly in the great depths where it is not obscured by the organic deposits. Some of this is of volcanic origin and may originate from submarine eruptions or from terrestrial volcanoes. Terrestrial volcanic dust may float through the air to settle to the sea over the deep areas; larger bits of air-packed pumice may lodge on the surface waters nearer shore to float for a long time, become waterlogged, and eventually sink to the bottom remote from the place of its first contact with the water. Dust from the desert is carried long distances through the air and is observable in deep-sea deposits. Floating icebergs may carry rock fragments of considerable size. As Murray remarks, materials of extraterrestrial origin do not bulk large in marine deposits: they are rarities, but extremely interesting. Naturally, such matter is noticed chiefly on the red clay areas, where other materials are so few. Interplanetary particles on the floor of the ocean are presumed to be fragments of meteorites; they are chiefly black and brown metallic spherules which, because of the iron in them, can be picked out by the use of a magnet. There are also products formed in the sea, concretions or nodules of manganese and barium, combinations of iron, potassium, and silica, and silicious and phosphatic concretions. The oxides of iron and manganese, especially noticeable in deep sea deposits, give the color to the deep sea clays. Red clay constitutes more than half of the floor of the Pacific and is estimated to occupy about one-third of the combined area of the floor of all the seas. Naturally, it is present in the greater depths to which the

3. Adolf Steuer, *Leitfaden der Planktonkunde.*

organic materials cannot descend because of the depth and the solvent agents in the water.

The red clay of the sea is not to be confused with the red clay of the land. There is no rock in the geological series that corresponds to the red clay of the ocean floor; in other words, no present area of land seems to comprise what has ever been the red clay of sea bottoms; this leads us to believe in the relative permanence of the deeper parts of the seas. It may readily be understood that deposits of this sort accumulate with exceeding slowness: Sir John Murray has estimated that there has been an increment of about one foot since Tertiary time! [4]

4. Although Murray's classification of marine deposits, as it has been outlined in the text, retains its essential validity, it must undergo some revision in the light of recent broader and more detailed observations. In the first place there can be no sharp distinctions between the different types of deposits, which necessarily are mixtures. Revelle emphasizes a distinction in color between terrigenous and pelagic bottoms. Terrigenous deposits build up relatively rapidly and are black, bluish, green, or gray. The more slowly built pelagic deposits are red, brown, yellow, or white. Revelle proposes a more detailed classification of the terrigenous muds and the pelagic oozes. Calcium carbonate oozes have more than 30 per cent $CaCO_3$ and are subdivided into various types of globigerina, pteropod, and coccolith oozes. Silicious oozes have remains of silicious organisms greater than 30 per cent and $CaCO_3$ less than 30 per cent and are divided into several types of diatom and radiolarian oozes. Red clay as contrasted with the oozes will have less than 30 per cent of organic skeletal remains and will be of one sub-type or another according to its composition in detrital, volcanic, silicious, or calcareous materials. The proposed classification is summarized on page 16 of *Marine Bottom Samples Collected in the Pacific Ocean by the Carnegie on Its Seventh Cruise* (Carnegie Institution of Washington, Publication 556 Washington, 1944, Pp. 180), by Roger R. Revelle.

CHAPTER 9

Sea Water in Motion: General Plans of Circulation

Broad Features of Circulation and Methods of Observation

THE BLASÉ TRAVELER LIKES TO REFER TO THE OCEAN HE HAS crossed as "the pond," but no pond is so restless as any one of the oceans. Besides waves, tides, and seiches, each ocean has its wide-reaching system of circulation. Furthermore, with even a little knowledge of ocean currents and drifts, we begin to see how all the seas together constitute a single body with all its members interconnected in a fairly orderly system of circulation; for in many cases the movements of great volumes of water from place to place, "movements of translation," in contrast to "movements of oscillation" in waves and tides, are not confined by the boundaries of oceans as we may sketch them on the map. As with all circulating systems, the circulatory mechanism that interlocks the seas involves transformation of energy—and, in this case, a notable amount of energy. The ultimate source of the energy, as far as we can trace it, must concern us in another chapter, but it is well to have in mind now that, with hardly any other mechanisms on earth, do we deal with so great regular income and outgo of energy.

By different means the oceanographer gathers data from many observations about currents, and, when he has arranged and organized the data he can prepare generally reliable maps showing, with lines and arrows, the broad eddies and great streams that move in some orderly fashion, although rarely with precise constancy of

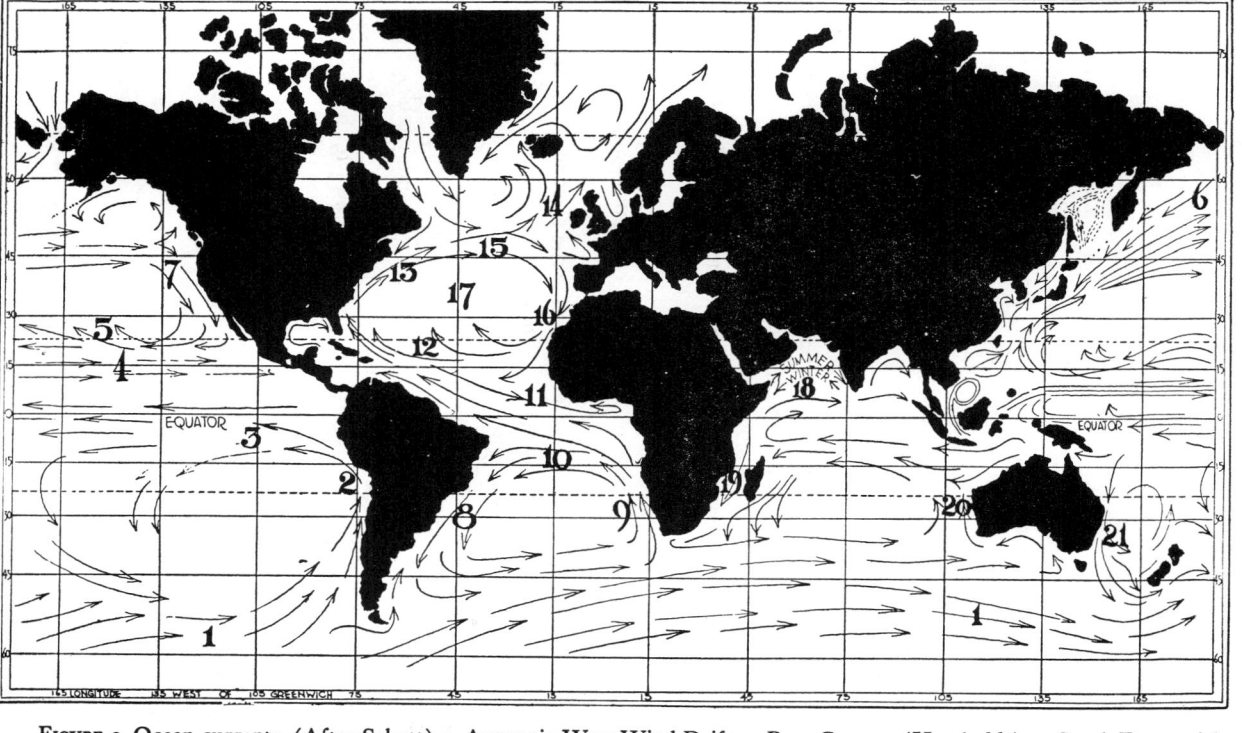

FIGURE 9. Ocean currents. (After Schott) 1. Antarctic West Wind Drift. 2. Peru Current (Humboldt). 3. South Equatorial Current. 4. Counter Equatorial Current. 5. North Equatorial Current. 6. Kuroshio. 7. California Current. 8. Brazil Current. 9. Benguela Current. 10. South Equatorial Current. 11. Guinea Current. 12. North Equatorial Current. 13. Gulf Stream. 14. Norwegian Current. 15. North Atlantic Current. 16. Canaries Drift. 17. Sargasso Sea. 18. Monsoon Drift (Summer East, Winter West). 19. Mozambique Current. 20. West Australian Current. 21. East Australian Current.

velocity or of direction. In some places the streaming movements are more rapid than are those of great rivers like the Mississippi or the Amazon; sometimes they are nearly as constant in direction, although far larger in volume. In other places the motion is so slow as scarcely to retard or accelerate the passage of a ship. The seaman and the oceanographer speak of the slow movements as "drifts," as for example, the great, eastward, circumpolar Antarctic Drift. These currents of the ocean, except as they may be bounded on one side by lands or shoals, are not confined in hard channels; so that the precise direction and the volume of flow may undergo minor changes. On occasion there may even be reversals of direction; while in a few cases, as in the Indian Ocean, reversal is seasonal.

The usual maps show the predominating or prevailing directions of surface currents and drifts; but it must be understood that there are deep flows, generally as slow drifts of immense masses of water, and that these are of equal significance with the superficial currents in the whole system of mixing and of interchanging of water masses between different regions of the hydrosphere.[1]

The surface currents have great influence on climates and on the activities of man, and they have been studied from ancient days. Various methods have been used to determine the direction and rate of movement of masses of water. The movements of water in sight of land may be observed with reference to some fixed object. Out in the open sea there are no fixed objects, and indirect methods must be relied upon. Information may be obtained from floating objects, "flotsam" in technical language, such as icebergs and wreckage; bottles may be deliberately set adrift, sealed and empty but for a card which the finder may mail to obtain a small reward. In these cases we cannot know just what course the drift has taken, how roundabout may have been its journey, or, sometimes, what part the wind, rather than the current, may have played in determining the course followed. Of course, "drift bottles" are designed to offer the least possible resistance to currents of air. To minimize the direct effect of wind on the bottle a "drift anchor" may be added in the form of a cross of sheet metal suspended a few feet below the bottle.

1. It is not only the lack of boundaries between oceans but also their general continuity with rivers and lakes, and the want of any definite break between all of these and the world-wide sheet of soil water, that gives basis for recognition of a continuous watery envelope of the earth called the *hydrosphere*, which, with the *geosphere* below and the *atmosphere* above, makes up the whole terrestrial globe.

Ships at sea can furnish much valuable information. A navigator keeps regular records of his course and speed, but finds that, from day to day, the position of the ship, as determined by astronomical calculation based on observations of the heavenly bodies, is not what should result from the recorded course and speed. The difference is attributable to currents, whose direction and rate can then be computed with some degree of approximation; but all allowance must be made for wind drift and for errors arising from deviations of the compass. A vessel at anchor in a current may determine the direction and velocity of the current by the use of a chip log or by setting loose drift buoys, whose direction and distance may be determined after a given period of time. Sometimes a vessel may trail a drifting buoy to determine its position at regular intervals. Such a buoy, in order to be followed by the eye or the vessel, must have a staff and flag that will give minimum resistance to the wind. The submerged part in the form of a cross, "the current cross," is broad enough in two directions to be carried by the water, no matter how the buoy may turn.

Still other methods of determining rate of movement involve the use of an instrument held in place and having a propeller which is turned by the flowing water. Sometimes current meters are left anchored to the bottom to be recovered after a certain period of time. Such current meters are so devised as to make a record both of the direction and of the rate of movement of the water. In the Ekman current meter there is a propeller and a vane that orients the instrument to keep the propeller always facing the current. There is also a compass box rigidly connected to the vane of the meter; the box is divided radially into a number of compartments, say thirty-six, each corresponding to an angle of ten degrees. The magnets of the compass, which adjust themselves in the magnetic meridian, are attached to a frame that turns with the magnets and carries a bar[2] through which a small ball drops at intervals into one of the compartments of the box. The box, rigidly fixed in the instrument, turns with the vane and is, therefore, oriented to the direction of the current. One ball drops for each thirty-three revolutions of the propeller, or more frequently, if desired. In consequence, the average direction of the current can be determined by the distribution of the balls in the compartments of the box, while the velocity is com-

2. The needle itself, if grooved to carry the ball, may serve in place of a special bar.

puted from the registered number of turns of the propeller. In the possible event that the balls are too widely distributed in the several compartments, the results may be considered invalid as to both the direction and the velocity of the current.

When the movement of the water is very slow, say a fraction of a centimeter per second, reliance must be upon the characteristics of the water as determined by the thermometer and by analyses made from samples; but see note, p. 137. This is particularly necessary in the case of deep drifts. *Precise determinations* of salinity, temperature, and dissolved oxygen identify different masses of water and enable the oceanographer to map their distribution and trace their movements.

Currents and other great movements of water have much to do with the shaping of climates in all parts of the world. With its strong component of hydrogen, water has the highest heat capacity of all ordinary liquids except ammonia (NH_3) which has even more hydrogen. This means that water has always exceptional capacity both to absorb and store heat with relatively little change in temperature and, when in motion, to transport heat from one place to another. Accordingly, ocean currents are most important agents for the transfer of heat from low to high latitudes. Winds blowing from the sea, as everyone knows, have marked effects on terrestrial climates, which indeed are determined to no little extent by the winds. The climates of a region depend then not only on latitude, but also on the direction from which the wind blows. Not everywhere is the predominant drift of air over the land from the cooler or warmer water of the sea, but in many regions this is the case. Notable examples of the tempering effect of ocean currents on the climate of the land are afforded by the Benguela Current, bringing cold southern water up the west side of Africa and keeping a long coastal strip relatively cool—and foggy; the Peru Current, conveying water of Antarctic origin almost to the Equator, so that at Lima, only 12 degrees of latitude from the Equator, the highest summer temperature is below 90°F. and winters are only continuous fog; and the Gulf Stream with its tempering effect on the climate of northwest Europe.

Ocean currents are caused by conditions existing in the water as well as by outside forces. Of the internal causes, most prominent are those due to differences in pressure; unequal pressure results when one part of the ocean is heated to a higher temperature than another or when the salinity is changed by evaporation or by inflow of rivers, by melting icebergs or by rainfall. Of outside forces, the winds are most readily observable; for strong winds obviously drive the surface water. In respect to direction of flow, the influence of the wind is easily seen; but the form of the coast line, the topography of the bottom, and the rotation of the earth cause modification of direction. Variation in atmospheric pressure causes rise and fall of the level of the sea in particular regions, with resulting disturbance of equilibrium to be corrected by subsequent shifts of masses of water. The greatest of outside forces is the rotation of the earth, which deflects currents to the right in regions north of the Equator and to the left in areas south of it. (See p. 139, below.)

A rough outline of the general picture of oceanic circulation is something like this. In each ocean that extends north-and-south across the belt of the earth, there are, in equatorial regions, two broad streams running from east to west and known as the North Equatorial Current and the South Equatorial Current. Between them is a narrow, equatorial Countercurrent directed toward the east. The equatorial currents are deflected, partly by land masses and partly by influences related to the earth's rotation, to the right in the northern hemisphere and to the left in the southern. In the northern hemisphere, the deflected streams move first in a northerly direction turning gradually eastward and then southward to complete the circle. In the southern hemisphere, the directions of drift follow in reverse order, first southerly, then easterly in high southern latitudes, and northerly; eventually they complete a great eddy in each part of the Atlantic and Pacific oceans by entering in part again into the equatorial currents. In the Indian Ocean this general scheme for currents is changed somewhat by the monsoons, which are winds that change direction with the seasons. In the southern hemisphere the Antarctic Drift, influenced by the prevailing winds, the distribution of land masses, and submarine topography, moves from west to east around the Antarctic continent at a calculated rate of 4.4 cm/sec to 15 cm/sec;[3] that is to say, at a rate of about one-third of a statute mile, or much less, per hour.

It may help to understand some of the very complex relations of currents and drifts to be discussed in the following pages if we have

3. 50 cm/sec is equivalent, approximately, to one knot, or one nautical mile of 6,000 feet per hour.

in mind that the oceanographers distinguish several strata of water; in order of vertical distribution, these are surface water, upper water, intermediate water, deep water, and bottom water. These masses find their relative levels according to their densities; water that is heavier, because of low temperature, high salinity, or a combination of the two, sinks below lighter water.

It must be observed that, when the density of surface water is increased by cooling, by evaporation, or by the formation of ice (leaving the water more saline), the water must sink until it meets water of equal density while subsurface water rises to take its place. The rising and falling currents are called *convection currents*. When conditions effecting the increase of density continue, the densest water accumulates at or near the bottom to flow out beneath the lighter waters except as they may be within an enclosed basin. Convection currents occur mainly in high latitudes but not usually to such an extent that *bottom water* is formed. In any event, whenever water of high salinity carried by currents is cooled in high latitudes, or when water of relatively high salinity freezes, the water may become of such density as to find its level only at the bottom.

The most striking examples of the formation of bottom water of great density are found in Arctic and Antarctic regions or in the Atlantic Ocean. "The deep and bottom water in all oceans is derived mainly from these two sources, but is to some extent modified by addition of high-salinity water flowing out across the sills of basins in lower latitudes, particularly from the Mediterranean and the Red Sea."[4]

Circulation in the Atlantic Ocean

A prominent feature of the circulation in the North Atlantic is the broad and warm northward flowing current off the east coast of the United States, which is known generally as the *Gulf Stream*. It was Maury of the United States Navy who first made a systematic study of this stream, although it had been known to some of the earliest explorers of America and had been roughly mapped by Benjamin Franklin. It has been studied intensively by the Coast and Geodetic Survey, with such leaders as Alexander Dallas Bache (a grandson of Franklin), Alexander Agassiz, and J. E. Pillsbury.

4. Sverdrup, Johnson, and Fleming, *The Oceans*, p. 747.

The last-mentioned investigator anchored the "Blake" in the midst of the swift stream, making observations and measurements at various depths, which "are among the classical data of physical oceanography."[5] The German physical oceanographer Wüst and the American Iselin have in recent years added much to knowledge of the Gulf Stream. Whence comes this water, what is its volume and where does it go? The answers to these questions are not simple; for the stream itself is not simple, but really a *system* of currents,[6] including: Florida Current, Gulf Stream proper and North Atlantic Current, to say nothing of secondary currents, eddies, and meanders. (See "The Gulf Stream System," by C. O'D. Iselin, in Proc. Am. Phil. Soc., 96: 600-603.)

We must go back to the westerly flowing North Equatorial Current, which, off the northeast coast of South America, is joined by a great branch of the South Equatorial Current bringing water from the South Atlantic. The combined waters move in part, through the Caribbean Sea and the Yucatan Channel, gathering speed, to pass on through the Straits of Florida; here, as the *Florida Current*, it is a body 95 nautical miles wide and about 2 miles deep. The velocity in the narrow part of the Straits is about 3½ knots, and the transport of water here has been estimated, somewhat roughly of course, at twenty-six million cubic meters per second. If this is correct the stream here has something like the volume of a thousand Mississippi Rivers at normal stages!

Past the Bahamas, the Florida Current is augmented by another branch of the North Equatorial Current; this is the *Antilles Current*, which has by-passed the landward seas and which carries water believed to be identical with that of the Sargasso Sea, to be mentioned a little later.[7] Passing Cape Hatteras as the *Gulf Stream*, with reduced speed of about one nautical mile per hour and with its flow deflected to the right, as is characteristic for all ocean currents in the northern hemisphere, it leaves the continental slope to continue in a more easterly direction and meet the southward flowing *Labrador Current* in the vicinity of the Grand Banks of Newfoundland, as we have mentioned above (page 54). Now it divides into branches to merge into the *North Atlantic Current*, which includes the easterly and northerly currents of the North Atlantic. Much of the Gulf Stream water is diverted southward into the great central eddy

5. *Ibid.*, p. 673.   6. Sverdrup, *op. cit.*, p. 173.   7. *Ibid.*, p. 162.

of the North Atlantic, the *Sargasso Sea*.[8] Part of its water warms the shores of Iceland and Norway, while some approaches the western shores of Europe in southerly drift and even passes into the Mediterranean.

Whatever the origin of the water in the nearly-enclosed Mediterranean, strong evaporation there increases salinity and density, so that the heavier upper waters sink to the depths, whence they flow out through the Straits of Gibralter to form a mass of deep and bottom water that can be traced far out into the Atlantic, southward across the Equator, and even around the southern extremity of Africa into the Indian Ocean.

To a considerable extent the winds over the eastern part of the United States are from the northwest, so that the Gulf Stream has a limited effect on our climate; but, through the agency of the prevailing southwest winds of northwest Europe, the warm air from waters traceable to the Gulf Stream moderates the climate of that region in marked degree. As evidence, we have only to contrast the habitability of Norway with that of Greenland or of Baffin Land on the North American continent, far north of Labrador but in the latitude of Norway. During recent years oceanographers of the Scandinavian countries have been interested in the possibility of long-time weather prediction for northwest Europe derived from observations of variations of the Gulf Stream near its beginning, across the ocean and far to the south.

Passing now to a consideration of the broad characteristics of the Gulf Stream, we find that its waters are differentiated from those of the open sea in some very definite ways. In general, the waters of this stream are deep indigo blue and transparent; they are saline and warm, relative to adjacent waters; the velocity of movements is high as compared with average movements in the sea. The surface velocity decreases from 3 ½ knots in the Straits of Florida to 1 ½ off the coast of Georgia and one knot off Cape Hatteras. The average temperature of surface waters is approximately 80°F. (27°C.) in the first 400 miles of the current, but subsurface temperatures decrease rapidly toward the bottom; the water on the eastern side of the current is warmer than that on the western side. The so-called "cold wall" between the Gulf Stream and the United States coast is due

8. *Ibid.*, p. 172.

to several factors. Among these are: mixing, to some extent, with water discharged from cold land streams; proximity to land having low winter temperatures, with prevailing breezes from the land; and cold waters from the Gulf of St. Lawrence, which are deflected against the American coast by virtue of the earth's rotation.[9] For the seas as a whole the salinity is hardly up to 35 o/oo, but the waters of the Gulf Stream have a relatively high salinity, 35-36.5 o/oo, although, as a whole they are distinctly less saline than the waters of the Sargasso Sea.

The westward flowing North Equatorial Current, the northerly and easterly Gulf Stream and North Atlantic currents, and the southerly Canaries Drift on the east side of the Atlantic complete the periphery of a great Central North Atlantic eddy. This is what has long been known as the Sargasso Sea, an area of relatively still or slowly turning water, where the floating "gulf weed," or sargassum, accumulates; the weed propagates vegetatively to form in some places floating islandlike clumps, but never, it appears, the allegedly solid and impenetrable masses which only legend has placed there. The water of this wide-stretched eddy, undiluted by melting ice or the discharge from rivers, and subject to constant evaporation, has relatively high salinity, as I have previously said (p. 82). It is relatively poor in nutritive material and has the deep blue characteristic of deep water with scant material in suspension.

We have seen that a great volume of upper water passes from the South Atlantic into the Gulf Stream system of the northern ocean and that the transport is estimated at something like six million cubic meters per second. We shall see later that other South Atlantic or Antarctic water enters the North Atlantic at intermediate levels. Naturally, there must somewhere be an equivalent "pay back" from northern to southern seas. The return of water from North to South Atlantic is understood to occur at low levels; but the sinking of heavy surface water to form the lower return water is believed to take place chiefly in three regions. As was mentioned before, surface water becomes heavy and sinks, either through excess evaporation or through lowering temperature, which may follow from the mixing of cold and therefore heavy water with saline water of a moderate temperature. The chief places of sinking in the North At-

9. Marmer, *The Sea*, Chapter XVIII.

lantic, as now known, are (1) outside the Straits of Gibraltar (saline Mediterranean water); (2) in the region southwest of Greenland (cold Arctic and North Atlantic water); and (3) in the region of Labrador, where saline Gulf Stream waters are mixed with cold Arctic waters. About two million cubic meters is presumed to sink each second at each of these three places.[10] Of course these are rough figures, but they are worth quoting as giving some idea of the volumes of water involved in such shifts.

The conditions described in outline for the North Atlantic illustrate the complexity of the dynamics of the sea. It is not the purpose here to give a systematic account of the circulation of the ocean. For that one must refer to the more technical treatises, some of which have been cited. It is hoped merely to give a rough picture of the general nature and scope of the world-wide mechanism for mixing ocean waters. A brief examination of outstanding features of circulation in other oceans will complete the chapter.

In the *South Atlantic* there is a somewhat analogous but reverse rotation in counterclockwise direction. The South Equatorial Current forms the northern boundary of a central eddy. That part of this current which does not join the Gulf stream turns south as the warm Brazil Current on the west side of the eddy. On the southern side is the easterly flowing Antarctic Current. The eastern side of the eddy is formed by the Benguela Current, one of the more conspicuous ocean streams, bringing cold water northward along the west coast of Africa and finally turning westward as the northern cooler part of the South Equatorial Current. Upwelling of deep waters (see page 140, below) along the African coast contributes to maintenance of lower surface temperatures than would otherwise be normal for the latitudes. In contrast to conditions in the North Atlantic, it is the cold current of the east side of the South Atlantic that is the most notable stream. The deeper waters of the South Atlantic are partly of Antarctic origin with northward drift and partly of Arctic origin with southerly drift, as mentioned on page 128, above, and page 135, below.

Circulation in the Pacific Ocean

In the Pacific Ocean the conditions of circulation are less well

10. Sverdrup, *op. cit.*, p. 173.

known than are those of the Atlantic and they appear to be somewhat more complex. In the broad South Pacific there is a great eddy in the eastern part, and there may be another with more erratic conditions in the western region. As in the South Atlantic the best defined current is on the east side. There we find the Humboldt Current, or Peru Current, as it is sometimes called, which carries a long way northward subantarctic water from the easterly drifting Antarctic Current (West Wind Drift or Antarctic Drift), a belt of easterly flowing water around the earth in high southern latitudes. Again, as in the case of the Benguela Current of the South Atlantic, the low surface temperatures maintained along the course of the stream toward the Equator is due not solely to the coldness of the subantarctic water received at the source, but, in considerable part, to the fact that the winds tend to drive the surface water away from the coast to be replaced by cold water upwelling from deeper strata.[11]

The Humboldt Current is not so well-defined as is the Gulf Stream, but it is a definitely tangible current running almost to the Equator and fairly close along shore. A voyager on a ship sailing south from Panama, if the Equator is to be crossed during the night, may be advised to put away his linen outers and don warm clothing in the morning. Having lolled for several days under tropical sunshine over warm waters, he may not heed the advice at first; but, if by morning the ship has entered the waters of the current, the passenger will not be slow to seek warmer clothing. Even at seaside points well within the tropical zone, the coastal water, in the sixties, Fahrenheit, is distinctly cold for swimming. The Humboldt Cur-

11. To quote Dr. Murphy, *Oceanic Birds of South America*, (p. 95):
"Significant features of the surface waters in the current are first, relatively low temperatures in close proximity to the land, with rising temperatures offshore along lines usually perpendicular to the trend of the coast; and second, extraordinary uniformity of temperatures throughout the greater part of the length of the current, a uniformity which is little affected either by latitude or season of the year. Both of these facts would strongly suggest that the low temperatures close to shore are due to upwelling from cooler intermediate layers, rather than to northward transportation of subantarctic surface waters. The latter would, of course, become gradually warmed during their progress into the tropics, and the Humboldt Current would show appreciably rising temperatures from south to north, which is not in accord with the facts. Upwelling would, in any event, be inevitable in view of the meteorological régime. An accelerated left-hand trend, and continuous vertical circulation, is caused by the steady southerly winds parallel with the coast, which tend to force the surface water offshore at an angle of 45° from their path."

rent is perhaps some 500 miles wide; but the offshore waters are relatively warm. At its northern limit near the Equator the greater part of its volume turns west in the South Equatorial Current.

Although the Peru Current, or coastal part of the Humboldt Current, is generally constant in rate and direction of flow over most of its course, there sometimes occur significant aberrations in its northernmost reaches. In northern summer a branch of the current crosses the Equator to continue northward alongside the Equatorial Countercurrent, which also turns north. In northern winter, the summer of the southern hemisphere, the easterly flowing countercurrent turns southward, when it is known as El Niño (referring to Christmas), to flow a few degrees southward from the Equator and close along the coast of Ecuador. Occasionally, but seemingly quite irregularly as to intervals of years, the southward-flowing warm current continues on along the coast of Peru. This unwonted substitution of warm for cool waters has disastrous effects upon the fish and other organisms of the coastal regions. There may ensue such a mortality of organisms and so much decomposition as to create decidedly foul conditions of water and air. The hydrogen sulphide liberated as a product of decomposition may blacken the paint of ships; this unpleasant and expensive phenomenon has long been known to seamen as "The Callao Painter." The valuable guano-producing birds, which feed upon anchobetas and other small fish and crustacea in the Peru Current, may also suffer heavy mortality or they may abandon the islands and the region with consequent great commercial loss.

In the Pacific, as in the Atlantic, we have the North and South Equatorial currents flowing westward, with the narrower Equatorial countercurrent flowing in the reverse direction; but these currents are all somewhat farther north in the Pacific, as compared with those in the Atlantic. The South Equatorial Current extends north of the Equator, and the countercurrent is entirely in the northern hemisphere.[12]

Conditions in the North Pacific, although different, are more nearly comparable to those in the North Atlantic. The North Equatorial Current, deriving water at or near its beginning in the east from the countercurrent and the southward flowing California Cur-

12. Sverdrup, *op. cit.*, p. 193.

rent, flows westward across the broad waist of the Pacific, gathering increments of Central Pacific water on its northern side. Approaching the Philippines on the west, a part is said to return as the Countercurrent, but the larger part turns northward and then northeastward, running eastward of Formosa and the Japanese Archipelago as the Japan Current or Kuroshio ("black current"), reminding us of the Gulf Stream in the North Atlantic. In the region above Formosa, the rate of flow is something less than 2 nautical miles per hour. The salinity is lower than that of the Gulf Stream, in keeping with the generally lower salinity of Pacific as compared with Atlantic waters (p. 82, above). On leaving Japan the Kuroshio divides into two branches: the larger southern branch runs due east and is distinguishable as far as 160° E. longitude, or nearly to the Hawaiian Islands; it merges into the easterly North Pacific Current. The northern branch becomes mixed with the southward flowing cold Oyashio, skirting the coast of upper Asia, the mixture forming the masses of subarctic water found below the Aleutians and Alaska. A certain degree of sinking seems to occur at the convergence of warm Kuroshio and cold Oyashio. From the easterly Aleutian Current, in the subarctic water, one branch turns north into the Gulf of Alaska; another swings southward along the coast of the United States to become the California Current which moves strongly southeastward to merge finally with the North Equatorial Current. The effect of the California Current is to temper the climates of our western states; but, as with the Peru Current, the relatively low temperature of the coastal water is attributable, not solely to its subarctic origin, but, in part and in some regions, to the upwelling of deeper cooler waters.

In the North Pacific the "deep water," in the technical sense, is reputed to be derived chiefly from the Indian Ocean, being Antarctic water of Atlantic and Indian Ocean origins. Between northern and southern Pacific there is believed to be little exchange of water across the Equator.

Circulation in the Indian Ocean

The Indian Ocean has its own distinctive form, being roughly circular in outline and with only a small part of its area north of the Equator. Its currents, while comparable in some ways to those of the Atlantic, are much more variable, and this is due, in part at least, to changes in the prevailing monsoon winds. In its southern part a current flows from Africa toward Australia, approaching close to that continent in southern winter. Interchanges of water with the Pacific southward and northward of Australia seem to vary with the season; but they need not concern us here.

As in other oceans, a South Equatorial Current flows toward the west, its velocity varying with the season, being greatest in southern winter. A part of this stream turns southward along the east coast of Africa to form the Agulhas Current, which may feed partly into the Atlantic around the Cape of Good Hope, but which mainly turns eastward to contribute to the easterly flow first mentioned. Between the eastward current and the westerly Equatorial Current there is pictured a large eddy. In northern winter, when the northeast monsoon prevails, there is found a westward-flowing North Equatorial Current north of an easterly Equatorial Countercurrent; but the westerly current disappears under the influence of the southwest monsoon, so that, in northern summer, the flow is all easterly.

An interesting feature of circulation in the Indian Ocean area is the interchange between the ocean and the Red Sea, where great evaporation produces water of notably high salinity. In winter the winds drive top water into the Red Sea from the Gulf of Aden, while highly saline and heavy Red Sea waters are flowing out in the depths. In summer, with reversed winds, water flows out from the Red Sea at the surface and, probably to some extent, at the depth of "the sill" at the gateway between sea and ocean, while cold and less saline waters are flowing into the Red Sea at intermediate levels. In the depths of the Indian Ocean there are found, accordingly, some waters of Red Sea origin, but also much of Atlantic origin.[13]

Circulation in the Antarctic Ocean

The Antarctic, as a whole, presents a very different picture from that of any of the other oceans. It surrounds a continent rather than being partially surrounded by continents. It is, thus, a continuous but ill-bounded circumpolar belt, northward on all sides of the Antarctic continent. With a drift from west to east, the Antarctic Current is irregular in width and in precise course, as its

13. Sverdrup, *op. cit.*, p. 215.

direction is affected by the distribution of land masses or of submarine ridges. This unceasing circumpolar drift of water is not however, to be conceived of as a particular mass of water in continuous circulation: there are continual interchanges between it and the oceans northward from it. Tongues of surface water are given off, as in the Falkland Current, which flows along the eastern side of the southern coast of South America, and contributions are received, as in the case of a considerable part of the Agulhas Current from the eastern side of South Africa.

We have already mentioned the masses of bottom water and intermediate water of Antarctic origin both of which drift northward in the South Atlantic below and above the southerly drift of North Atlantic deep water. Antarctic bottom water has indeed been traced as far as 35 degrees north latitude in the North Atlantic, or to the approximate latitude of Cape Hatteras. Antarctic intermediate waters also move far up in the South Pacific and the Indian Oceans. Presumably much of this Antarctic water becomes mixed with the deep waters moving southward and returns to the Antarctic region along with Indian and Atlantic and perhaps Red Sea water.

There is also, as may already have been inferred, a distinct vertical movement of water in the Antarctic region. The cold waters that sink to form the great masses of intermediate water are rarely over two degrees above the freezing point of fresh water and are heavily charged with oxygen. This, of course, is true also of deeper waters formed in Arctic regions.

The Arctic Ocean

In contrast to the Antarctic, which is hardly more than the southern extension of Pacific, Atlantic, and Indian oceans to the borders of a polar continent, the Arctic is a small polar sea hemmed in by continental land masses. Broadly speaking, the Arctic is supposed to include the oceanic waters north of latitude 60°N. and the Antarctic those south of latitude 60°S. With less than one-fifth the area of either the Atlantic or Indian Ocean, the Arctic is proportionately much less in volume because its average depth is less than a third of either of those oceans. Nevertheless, it has depths up to about three and one-half miles with an average of some three quarters of a mile. Its waters are low in salinity, less than 30. Throughout much of its extent, the surface temperatures are well below the freezing point of fresh water. It is characteristically an area of sea ice, 5 to 9 feet in thickness, but, as a result of the pressures of moving ice floes, the ice may become piled up to a depth of 15 feet or more. Even in the summer the Arctic is never half free of ice.

Largely enclosed by land, as it is, the significance of the Arctic to general oceanic circulation arises chiefly from the sinking of its cold waters when they come in contact with warm Gulf Stream and North Atlantic waters to form Arctic "intermediate water" which spreads out over a part of the North Atlantic. It also contributes icebergs, which flow into the Atlantic with the southerly current along the west shore of Baffin Bay, passing out through Davis Strait, and entering the Labrador current to drift on to the region of the Grand Banks off Newfoundland. The thawing of these great·masses of ice has noticeable effects on temperature and salinities of waters in certain regions. The Arctic has little relation to the North Pacific, in which there are virtually no icebergs. The Arctic Ocean is connected with Bering Sea only through the narrow Bering Strait, some miles wide; and Bering Sea is to a great extent shut off from the Pacific Ocean by the Alaska Peninsula, the long loop-like chain of Aleutian Islands, and the Asiatic peninsula of Kamchatka.

The Antarctic is a much more prolific producer of icebergs, which are longer-lived than those from the Arctic, the upper limits of life of individual icebergs being approximately two years in the North Atlantic and ten years in the southern oceans. In each region they may range to about 40 degrees in latitude. We need not here concern ourselves particularly with the westerly drift of ice in the Arctic, which has been the subject of a good deal of careful study, notably by the Norwegian explorer Fridtjof Nansen in the drift of the "Fram" in 1893. After being allowed to become frozen in the ice near the New Siberian Islands, the vessel drifted with the mass of ice northerly and westerly, to reach Norway, nearly a third of the way around the earth, after almost three years in the ice.

Conclusion

In short, we find no sea independent of any of the others, and no resting place for sea water anywhere, unless it is in some of the semi-enclosed "deeps." If we may repeat what has been said or suggested more than once, the seas, all together, constitute a great dynamic system with an intricate and world-wide mechanism for mixing everything soluble that comes into it—and a certain amount of everything soluble on the face of the earth must some time drain into the sea. This is the great concept of an integrated and world-wide circulation of ocean water which Maury sensed a century ago, not from much knowledge of the circulating mechanism, but from the knowledge of the general uniformity of proportions of dissolved matter in the sea.

NOTE: There is now an intriguing device for ascertaining direction and velocity of surface flow of water while the vessel is in motion. Much more than a century ago, the great English physicist Faraday suggested that "where water is flowing, there electric currents should be formed," since the moving water is "cutting the magnetic curves of the earth." It remained to perfect a device to measure electric potentials developed by the movement of water through the earth's magnetic field. This is now done with the *Geomagnetic Electrokinetograph* ("G.E.K."), which is towed behind a vessel under way. With a competent observer aboard and with appropriate manipulation of the vessel, without stopping, direction and velocity of flow are of continuous record. (William S. von Arx, "An Electromagnetic Method for Measuring Velocities of Ocean Currents from a Ship Under Way," Papers in Physical Oceanography and Meteorology, M.I.T. and W.H.O.I., *11* (3), 1950.

CHAPTER 10

Sea Water in Motion: Water Moved by the Winds

Horizontal currents

ANYONE OF EXPERIENCE ON LAKES OR ON COASTAL WATERS WILL readily observe that, when there is a wind of sufficient force and duration, the surface water is caused to flow in the general direction of the wind, except as the direction may be modified by coastal formations and bottom topography: water in movement naturally follows the lines of least resistance. Wind blowing over water exerts stress on the water, and it is this sheering stress which initiates the flow at the surface. The surface water moving over the next deeper water exerts a sheering stress to cause a movement there; and so the translation of stresses and the consequent movements proceed downward from level to level. A steadily blowing wind may put into motion the whole mass of water from top to bottom. The rate of movement would, of course, decrease with depth, and physical studies have shown that the decrease is in direct geometric proportion to distance below the surface.

There is nothing in these phenomena as they occur in confined or coastal waters that would be contrary to the expectation of the uninitiated. When, however, we consider the movements of wind in the open ocean, where the depths are great, we find that the current formed by the wind is not actually in the direction of the wind. The effect of the rotation of the earth comes into play with notable effects. Thus, it has been found (mathematically) that the direction of movement of the surface water caused by the stress of the wind deviates from that of the wind to the amount of something like 45 degrees, to the right of the wind direction in the northern hemisphere, and to the left in the southern. The movement of the surface water exerts a stress on the water beneath, which moves in a direction deviating somewhat to the right (or to the left, according to hemisphere) from the direction of movement of the surface water. Since each layer exerts stress on the next layer below, and at every level the deviation is always to the right (or to the left), the surprising conclusion is reached that there will be a depth (depending upon the strength of the wind and the viscosity of the water) where the movement of the water is exactly the reverse of the direction of the wind which exerts the original stress. But the velocity of movement decreases with depth in geometric proportion, so that, at the depth where the current is in a direction the reverse of that of the wind, the velocity is very slight (about 4 per cent of the surface rate), and it is virtually zero below that level. The total transport of waters under the influence of wind is said to be at right angles (normal) to the direction of the wind.

The conditions described in the last paragraph have theoretical soundness, but there must be some modifications. The velocity of movement of the surface of the earth is, of course, greatest in the region of greatest diameter, which is at the Equator. In contrast, a particle at either pole of rotation has, of course, no velocity of translation about the axis: it revolves but is stationary with reference to the axis of the earth. Consequently, water that flows in the general direction of either pole is moving from a region of greater to regions of lesser velocity of the surface of the earth. If it carries its momentum, as it must to some extent, it is moving to the eastward more rapidly than a particle fixed at the latitude at which it is arriving. In other words, the motion relative to the axis of the earth is eastward. This means that water flowing away from the Equator necessarily turns eastward, which is to the right in the northern hemisphere, to the left in the southern hemisphere. The general principle of movement of water as influenced by the earth is broader than is expressed by the illustration just given, which, however, points to the basic fact that in the northern hemisphere currents tend to have a clockwise rotary motion and in the southern a counterclockwise motion. This is in accord with statements in the preceding paragraph regarding the direction of wind-driven currents with reference to the wind, with a deviation of 45 degrees, to the right in the northern hemisphere and to the left in the southern hemisphere. There must, however, be some qualifications in respect to latitude and depth.

As Marmer has so clearly stated: "But it is to be noted that this result is derived on the assumption of an ocean of infinite depth. The sea, however, is not of infinite depth and this abrupt change of 90 degrees (at the Equator), in Ekman's words, 'has, of course, no correspondence with reality.' Actually, the angle of deflection would begin to decrease in the neighborhood of the equator and be zero at the equator. In fact, for an ocean of finite depth Ekman's equations show that the angle between the surface current and the wind depends on the depth. In a very shallow ocean his calculations make this angle very small, that is, the current sets nearly in the direction of the wind; but as the depth of the ocean increases, the angle increases and approximates to the value of 45 degrees."[1]

Other qualifications with reference to wind-driven currents relate to the directions of coast lines and to differences in density. The effect of the wind in causing movement of water at some depth will depend in part upon changes of density with depth. When the upper waters are lighter because of reduced salinity or higher temperature, the influence of the wind on the movement of the water may not extend to as great a depth as in more homogeneous waters and we may find a fairly homogeneous layer of water circulated by the wind above the more stable water of the deeper zone. We are told, however, that, in the sea generally, the changes in density with depth are not great enough to cause directly any great modification of the effects of wind action in a vertical direction, except as the variations in density influence eddy viscosity, with notable indirect effect.

Upwelling

There are conditions when the influence of wind is such as to cause the water to move continuously either toward or away from the shore. This, of course, may result in secondary currents running parallel to the shore and also in raising or lowering the level of the coastal water. The resulting disturbance of equilibrium leads in

1. Marmer, *The Sea*, p. 260.

turn to vertical movements of the coastal waters upward or downword, according to whether the surface drift is toward or away from the shore. When the lighter coastal water is carried away from the coast, the water from below, which is generally colder and heavier, rises to replace it. This "upwelling" of deeper, colder water occurs most notably along the coasts of California, Peru, and West Africa, where the conditions are most favorable in respect to direction of prevailing winds and precipitateness of the coastal slope. According to the more recent investigations (of McEwen particularly) the water drawn to the surface along the coast of southern California comes from a depth of only 200 to 300 meters, so that what actually occurs is an overturn of a relatively superficial layer. The rate of rise on the coast of California has been estimated at about a yard a day.

Rise of water from below must occur wherever there is *divergence* of streams, attributable to winds or to other forces that move oceanic currents. Such a divergence must occur, for example, in the region of the Equator where, because of the rotation of the earth, there is a trend to the right in the northern hemisphere and to the left in the southern hemisphere. Obviously a deepening trough would develop were it not for the rising of waters from a lower level. Conversely, in regions of *convergence* of currents, piling up is obviated by the subsidence of surface waters to flow away at a lower level. Principal convergences are the Antarctic convergence which is said to be traceable all around the Antarctic continent, a subtropical convergence farther northward and a tropical convergence.

Another form of vertical movement occurs when surface waters, because of cooling or evaporation, become heavier than those beneath. A change of level takes place, the heavier surface waters sinking to the level appropriate to their density. Such convection currents on a grand scale may result in an "overturn" in the fall; it is thought to affect only a relatively thin upper stratum. Upwelling is understood to occur all around the Antarctic continent, in compensation for the sinking of heavy surface waters to form Antarctic bottom water.

To the upwelling of a deeper water is attributed in large measure the relative coldness of certain coastal waters. The upwelling waters seem also to bring into the surface zone of active photosynthesis a good deal of dissolved nutritive matter to enrich the region and promote the growth of plankton and fish. Accordingly, regions of upwelling are likely to support extensive fisheries. The great guano deposits on islands off the coast of Peru, formed by the innumerable cormorants, gannets, and pelicans, are undoubtedly traceable in considerable part to the abundant anchovies and other small fishes upon which the birds feed; the anchovies are traceable to the plankton and the plankton, in part, to the nutritive materials brought back to the upper waters by upwelling.

Waves

To the ordinary observer nothing is more characteristic of the ocean than the continual prevalence of wave motion. The waves may be low and seemingly regular, or, in times of storm, high and terrifying. They beat unceasingly on the shore and give zest to bathing as they roll in and break in the shallowing water. Away from shore they mark the continuing uneasiness of the surface and give rise to seasickness or, perhaps, after some experience, to the soothing cradle-roll or pitch of the vessel. They may be obviously driven by the winds or, in times of calm, there may be only a long, low heaving movement which we designate as "swell," but not necessarily employing that term in its slang meaning of superb or delightful. Even the swell, particularly in the broad Pacific, may be marked by very great differences in elevation between crest and trough and, on reaching the coast, cause tremendous damage as they break on the exposed shores. Such is the case with the *mar brava*, or "wild sea," occurring at times on the coast of Peru, which, in the absence of local strong winds, drags ships at anchor in the ill-protected harbors, often beaching them or causing damaging collisions and wreaking havoc upon docks and the strongest steel piers.

Everyone associates waves with winds, recognizing the persistence of high waves for some time following wind storms and the spread of waves from regions of storm to regions where only normal air movement may have occurred. The mechanics of wave motion and the relations of waves to winds are much too complex to be grasped by the ordinary student. Yet there are a few facts about waves that may be of interest to anyone. We know that waves have different heights, lengths, periodicities, and velocities. We know that they are not regular, but differ in size and form; that they do not always run in the direction of the wind, that some are marked by breaking

Pl. 6. "Sandfall" in the Cape San Lucas submarine canyon, Baja California, during the Scripps Institution's Vermilion Sea Expedition. The "fall" is about 30 feet high. Currents feed sand from the nearby beaches into the canyon.

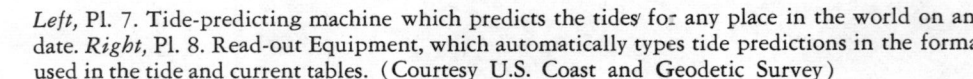

Left, Pl. 7. Tide-predicting machine which predicts the tides for any place in the world on any date. *Right,* Pl. 8. Read-out Equipment, which automatically types tide predictions in the format used in the tide and current tables. (Courtesy U.S. Coast and Geodetic Survey)

Above, Pl. 9. Standard automatic tide gage with transmitter for remote recording. (Courtesy U.S. Coast and Geodetic Survey) *Below*, Pl. 10. The amount of heat flowing through the crust of the earth into the ocean waters varies considerably over the Pacific Ocean. The cause is unknown. It may be that vast convection cells underlie the crust. Some of the first such measurements made were taken on Capricorn Expedition, 1952-53. Here scientists lower the temperature probe. The probe itself is the slender steel rod; the larger section at the top houses recording instruments. (The University of California, La Jolla)

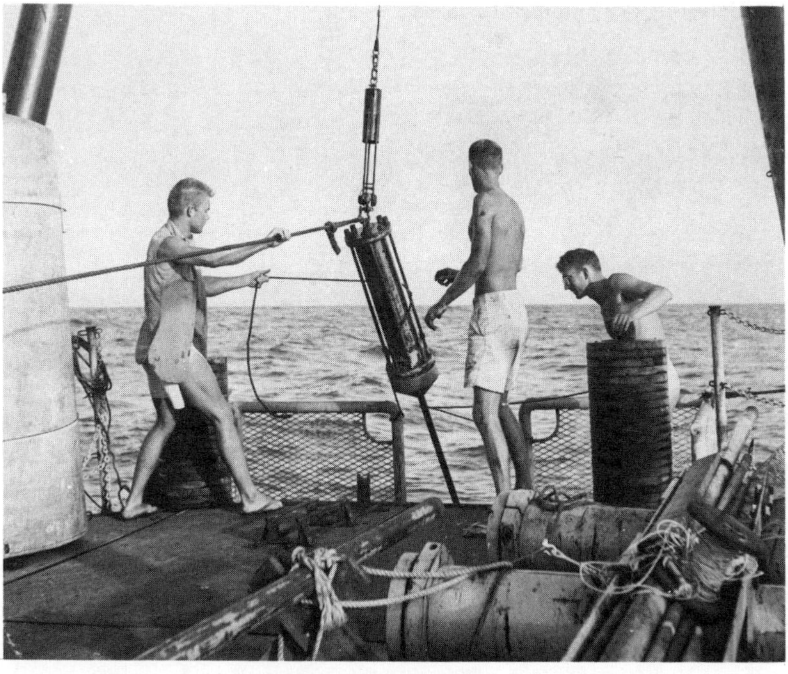

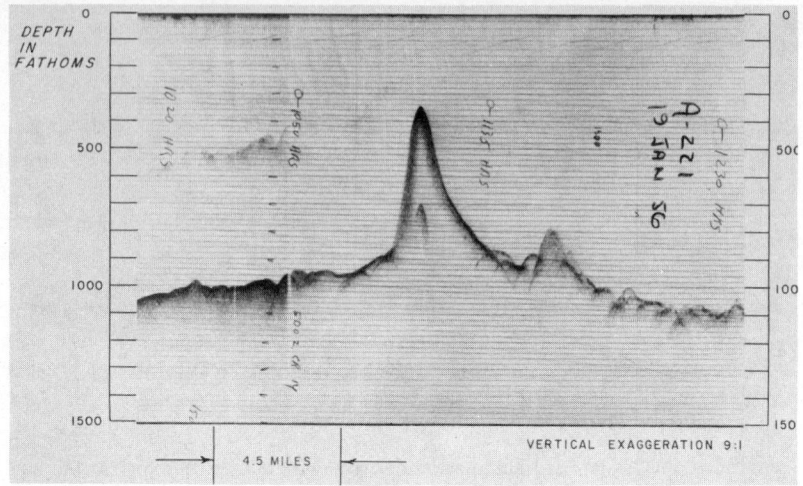

DEPTH IN FATHOMS

0
500
1000
1500

VERTICAL EXAGGERATION 9:1

4.5 MILES

Above, Pl. 11. Sea-mount—or underwater mountain, as tracked by Woods Hole Oceanographic Institution echo sounder in the Caribbean area. Depth is determined by the time it takes echo to go to bottom and return to shop. (Courtesy Woods Hole Oceanographic Institution) *Below,* Pl. 12. Marine Technician attaches a Nansen bottle to the hydrographic wire. The Nansen bottle is one of the standard tools of oceanography throughout the world. Actuated by sliding weights called messengers, the bottles on a line reverse and collect a sample of sea water at a specified depth. Thermometers on the side of the bottle record temperature *in situ.* (The University of California, La Jolla)

Pl. 13. This six-ton crane aboard the Scripps Institution research vessel
ARGO enables oceanographers to lower heavy equipment to the deepest
parts of the ocean.

Above, Pl. 14. This underwater camera, designed by Carl J. Shipek of the U.S. Navy Electronics Laboratory, was used on Capricorn Expedition to the South Pacific in 1952-53. *Below,* Pl. 15. Lowering the chain dredge from the stern of the research vessel HORIZON. The ship is one of the oceanographic fleet of The University of California's Scripps Institution of Oceanography. She was engaged in Northern Holiday Expedition to the Gulf of Alaska at the time this photograph was taken. (The University of California, La Jolla)

and foaming crests while others are not, that the "breaks" do not occur uniformly along the crest of any particular wave, and that the sloping surfaces are not necessarily smooth but may be marked by various sorts of irregularities. Doubtless most of us understand, too, that, despite the appearance of linear movement, there is no substantial flow of water resulting from the waves. With wind blowing across a field of wheat, each head of grain moves forward and falls, rises and moves backward, but keeps its basic position. In water, each particle in wave movement rises and moves forward, falls and moves backward; its path is nearly circular, if the water is deep, or elliptical if the bottom is nearer; but there is some slight advance. The floating log, passed by succeeding waves and appearing now at the crest and now in the trough and seemingly stationary does make some progress, independently of the effect of direct wind action on the log. Waves caused by wind, in contrast to currents, are "movements of oscillation," not "movements of transport."[2]

One fact about the relation between winds and waves that is easily grasped, once our attention is called to it, is that, so long as the wind blows faster in the direction of the wave movement than the waves are moving, each wave acts as an obstacle to the movement of the air, so that an eddy must form on the leeward side; consequently, the pressure of the wind is greater on the windward slope than on the other side of the crest and this pressure tends to increase the velocity and the height of the waves.

The friction between air and water, the relative densities of air and water, the surface tension and the viscosity of the water, and the rate of movement of the air are all factors in the formation of waves. It is said that wind velocities below about 2 miles per hour will not cause disturbances of a smooth water surface but, as Sverdrup says, "as yet the problem of the generation of surface waves is not satisfactorily solved."[3]

In general the height, profile, and velocity of progress of waves depend not only upon wind velocity at the time, but also upon the length of time the wind has blown, the state of the sea when the wind started blowing, and the dimensions of the area over which

2. There are, however, "waves of translation," representing the progressive forward movement of water, as when, by the breaking of a dam, a mass of water is added to that below to move on over the smooth water—or when, along shore, "the crest of a breaking wave topples over and crashes down on the water surface in front."—Sverdrup, *op. cit.*, p. 147. See also Bigelow and Edmondson, 1947.

3. *Ibid.*, p. 134.

the wind has blown. Practically all winds are variable in strength, marked, as we say, by gusts. This inconstancy of the wind has much to do with the irregularities of wave surfaces. The greatest wave *heights* observed in most oceans are about 12 meters, although heights up to 30 meters (98.4 feet) have been reported. Fifty feet is thought to be "the extreme height of the waves of the sea due to wind."[4] Of course a great wave breaking over a ship or on a steep shore may throw water to a much greater height, even up to 100 feet. A particular series of high waves had a *length* between crests of 310 meters (about one-fifth mile), a *period* of 13.5 seconds (the time interval between crests passing a given point), and a *velocity* of the order of 40 knots (about 48 miles per hour). Heights, lengths, periods, and velocities may be increased on approach to shores, and all of these characteristics of waves vary greatly with many conditions.

The length of a wave may be 15 to 30 times its height. For wind waves it may be given as a general rule that the velocity is $2\frac{1}{4}$ times the square root of the length. In other words, if the distance between crests is 100 feet (the length), the rate of advance (velocity), measured in feet per second, would be about $2\frac{1}{4}$ x 10, or 22.5 feet per second. The period, which is the interval of time elapsing between passages of successive crests at a given place, would, of course, depend upon length and velocity. It is usually about one-half the square root of the length, or, in the instance mentioned, about five seconds. These remarks refer to waves caused by the wind. Waves resulting from earthquakes or other seismic disturbances may have very great velocities, even approximating the velocities of present day airplanes.

Wave motion is largely a surface phenomenon, the wave motion decreasing rapidly with increasing depth. A descending submarine vessel easily gets below the level of disturbance from ordinary surface wave action;[5] yet we know that, after great storms, bits of coral, Baltic amber, or other material from the bottom at some depth, may be dislodged and cast up on the beach. Murray in *The Ocean*[6] tells of the disturbance of sand on the bottom at nearly 200 fathoms

4. Marmer, *op. cit.*, p. 181. Wave height is the vertical distance from trough to crest.

5. This is "by the book": a former submarine officer in the U. S. Navy assures me that wave action is felt far down.

6. Pp. 105, 106.

(almost one-fourth of a mile) during heavy gales. We are speaking now of the subsurface effects of wind waves: it will be seen a little later that there are also disturbances in the depths which are independent of surface waves.

The irregularities of wave motion on the ocean are attributable in part to the fact that two or more patterns of wave movements may prevail at the same place and time, superimposed upon one another. Waves with different periodicities and lengths will, at different points and moments, combine to cause a higher lift of the water or, at another place, partially cancel each other to form a shallower trough. For example, a long, low, swell running concurrently with a series of waves may not be directly observable at all, but will have the effect of causing noticeable irregularity by raising some crests and lowering others, by making troughs between waves deeper or shallower, and by slightly advancing or retarding crests, and thus producing observable irregularities in periodicities, as well as in heights of waves and depths of troughs.[7]

As waves approach the shore, their velocity is retarded in the shallow water, the lower part being retarded more than the upper, so that the crest "breaks" over, as is characteristic of the condition of "surf." Another effect of the slowing down in shallow water is to cause waves that were originally oblique to the shore to become roughly parallel to it. The first part of an oblique wave to approach the shallow water is slowed down while the free outer part continues with undiminished velocity, so that the front of the wave is steadily turned toward the shore. Such a change in direction of a wave as occurs on approaching the shore may also occur as the wave advances over the relatively shallow water of an isolated shoal. Consequently, pictures taken from an airplane may reveal the presence of a shoal that has not been located by actual soundings.

7. See Sverdrup, *op. cit.*, p. 140, Fig. 38.

CHAPTER 11

Sea Water in Motion: Tides and Other Movements

The Tide

WE HAVE DEALT WITH THE WAVES, THE SWELLS, THE CUR-rents, and drifts. If by some miraculous intervention we could stay any of these significant features of dynamic action in the sea, the waters would still not be at rest. "The sea moves also in a slower tempo. Twice each day, in rhythmic fashion, it rises and falls in response to the mighty pulse of the tide-producing forces. These stir the sea to its depths and bring about the phenomena which for short are called the tide."[1] The tides are "the largest waves in the ocean."[2]

The relation of the tide to the moon is apparent when we observe that generally the tide, like the moon, comes approximately fifty minutes later each day. Its relation to the sun becomes evident when our observations cover a longer period and we find that the tide varies in height from day to day. It is a general rule that the tide on the flood is highest, and on the ebb is lowest, when the moon is "full" or when it is "new"—that is to say when sun, moon, and earth are in line; and the tide is least high at flood, and least low at ebb, in the first and third quarters of the moon, when the three bodies are farthest out of line. The extreme tides of the full and new moon we call the *spring* tides; the moderate tides on the quarters of the moon are called the *neap* tides. Spring and neap tides

1. Marmer, *The Sea*, p. 203.
2. Sverdrup, Johnson, and Fleming, *The Oceans*, p. 545.

are said to have the general relative quantitative relation of 13 to 5. Actually, there is usually a lag, the spring and neap tides following a little after the alignment of sun and moon. So also the semidaily tides fall behind the primary tide-producing forces of the moon and the sun—as someone has said, like a dog pulled by a chain but fol-

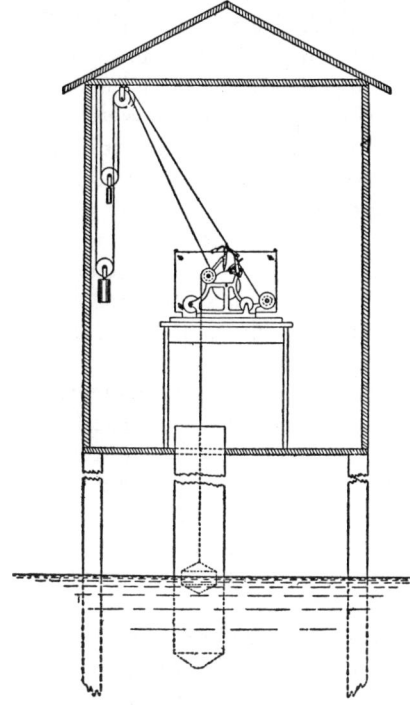

FIGURE 10. Diagram showing the plan of the standard automatic tide gage. (Courtesy U. S. Coast and Geodetic Survey)

lowing behind, rather than closely accompanying, the agent that pulls the chain.

The tides are not, of course, entirely regular. They vary from day to day in the same place, they manifest themselves differently in different places in the same general area, and they have characteristic features in particular regions. The partial inconstancy and the diversity of tides are attributable to the fact that there are many variables to which the tide is responsive. Among these are: the elliptical orbits of earth about sun and of moon about earth, giving changing distances between earth and sun, and between moon and earth; the declinations (see p. 150, below) of sun and of moon, which have slow rhythms; the latitude of the place; the changes in barometric pressure; the prevalence of off-shore or on-shore winds; the width and the depth of the water on which the tidal forces act; and the contours of shores.

Considering tides the world over, we can distinguish three types or "species." A *semidaily* (semidiurnal) tide is the common form of tide in the Atlantic, where the successive high tides of a day are of nearly the same height, and the two low tides are about equally low. A *mixed* tide is more common in the Pacific and Indian oceans, where alternate highs may be nearly equal and the lows very unequal, or vice versa. One low is very low, while, at the next low, the waters scarcely fall to mean sea level; or the lows may be nearly the same, while alternate floods bring the water barely, if at all, to mean sea level, as at Honolulu. A *daily* (diurnal) tide prevails in places on the Gulf of Mexico, where alternate lows or highs are more or less completely effaced and flood and ebb tide seem to follow one another at about twenty-five-hour intervals, as at Pensacola and sometimes at Galveston.

The *mixed* tides are actually combinations of *daily* and *semidaily* tides, with different combinations at different places. The fundamental question, then, is: Why should there be daily and semidaily tides? Without going too far into explanations that would lead us considerably into the realm of the mathematician and the physicist, the chief types of causes responsible for the two tides may perhaps be suggested. Let us forget the diurnal tide for a moment and consider only the semidiurnal tide.

The gravitational attraction between sun and earth and between moon and earth supplies the force inducing the mass movements that we know as the tide. The seas are upon the surface of the earth and the differential "pull" of gravitation on parts of a whole depends upon distances of the several parts from the center of mass. Obviously, the sun pulls more strongly on water of the surface that is toward the sun than on the center of the earth, while its pull on the center of the earth is stronger than its pull on water of the more distant surface. If the surface of the earth were entirely water,[3] the pull of the sun would change the sphere into an

3. The surface of the earth is not all water, but we are not concerned here with tidal strain over terrestrial areas. These are to some extent measurable, but the

oblate spheroid with increased diameter in a line running directly from the sun through the earth and with decreased diameter in a plane perpendicular to this long axis.

Let us imagine for a moment that the sun is directly over the Equator: then, along the equator, two conditions of high tide will prevail at one time, one at each extreme of the long axis—that is to say, on the face toward the sun and on the face away from the sun. Halfway between, on each side, low tides prevail; thus there are two lows at intermediate points. The four tides, two high and two low, must prevail somewhere around the circumference of the earth at all times. This is true, not only at the Equator, but, to a less extent, at any latitude, although the effectiveness of the tide-producing force will be somewhat reduced as we proceed away from the Equator toward the poles.

But the earth makes a complete rotation about its axis in a day; so that the two states of high solar tide and the two states of low solar tide must pass completely around the earth in the course of a twenty-four-hour period. This means that, at any place on the earth, there must be two high solar tides, generally one in the day and one in the night, and two low tides in between. Of course, this is not exactly what we seem to find. Our failure, so far, to arrive at any close approximation to the actual conditions is due to the fact that we have not yet considered the influence of the moon which, as a tide-producing force, is definitely stronger than that of the sun.

The moon revolves around the earth relatively slowly, but at such a rate that the *lunar day*, resulting from the rotation of the earth on its axis, is about fifty minutes longer than the *solar day* of twenty-four hours. Just as, with the sun alone, we should have at any place four solar tides in a period of twenty-four hours, so, with the moon alone, there must be four lunar tides, two high and two low, during a period of about twenty-four hours and fifty minutes. The tides caused by the sun and those caused by the moon run with slightly different periods; so that they are sometimes partially cancelling and sometimes supplementing each other; lunar and solar tides will coincide and be fully cumulative only twice each lunar month, when,

---

solid earth yields too little to tidal forces to make the changes ordinarily observable to man. It may be, however, that these strains set off some earthquakes, and that something is felt by the catfishes whose movements are said to presage by many hours the occurrence of earthquakes on Asiatic shores. Tidal effects in the air mass around the earth are also too slight for ordinary attention.

as previously mentioned, sun, moon, and earth are in line at full or new moon; at other times lunar and solar tides will partly cancel one another or be only partly in summation.

We see, then, in a general way, why there should be semi-diurnal high and low tides and why the tides should vary in degree of highness or lowness in a somewhat regularly rhythmic fashion. But, it may be asked, why should the general rhythm of the semidaily tide, as we see it, follow the lunar period rather than the solar period. The answer takes us back to two basic laws: the tide-producing force of a celestial body varies *directly with the mass* and *inversely with the cube of the distance*. The sun has twenty-six million times the mass of the moon, but it is 389 times farther from the earth than is the moon, and the cube of 389 is nearly fifty-nine million. Consequently, the relative tide-producing powers of moon and sun are as 59 is to 26; the influence of the moon in this respect is about 2 ¼ times that of the sun. Naturally, then, the tides display a *lunar* rather than a solar period. What we see of the *solar* tide is little more than the changes it effects in the highness and lowness of the tides on successive days. Consequently, the tides are most marked in January, when the sun is nearest the earth and exerts the most force with or against the moon.

What is known as the *declination*[4] of the moon is also a factor in the height and rhythm of tides. In an earlier paragraph we assumed that the moon and the sun stood directly over the equator. As everyone knows, the sun is in this position only twice each year and the moon only twice in approximately 27 1/3 days. Let us imagine for a moment the moon at its maximum declination to the north. That point on the surface of the earth which at a given minute is nearest to the moon may be expected then to have its highest lunar tide; at the same time, a point on the other side of the earth an equal distance below the equator, and, therefore, farthest from the moon, has also approximately its highest lunar tide. As the earth revolves on its axis, each of these points comes, half a day later, to a position where it is as far out of line with the moon and the center of the earth as it can get on that day: in this position it is subject to greatly reduced tidal force. It is time for "high tide," but this high

---

4. Meaning the angular distance with reference to the celestial equator. We are concerned here with the angle of the moon with reference to the axis of the earth.

will not compare with the last high. Consequently, there is only one very high tide in the course of the day, and one that is moderately high. For this and other reasons, there is a *diurnal* rhythm as well as a semidiurnal rhythm.

Various sorts of mixtures of the diurnal and semi-diurnal lunar and solar tides give us various types of tidal manifestation in different regions. "To a very large degree, the various oceans may be said to show preferences for one or other of the three types of tide. In the Atlantic Ocean the semidaily tide is the prevailing type, while in the Pacific and Indian oceans the mixed tide is the prevailing type. The daily tide is found in certain parts of the Gulf of Mexico, the China Sea and in other like bodies of water."[5]

From what has been said so far it may be assumed that, generally speaking, and theoretically at least, the semidaily tides will be greatest in equatorial regions and least as we approach the poles, while the diurnal tide will be nearly zero around the equator and greatest toward the poles.

Still another important set of conditions, as yet unmentioned, has much to do with the form and rhythm of the tide. Every container of water has, for the contained water, a *natural period* of *oscillation*, depending on its length and depth, assuming that the water is made to swing back and forth. A number of different basins of different sizes and depths will offer an equal number of periods of oscillation. If we apply a certain force to all of these containers we can expect the greatest rise and fall of the water when the period of the applied force is the same as the natural period of oscillation, so that the two factors reinforce each other; and we shall have the least rise and fall when the period of the applied force differs most from the natural period of oscillation, so that one factor of oscillation tends to cancel the other. We have various combinations of "free" oscillations comparable to *seiches* in enclosed bodies of water, with periods dependent upon the geometric shape of the lake, bay, or ocean, and "forced" oscillations, with periods dependent upon the outside forces producing them. The seiche (pronounced *sāche*), it may be explained, is a sort of "see-saw" or back-and-forth swing of water such as one causes in a long pan by suddenly raising one end.

We have seen, although in a very general way, that both daily

5. Marmer, *op. cit.*, p. 215.

and semidaily rhythms characterize the chief tide-producing forces. "Now it happens that the lengths and depths of the various parts of the Atlantic Ocean are such as to make their natural periods of oscillation much more nearly half a day than a day. Hence, in this ocean there is little daily tide. In the Pacific and Indian oceans, depths and lengths are such as to permit oscillations of both the daily and semidaily periods. In these oceans, therefore, both daily and semidaily tides are brought about, the combination of the two giving rise to the mixed type of tide characteristic of these oceans. Finally, in the Gulf of Mexico the natural period of oscillation more nearly approximates the daily rather than the semidaily tide, so that here we find the daily tide well developed."[6]

We have said nothing of tidal modifications resulting from variables such as the changing distances between moon and earth and between earth and sun, the varying barometric pressure, the changing direction of the wind and the diversity of bottom and shore forms. There are, indeed, so many complicating factors affecting the tides that a full explanation of them taxes the most competent mathematician equipped with the best mechanical devices. To forecast the tide at any particular place and time, the U. S. Coast and Geodetic Survey employs an extremely complex and ingeniously devised machine which automatically summates the effects of more than a score of variables. We will do well now to emphasize the fact that this cursory account is not intended to offer an explanation of tides but merely to be suggestive of the principal forces behind them, and behind their variable manifestations.

At this point we may distinguish three types of manifestations of tidal phenomena. The "progressive wave" type, the real tide, proceeds around the whole earth; it reflects the external tidal forces and in some places is essentially what is observed. There is also a "standing wave" type where the rhythmic rise and fall is strongly modified by the swing of water, or seiche, caused within a nearly enclosed basin, such as a bay or harbor; the seiche reflects the form of the container. As already indicated, even the great oceans function as basins whose seiches modify the progressive wave form of tide: in bays there may be, over considerable areas, synchronous rather than successive rises.

6. *Ibid.*, p. 218.

The "standing wave" is best illustrated by picturing a tub of water in which, by tilting, the water is caused to swing back and forth. It rises on one side and then on the other with no wave running across the surface. If a similar tub of water is not tilted but the surface is disturbed at one place, the "progressive wave" moves across. In the first case, the rises at all points on one side come nearly synchronously; in the other case, the crest of the wave proceeds successively from point to point. In our terrestrial containers, which may be bays, harbors, semi-enclosed seas, or even a great ocean, the mighty tide-producing forces, together with the forms of the several bodies of water, give rise to both standing and progressive waves, with one or the other, or mixtures of the two, playing in each case the greater part in determining what may be observed at a particular place.

If, now, we add to our tub a shallow spout near the surface, then either type of wave may cause a flow of water through the spout and this flow is suggestive of the third type of tidal phenomena, "the tidal current" through inlets and in the mouths of rivers and narrow bays. The shape of the spout, as well as the type of wave, will have much to do with determining the rate and height of flow. Where the entering tidal current is cooped within a narrow estuary, or under some other conditions, it may be transformed into a high and powerful advancing wave or *bore*. Probably the tide in the ocean offshore will rarely exceed 2 or 3 feet, but in the tidal current of the Amazon we may have a rise and fall of 10 and 15 feet. In the Bay of St. Malo, on the northwest coast of France, there are "tides" of 39 feet; in Noel Bay, a part of the Bay of Fundy, the spring tides may cause the water to rise more than 50 feet (15.4m.); there are even records of a vertical tidal range of 66 feet for the Bay of Fundy. The exact causes for the extreme tides in the Bay of St. Malo are said to be different from those causing the still greater extremes in the Bay of Fundy, but we can not go into an analysis of these conditions. A famous "bore" is that in the Tsientang River in China, south of Shanghai, where a towering, rushing and roaring wall sometimes offers great danger to those who do not know enough to anticipate its coming and to be out of the path; although, with properly constructed sampans, the bore can be utilized for rapid advance up the river.

Internal Waves

We think of waves as surface phenomena, because it is only'the top that we see. Even the surface waves extend below, although with greatly diminishing degree of action with increasing depth: they are not felt very far down. There can, however, be independent subsurface waves, or, perhaps we should say, waves at surfaces other than that between sea and atmosphere. Actually, the waves that we see and call surface waves are not at the true surface of the earth, which is the outer limit of the atmosphere; they are at the boundary between water and atmosphere, that is to say, between two media of very unequal density. There can be waves at any boundary between layers of unequal density. Thus, we can have waves at the surface of a layer of heavy liquid overlaid by a thick layer of water, waves that are scarcely if at all apparent on the surface exposed to the atmosphere: this is easily demonstrated in the laboratory.[7] So in the ocean, where there are, perhaps far down, boundary lines between layers of water of unequal densities, waves can occur at any boundary without being obvious at the surface of the sea, and quite independently of surface phenomena. Actually the deep wave will have an effect extending upward to the surface, but with amplitude diminishing so rapidly toward the surface that the resulting wave motion there will be much too slight for ordinary observation or consideration. That such internal waves occur, although, of course, they are not directly observable, seems now an established fact; their origins or causes remain to be discovered.

Although the greater number of observations and analyses of data concerning internal waves seem to have been made within the past fifteen years, the occurrence of such phenomena was divined by Helland-Hansen and Nansen as long ago as 1909. The latter, in

7. An experiment with relatively immiscible liquids of unequal density, such as carbon tetrachloride colored with crystals of iodine, overlaid by plain water, is simple and convincing as to the possibility of internal waves. There should be warning, however, that conditions are not precisely the same where the two liquids of unequal density are miscible, as in the case of sea waters of different densities. In the latter case it would seem to be natural for eddy effects to lead to some slight degree of mixing, yet, speaking of the transition zone (halicline) between upper and less saline water and the deeper and more salty water, Professor Thurlow C. Nelson of Rutger's University has made the following interesting comment (by personal communication): "Our studies of the halicline in Barnegat Bay show it to be remarkably stable, broken only by fairly heavy waves. Even in a dead calm, however, the surface of the halicline rises and falls about .2m in rhythmic fashion due to submarine waves."

his chapter on "Physical Oceanography" in Murray and Hjort, *The Depths of the Ocean*, gave vivid suggestions of the phenomena of deep turbulence.

"We arrived at the conclusion that there must be many forms of motion of great and far-reaching importance, though hitherto hardly known at all, among them vertical oscillations of the water-layers and vortex movements. Many things go to prove that these are phenomena of general occurrence. We must picture to ourselves great submarine waves moving through the water-masses, alterations of depth in the layers according to changes in the velocity of the currents, standing waves, and great vortices. We must further conceive of constant fluctuations in the velocity, partly also in the direction, of the great ocean currents, not only by reason of the tides and as the effect of the wind, but also because the currents are subject to a sort of pulsation, the nature and origin of which are as yet unknown. There is an interplay of many different forces, producing an extremely variegated picture; the sea in motion is a far more complex thing than has hitherto been supposed. Physical oceanography is confronted with a host of new problems, the solution of which will be a matter of the highest interest."[8]

Much remains to be learned about the nature, extent, and general prevalence of internal waves, as well as concerning their causes. There are "short" internal waves; in the open ocean there are also long waves of low velocity, although these may be short in comparison with tidal waves. They may have considerable amplitude, perhaps much greater than that of surface waves. Seiwell (1937) found evidence of vertical displacement of as much as 80 meters, with a primary twenty-four-hour period, but with complicating oscillations of twelve and eight hour periods. Sverdrup has found evidence of internal waves with periods of about seven and fourteen days.[9]

It may be asked how knowledge of such invisible and, to the observer, impalpable, waves can be gained. In partial answer it can be said that, where an oceanographic vessel, remaining approximately in one place, discovers at given depths periodic changes in temperature, density, and oxygen content, it is reasonable to infer that at a particular depth, different strata of water are being sampled at different hours, in rhythmic alternation; the instruments of collection

8. Pp. 283-85.
9. See Sverdrup, *et al., op. cit.*, pp. 585-602.

at a fixed depth are at certain hours in one layer and at another in the next lower layer: rise and fall, or wave action, is indicated. If on a dark night an object suspended from a pier were found to be in the air and in the water in periodic alternation, the existence of waves would hardly be questioned; so our sampling device in the depths may yield alternating results that can be accounted for only by the assumption of deep wave motion.

Between the top of the ocean and the bottom there may be a number of different boundary surfaces between layers of different densities associated with different conditions of salinity or of temperature. Consequently, there may be internal waves at several different levels, and each series of waves may have some effect on those above and below. The whole subject of internal waves is too complex for our further consideration in this place; but, in the words of Sverdrup, Johnson, and Fleming "The internal waves probably are important to the process of mixing,"[10] and they "greatly complicate the actual movement of water masses and lead to the existence of extremely intricate patterns of currents and vertical displacements."[11]

"Tidal Waves"

The term "tidal wave" is applied loosely to destructive advances of the sea upon the coasts, and these have at least two distinct origins: earthquakes and storms. Neither type is related to the tide and those of the latter type are not actually waves.

The waves resulting from earthquakes arise in different ways: They may occur through mere oscillations, or through liberations of gas that rise to "lift the surface up like a great dome and produce a transverse wave" which spreads in all directions. Again there are waves resulting from submarine landslides. Earthquake waves may be enormously high and may travel long distances. The wave accompanying the Lisbon earthquake of 1755 and causing most of the damage there is said to have reached across the Atlantic to the West Indies as a tidal wave 4 to 6 meters high. The wave resulting from the eruption of the volcano Krakatao in 1883 caused great damage and the loss of thousands of lives in the East Indies and, in

10. *Ibid.*, p. 601.
11. *Ibid.*, p. 596, 597.

a round-about way, even reached England with a small but measurable height. Such waves are now called "tsunamis."

The great "tidal waves" that caused so much loss of life in Galveston, Texas, in 1900 and in the Buzzard's Bay, Massachusetts, region in 1938, were much more than actual waves. The flooding of the coastal regions in these cases was in considerable part the result of direct transportation of water under the influence of exceptionally strong winds. True "wave" motions are not transport but *periodic oscillation* of water particles within a limited space. It is not unnatural that confusion of thought and language should occur, especially since great waves and seiches usually accompany the movements of masses of water before the wind. In some cases, indeed, high waves break upon the shores with destructive effect even before the strong winds are felt at the coast. The base level of water along shore may also have been raised. The following flow of water in the tidal wave (which is neither wave nor tide) only increases the destruction.

Biological Relations of Waves, Tides and Upwelling

A whole book could be written on the subject of the significance of waves and tides to life in the sea. Some of the relations will be discussed in later chapters on biology. It is appropriate here only to suggest some of the bearings of tidal and wave movements on plant and animal life. That the rise and the fall of the tide and the tidal currents are of significance to the living world must be apparent to anyone who wanders even casually along the shores of bays and harbors. There are great numbers of organisms, plant and animal, whose preferred home is above extreme low water, "between the tide lines," where, for part of the time, they are washed by flooding and ebbing water, with almost constant renewal of supplies of food and oxygen. This is only a small part of the story. Because of special conditions, commercial fishermen in harbors, employing seines, seek the fish as they follow the rising tide over the shoals, while sport fishermen know the advantages of fishing at the slack of the tide.

Conditions of turbulence associated with waves promote interchange between sea and atmosphere, as well as circulation and distribution of oxygen, heat, etc. within the upper layers. The processes of diffusion and conduction, by which oxygen and heat are carried downward from the surface are extremely slow and of little effect on distribution. That part of the sea which profits by interchange of temperature and gases between sea and atmosphere would be restricted to a thin surface layer, were it not for the mixing effects of waves and for certain density changes. The tides are responsible for some coastwise currents and, in coastal regions, for much *mixing;* but, well out in the open sea, waves are probably most significant in mixing the upper waters and in preventing sharp superficial stratification.

For animals such as oysters that have locally fixed stations on the bottom or for those like clams that are relatively immobile, tidal currents and wave movements circulate the supplies of food and oxygen. Were it not that the sea water is virtually always in motion we could not have in salt or brackish waters the great populations of oysters, corals, sea anemones, barnacles, and other sedentary animals, for which there are no corresponding populations in fresh water (p. 240, below.)

Animals of fixed habit and others that are mobile but sluggish have larvae that live freely in the water for a while and then, when properly developed, settle to the bottom wherever they happen to be. For such the tidal and other currents permit limited migration and, in great part, determine distribution.

As early as 1911, Otto Pettersson had found a relationship between the occurrence of herring in certain Swedish fiords and the deep internal waves that one never sees at the surface. When great submarine waves enter those fiords, they force out the less salty upper waters; the herring go in with the deep waves or are drawn in by them. These phenomena of the deep, although unseen by man, may be of notable practical significance to those who "live by the sea."

In certain regions upwelling of deeper water brings back in circulation nutrient substances that had sunk and been lost. They had been lost to the organic world, because, while they were in the deep, they had been out of reach of the green and yellowish plants that grow and multiply only in sunlight. These conditions must be treated in more detail when consideration is given to the cycles of life (see p. 190, below). A particular region may be cited here. The region off the coast of Peru has been mentioned as a place where upwelling of deeper cold waters is most notable. At another time[12] I wrote regarding that region:

"In contrast to the barrenness of the coast there is a peculiar wealth of certain forms in the open ocean. The great red seas, formed, sometimes at least, of myriads of microscopic dinoflagellates, are of common occurrence. . . . Sometimes, too, great areas of the surface of the sea are reddened by the vast numbers of small crustacea *(Munida)*, which then play a part of great importance as food for the fishes and for the guano-producing birds. More striking still are the immense schools of small fishes, the 'anchobetas' *(Engraulis ringens* Jenyns), which are followed by numbers of bonitos and other fishes and by sea lions, while at the same time they are preyed upon by the flocks of cormorants, pelicans, gannets, and other abundant sea birds. It is these birds, however, that offer the most impressive sight. The long files of pelicans, the low-moving black clouds of cormorants, or the rainstorms of plunging gannets probably can not be equaled in any other part of the world. These birds feed chiefly, almost exclusively, upon the anchobetas. The anchobeta, then, is not only an article of diet to a large number of Peruvians, and the food of the larger fishes, but, as the food of the birds, it is the source from which is derived each year probably a score of thousands of tons of high-grade bird guano. It is therefore to be regarded as the most valuable resource of the waters of Peru. No more forcible testimony to its abundance could be offered than the estimate, made roughly, but with not wide inaccuracy, that a single flock of cormorants observed at the Chincha Islands would consume each year a weight of these fish equal to one-fourth of the entire catch of the fisheries of the United States."

12. "The Fisheries and the Guano Industry of Peru," *Bulletin U. S. Bureau of Fisheries,* Vol. XXVIII (1908). See also "Peru's Wealth-Producing Birds," *National Geographic Magazine* (June, 1920), and "Habits and Economic Relations of the Guano Birds of Peru," *U. S. National Museum Proceedings,* Vol. LVI (1919).

CHAPTER 12

The Sea and the Sun

The Sea a Dynamic Body

WE HAVE HAD REPEATED OCCASION TO EMPHASIZE THE FACT that the great mass of water covering most of the globe is not a static body. However it may seem to those on a becalmed ship, and however smooth may be the action of its internal members, it is everywhere and at all times a dynamic mechanism, an engine in restless action. There are surface waves and tides and deep movements of the same nature. In the upper waters there are great currents, swift and relentless, or slow and fluctuating. There are eddies of oceanic dimensions and small ones as well. In the deep, there are slow and almost impalpable, but never insignificant, drifts. There are vertical movements, the sinking of heavy and the rising of lighter waters. There are, indeed, all sorts and manner of shifts resulting from the rotation of the earth, and from the rays of the sun that effect changes in temperature and concentration and, therefore, in density. Put in another way, there are everywhere continual disturbances of equilibrium which require compensatory movements, and the sea, as a continuous fluid, has widespread freedom of movement.

Water moves easily, but not without energy: it has mass and it has viscosity, or internal resistance to circulation; so that, where movements of such great volumes are involved, there must be immense *transformations* of energy. There must also be one or more *sources* of the energy that is subject to world-wide change in the sea. The rotational movements of earth and moon and the movements of these planetary bodies relative to the sun constitute one source or set of related sources. It is for the astronomer or the physicist to trace this energy to a more remote origin; but, undoubtedly, so far as the sea absorbs the energies of movement of celestial bodies, there must be a proportionate slowing down of the movement of those bodies. The energy concerned directly in the movements of water is probably not nearly so great as that involved in bringing about the changes (heating, evaporation, etc.) that lead to disturbances of equilibrium and the resulting movements.

The chief source of energy for the sea is the sun, and the means of transfer of energy from the sun to the sea or land is what we know as solar radiation, some of which is reflected, some absorbed. The smaller part that is reflected can have no direct effect on the sea. What is absorbed is converted into other forms of energy, for that is the meaning of "absorption" of radiation. A most significant feature of the energy relations for us is that the absorbed radiation is not just retained within the sea. Not all the energy received by the sea is manifested in movements of water—probably only a small part. There are interchanges of a high order of magnitude between sea and atmosphere, between sea and land, giving the oceans great significance to weather, to terrestrial climates, and to the lives of plants and animals everywhere. We are interested in many of these relations, but let us consider first the reception and distribution of the energy of radiation.

The Sea as a Reservoir of Heat[1]

Energy is received in the form of radiation, which, whatever it may actually be, is generally described as wave motion. The different forms of radiation have different wave lengths, but an object may receive energy of one wave length, transform it into another, and radiate it again in the changed form. Thus energy may be received in the short-wave form, the range of visible light, and be radiated again in the long wave form that we recognize as heat. Speaking very roughly, let us say: the earth receives light and emits chiefly heat. Transformations may give what we call work. It is the transformation of energy, always without loss, that is significant.

1. The interested reader who is qualified in physics or mathematics is referred to the authoritative discussion of radiation and heat budgets in Sverdrup, *Oceanography for Meteorologists*, Chapters I-IV. We draw freely upon that source for some of the data in this chapter.

All the work we know of, including the growth and reproduction of living things, represents transformation of energy. The trend is always toward heat; this is the well known law of the degradation of energy.

If we consider all forms of radiation, the wave lengths have a very wide range; but we are now concerned only with radiation that has importance to the energy changes in the sea and this comes within a relatively narrow range. Wave lengths may be given in the unit μ (micron), which is 1/1000 of a millimeter, or it may be measured by the smaller Ångström unit (Å), which is 1/10,000 of a micron or 1/10,000,000 of a millimeter. The wave lengths visible to man—that is to say, the wave lengths of light—fall between about 3,900 and 7,600 Å, or 0.39 to 0.76 μ. Wave lengths important to the heat budget of the earth are between 0.15 μ (1500 Å) and 120 μ (1,200,000 Å), but the radiation from the sun with which we are mostly concerned is chiefly short-wave radiation, with little of wave lengths greater than 2.6 μ (26,000 Å), and with maximum intensity close to 0.5 μ (5,000 Å), or at about the lengths of the longer blue and the green rays in the visible spectrum. On the side of the short rays, the energy of radiation falls off very rapidly to the shortest ultraviolet, but very much more gradually on the other side through the infrared. In this connection it may be mentioned again that the energy radiated *from* the earth is largely in the long wave. The earth receives short-wave (chiefly visible light) but emits long-wave radiation (heat.)

Energy from the sun is constantly coming into the earth directly or indirectly; part (about 57 per cent) is absorbed and part (about 43 per cent) reflected.[2] That part of the radiation from the sun that is reflected from the surface of the earth or from the upper surface of the clouds, and is not absorbed by the earth or the atmosphere, makes no contribution to the heat budget of the earth. It may be said that about 40 per cent of the energy reaching the outer limits of the earth is reflected back into space, while some 60 per cent is absorbed by the earth or its atmosphere. On the other hand, the earth is constantly losing energy to space by radiation from the

2. The "solar constant" is stated as approximately 1.94 g cal/cm²/min. The average solar radiation reaching the limit of the earth's atmosphere is found to be one-fourth of that, or 0.485 g cal/cm²/min, of which 0.209 is lost by reflection and is of no concern to life on earth. The remainder 0.276 is ultimately lost by back radiation to space.—Sverdrup, *op. cit.*, p. 3.

earth's surface or from the atmosphere, and, unless the earth is constantly becoming warmer or colder, the outgoing energy must be in approximate balance with the incoming energy.

Considering now the 60 per cent that is absorbed and then lost by back radiation to space, we have loss by radiation from water in the atmosphere and loss by radiation from the earth's surface, so far as the latter escapes being absorbed by the water vapor and carbon dioxide in the atmosphere. Water vapor is particularly mentioned because at prevailing temperatures, it is the chief component of the atmosphere that absorbs or emits amounts of radiation, and water vapor absorbs only certain wave lengths, being transparent to others (between 8.5 and 11 μ), where the outgoing radiation is nearly at a maximum. The radiation lost from the earth and its atmosphere to space is, as previously mentioned, long-wave radiation (which gives heat) with maximum intensity at 10 to 15 μ.

It is important for us to keep in mind that the oceans, the land areas, and the atmosphere are not to be regarded separately, but are really parts of one great system. Since most of us are not skilled physicists, let us itemize here a few basic facts that we can accept from the physicists and oceanographers and that we need to keep in the backgrounds of our minds if we are to understand the principal oceanographic phenomena.

(1) We must first recall some of the peculiar qualities of water itself. The same amount of heat that would raise the temperature of a given quantity (by weight) of water by 1°C. would raise the temperature of the same quantity of chloroform more than 4°C. or that of the same weight of iron about 10°C. Water then, has high "specific heat" or heat capacity; that is to say, capacity for storage of heat relative to rise in temperature. This is true of other substances having much hydrogen in the molecule, such as liquid ammonia (NH_3), which has even higher specific heat than water but much less than pure hydrogen. Putting the idea in another way, water, because it has high heat capacity, can absorb a great deal of heat without getting particularly "hot," as temperature is measured by the thermometer or by other common standards. Conversely, it can lose much heat without being brought to a very low temperature. Other notable features of water are associated with changes from the liquid to the solid state and the reverse. The formation of a small amount of ice goes with the loss of a great deal of heat, and,

conversely, a large amount of heat is required to melt a small amount of ice. Incidentally, water freezes at a temperature that is relatively high in relation to temperatures that occur on land. A mixture of water and ice forms a fairly accurate thermostat. In short, liquid water is one of the best possible media for use in absorption, storage, and transport of heat.[3]

(2) Perhaps even more significant characteristics of water are related to its change from the liquid to the gaseous state. Water evaporates at all ordinary temperatures (with a wide range), but evaporation always requires the absorption of heat. No other substance has such a high heat of evaporation as does water. It requires approximately as much heat to vaporize one gram of water at its normal boiling point as it does to raise the temperature of 539 grams of water by 1 °C. Evaporation, therefore, involves prodigious storage of heat. It has been estimated that in the region of the equator something like one million horsepower per square kilometer is used each year in evaporation. Computations by various methods have indicated that over the whole ocean evaporation averages something like a meter each year. At any particular place and time the amount of evaporation depends upon the humidity of the atmosphere, the temperatures of sea and air, and the velocity of the wind.

Not only does evaporation result in great initial storage of heat in the atmosphere, but also it is the water vapor in the atmosphere that intercepts and absorbs direct radiation from the sun, which, otherwise, would pass through the mostly transparent atmosphere. Hence water vaporized at the surface of the sea serves a double function: as it goes into the atmosphere it carries heat from the sea; in the atmosphere it continues to accumulate heat. Furthermore, water vapor is even more mobile than liquid water; so that heat absorbed at one place and carried in the vapor, is easily transported by the wind to other and distant places. Condensation of the water, wherever its occurs, releases the latent heat stored. It is easy to see, then, how the evaporation of water plays such a great part in the distribution of heat over the surface of the earth—and why the sea and the water vapor of the atmosphere may be regarded as great reservoirs of heat.

---

3. Hence we use it in our domestic heating systems, although ammonia, at least, has advantages over water in respect to specific heat and latent heat of fusion—but not in some other respects.

(3) Since in the atmosphere it is the water vapor, principally, which absorbs, holds, and emits radiation, we want to know how this vapor gains heat. This is only in very small part by *conduction* from the earth's surface, where air and earth are in contact. (Where any two bodies of unequal temperature are in contact, the warmer tends to give heat to the cooler by conduction.) Atmospheric water vapor acquires much more heat by *direct absorption* of both short-wave radiation coming from the sun and long-wave radiation given off from the earth, so far as it is not "transparent" to such rays. But, as has already been suggested, there is another source of heat for the atmosphere: and that is by *condensation*, since the condensation of water vapor releases the energy that was stored when and where evaporation originally took place. Probably the atmosphere gains as much heat through condensation of water vapor as through direct absorption of passing radiation.

What the atmosphere gains, year in and year out, it also loses. This must be true because the atmosphere does not get progressively warmer from year to year. It is said, by the way, that the gain of heat by the atmosphere through absorption of long-wave radiation from the earth and through condensation occurs at relatively low altitudes. Loss of heat from the atmosphere to space is said to take place chiefly at high altitudes by radiation from the water vapor and from the upper surfaces of clouds. In short, heating of the atmosphere takes place below and cooling above.

(4) For the earth as a whole, evaporation, which, to repeat, is (in one aspect) the storage of heat in water vapor, takes place predominantly at the surface of the sea—simply because the greater part of the face of the earth is sea. This much is obvious, but the point of special interest to us here, is that evaporation does not necessarily occur where the heat is absorbed: Heat absorbed in one locality at a given time may be used for evaporation *later* and in *another place*. By currents in the sea and by winds in the atmosphere, heat is transferred from regions of surplus receipt in low latitudes (from the Equator to about 35°N. and S.) to regions of deficiency in high latitudes. Movements of masses of water transport heat slowly; movements of water vapor by the winds transport it more rapidly. Hence, movements of air masses and of water masses influenced by winds or other conditions have much to do with determining when and where evaporation will take place. Evaporation depends on differ-

ence in vapor pressure, between the water and the air in contact with it. In general, water evaporates more rapidly when it is warmer than the air mass above it and warms the air immediately at its surface. "It must, therefore, be expected that the greatest evaporation occurs when cold air flows over warm water."[4] In middle and high latitudes, this condition on the sea occurs more generally in winter than in summer. More heat is *absorbed* in summer than in winter; but the *transfer of heat to the atmosphere* may be much greater in winter! Even though the surface water is cooler in winter than it is in summer, it may evaporate more rapidly in the cool season, simply because the air above it is still colder and is capable of being warmed by the water with corresponding decrease in vapor pressure.

(5) On the other hand, warm air holds more water vapor than does cold air and, as everyone knows, the cooling of warm moisture-laden air to below the dewpoint causes condensation. If the air over water is decidedly colder than the water and takes up vapor to the point of saturation, there may be some condensation, giving rise to a particular sort of fog, called *steam fog* or "smoke." It occurs chiefly over small bodies of water, where the air mass is not in contact with the water long enough to be brought generally to the same temperature as the water; over the open ocean where the air, even though in movement, has prolonged exposure to sea water, the differences of temperature leading to smoke fog are less common. Some fogs are caused by cooling of the air over a calm sea or land whose temperature is being lowered by radiation. The usual heavy fogs that hamper navigation are of another type called *advection fog*. Such a fog occurs when warm moisture-laden air from sea or land drifts over cool water, or land, and has its temperature lowered to the point of condensation.

(6) The biologist will not want to lose sight of the fact that a certain amount of short-wave radiation is absorbed by green plants,[5] particularly on land, to be stored through photosynthesis in the form of food materials that will supply the energy of living organisms. Eventually this energy employed in photosynthesis is changed to heat through the metabolic activities of both animals and plants. The

---

4. Sverdrup, *op. cit.*, p. 64.

5. "About [0.15] per cent of that part of the sun's energy which falls on the earth is caught annually and stored by plants."—W. J. Robbins, "The Importance of Plants," *Science*, C. 1944, 440. (By typographical error in the publication a larger figure is given. Correction is based on personal communication from the author.)

heat returns chiefly to the waters of the earth or to the water vapor of the atmosphere. The biologist will remember also that a good deal of the water vapor in the atmosphere is derived from the soils through the transpiration of plants and, much less significantly, through evaporation from animals. The heat liberated through evaporation from lungs, mouths, and skins of animals is, of course, principally a product of metabolism and is thus a part of that originally stored by the green plants. As will be seen later (p. 169) the amount of energy stored and released by organic life in the sea is computed to be a relatively minute part of the energy transformation in the sea, although it is of the greatest importance to marine life.

(7) *Conduction* is the transmission of heat without motion of the body as a whole; *convection* is the conveyance of heat by motion of particles. In water heat is conveyed upward by convection, but, because solar radiation, the main source of heat for the sea, is applied at the surface, convection, as a means of distribution of heat, is almost negligible. Conduction from the surface downward is likewise relatively insignificant, although water conducts heat more effectively than most liquids (much more slowly than most solids). But a feature of the sea, as compared to the land, is its mobility in both vertical and horizontal directions. The waves that stir the surface distribute heat downward to a significant extent. And there are other movements to promote circulation of heat.

Even though warm water is lighter than cold water having the same concentration of salts, yet, if through evaporation the surface water becomes sufficiently dense, it may sink to replace colder and less dense water: in this way, some heat is carried below the surface, although not ordinarily to any great depth. Horizontal movements play a great part in distribution. We have seen that heated sea water may be conveyed long distances from warm to cold regions, to release the transported heat either by radiation or evaporation in regions that receive less direct radiation.

Let us make a rough summary of this section. The energy that makes possible the circulation and the turbulence of the sea is derived directly or indirectly from the sun through radiation. The incoming energy received is chiefly short-wave radiation (in and around the wave lengths of visible light). An equal amount is lost by reflection or, after transformation, as long-wave radiation (roughly characterizable as heat). Because the sea occupies the greater part of the surface of the earth, the predominant share of energy available to the earth comes directly or indirectly to the surface of the sea. As compared with nearly all ordinary substances, water, in liquid, gaseous, or solid form, has exceptional qualities for the absorption, storage, transport, and release of heat. It stores much heat without relative rise of temperature. It absorbs heat at one place and time to release it later at another place, which may be a little deeper in the water, higher in the atmosphere, or at distant-places on the surface of the earth. Its mobility as liquid or vapor facilitates this transfer in all directions, vertically in sea or atmosphere, and horizontally over the surface of the earth. All this is true of fresh or salt water; but the liquid sea water has the further quality of undergoing change of density with loss by evaporation. The changes in density play no little part in the setting of conditions for both vertical and horizontal movements.

Water goes back and forth between sea and atmosphere. With a virtually unlimited amount of water for evaporation and storage of heat, and with its mobility, the sea, like the atmosphere, is a great *reservoir* of heat and a means of its *wide distribution.*

How the Seas are Warmed and Cooled

We are concerned with what might be called the "heat budget" of the ocean, the income and outgo of radiation. As a basic fact, we recognize that the oceans as a whole seem to be neither warming up nor cooling down from year to year. This means that income and outgo are approximately in balance: in respect to heat, the oceans lose each year approximately what they gain. There are three chief sources of heat for the sea. The water gains some heat from the atmosphere where two media are in contact. It gains more by absorption of radiation, coming directly from the sun or indirectly from the sun by reflection from the sky. It is heated to some extent by the condensation of water vapor. We can think of other sources of heat, such as conduction from the interior of the earth through the ocean bottom, transformation into heat of the kinetic energy of currents through friction, and heat released through chemical and biological processes within the sea. The effects of these last-mentioned agencies of conversion of energy are considered practically negligible. Conversely, there are three chief ways in which the seas suffer loss of heat: back radiation from the sea surface to the atmosphere and to space, loss to the atmosphere by conduction, and loss by evaporation through storage of heat in water vapor transferred to the atmosphere. Of course, a certain amount of radiation is used by plants in photosynthesis; but the amount so used in the sea is estimated at only a fraction of one per cent of the energy transformation in the sea.[6] Furthermore, most of the energy used in photosynthesis must be returned to the sea through the metabolism of plants and animals, and so, either directly or indirectly, as heat.

Now, although for the seas as a whole gains and losses in heat are in approximate balance, yet for a particular locality or a given depth at any one time, the conditions are quite different—income and outgo are not in balance locally and seasonally. The temperature of the water at a particular place, level and time may be changing one way or the other, and these changes might be cumulative to a more notable degree were it not that, as the waters are being warmed or cooled, they are also being regularly transferred by currents to other localities or depths. In short, as we may seem to emphasize repeatedly, the circulatory mechanisms are significantly interrelated with the heat budget, as with every other feature of ocean economy.

So far as the incoming short-wave radiation, chiefly in the range of visible light, comes directly from the sun to the surface of the sea, the amount must vary with place and time—that is to say, with latitude, season, and hour; and, we might add, with condition of the atmosphere. When the sun is at a low altitude with reference to a particular place, the rays must, of course, pass a greater distance through the air and be subjected to more scattering against the larger molecules in the air, chiefly the water molecules and carbon dioxide: but, regardless of the altitude of the sun, the amount of water vapor in the atmosphere affects the amount of scattering. Much of the short-wave radiation "scattered" in the sky still reaches the sea,[7] and much of that coming from the sun to the clouds, rather than directly to the sea, may be reflected from the clouds to the surface of the sea. Reflection from sparse clouds may, indeed, be so much that even more radiation reaches the sea on an overcast day

6. The comments of Sverdrup (*op. cit.*, p. 50) indicate that less than one-tenth of one per cent of incoming radiation is utilized by plants in the sea for photosynthesis.

7. The reflection of diffused radiation reaching the sea as scattered or reflected radiation is estimated at 8 to 28 per cent. Such estimates are approximate, and different figures have been given by different investigators.

than on one which is clear and cloudless. Most of us have experienced the severe sunburns gained on slightly cloudy days. On a really dark and rainy day, however, there is great reduction in radiation at sea level, even to less than one-tenth of what is received on a clear day.

The altitude of the sun varies, of course, not only with latitude and season, but also with the time of day. We shall see a little later, however, that the effect of the altitude of the sun and the obliquity of the rays is minimized in considerable degree by the refraction or bending of light rays entering the sea at an angle to the surface. On the other hand, not all of the radiation coming to the surface of the sea enters the water to be transformed into heat. Waves increase reflection, but, by and large, the greater part of incoming radiation is absorbed. The proportion reflected changes significantly with the altitude of the sun, increasing greatly as the altitude is diminished. Thus, it is calculated that, while only 2 per cent of solar radiation is lost by reflection when the sun is at the zenith, and only about one-tenth of one per cent more when the sun is at 60°, three times as much (6 per cent) is lost by reflection with the sun at 30 degrees, and more than seventeen times as much (34.8 per cent) with the sun at 10 degrees above the horizon. If water existed near the poles much of the small amount of radiation coming to the sea would be reflected even at the most favorable times of day; but the sea near the poles is frozen and sea ice, especially if covered by snow, reflects much more strongly than water—even up to 50 or 80 per cent of all the radiation received. It may be mentioned in this connection, too, that snow also radiates more strongly than water; the actual loss by back radiation so lowers the temperature of the ice as greatly to increase its thickness; furthermore, the cooling of air over ice and its spreading leads to further extension of the ice field.

When we consider the loss by back radiation, we find a basic difference between conditions on sea and on land in that the diurnal and annual variations of sea surface temperatures and of the humidity of the air over the surface are relatively small. Consequently, the effective back radiation changes little with the hour of the day or the season, notwithstanding that incoming radiation shows the same wide diurnal variations over sea and over land. Of course, clouds, which radiate heat to the sea, do cut down the effective back radiation.[8]

8. See Sverdrup, *op. cit.*, pp. 59–60.

Finally, it has been found that, for the sea itself and in any latitude, the incoming radiation is decidedly more than the outgoing back radiation. The surplus received does not, however, serve to heat the sea indefinitely. It is the exchange of heat and water vapor with the atmosphere and with the land that plays such a great part in maintaining the balance and in regulating ocean temperature and salinity.

As we shall see in consideration of the penetration of radiation, most of it is absorbed in the first meter, so that only the uppermost layers are directly heated. Even in the clearest ocean water, only about one-sixtieth as much heat is absorbed at the ten-meter level and something like 1/4,000 at the hundred-meter level. Were the water absolutely at rest, the temperature changes from the surface downward might correspond to this gradation in absorption; but, in any body of water of substantial size, mixing takes place as the result of the winds, and, in the sea, evaporation increases the density of the warmer surface water, causing it to sink. For lakes, most of the summer rise in temperature of the lake, as a whole, is described as "wind-distributed" heat. In the sea, we may refer not only to wind-distributed heat but also to gravity-distributed heat, while recognizing also that much of the distribution of heat is attributable to the rotation of the earth as it affects the movements of masses of water.

The Penetration of Radiation

Most of the energy that reaches the sea is in the visible arc of the spectrum. That is to say, it is in the form of visible *light* (0.39 to 0.76 μ) without much ultra violet or infra-red. The energy taken in is greatest at about 0.5 μ, the region of blue to green; it declines rapidly on the short-wave side being very slight in the region of the violet and zero at about 0.35 μ. On the other, or long-wave side, the energy is considerable, but it declines somewhat steadily to about 2.5 μ.[9]

The radiation that enters the water decreases in passage downward, partly because it is absorbed (converted into another form of energy) and partly because it is scattered laterally by impact against suspended particles or color substances or even against the molecules of the water. Because the materials in the water effect scattering, the amount of scatter varies in different waters. Everywhere sea water contains suspended matter, living or non-living, to scatter

9. Sverdrup, *op. cit.*, fig. 8, p. 54.

radiation; and, therefore, there is greater absorption and rise of temperature within the same thickness of water than there would be in pure water. Actually it is not yet altogether clear why there is so much increase of absorption in oceanic water as contrasted with pure water. Presumably, there is a certain amount of finely suspended matter which is not yet definitely identified. There seem to be minute suspended particles, which, in our ignorance of their structure, are called "yellow substances" and which are perhaps stable metabolic products of phytoplankton.

We are now concerned with the rate at which downward traveling light decreases with depths: its mathematical expression is called the "extinction coefficient" and, of course, it is different in different waters and in the same water at different times. Penetration of light has been determined by means of the Secchi disc, a white disc 20 centimeters (8 inches), or more, up to 2 meters in diameter, or by lowering photographic plates. Helland-Hansen exposed panchromatic plates in the region of the Azores at noon, June 6: at 500 meters, with forty minutes exposure, there was some blackening; at 1,700 meters with two hours exposure, there was no blackening. When color filters were used with such plates it was found that the red was absorbed more rapidly, the green and blue less so.

Spectrophotometers have been used, but have not proved practicable. Photoelectric cells with suitable color filters and with readings from a galvanometer on the boat, are now most widely used and most effective.

Much of the radiation that passes through the surface of the sea is absorbed quickly, some 62 per cent in the first meter in clearest water and much more in coastal or turbid waters. The absorption is, however, highly selective. Roughly speaking, sea water is translucent for visible radiation only, and most penetrable for just the wave lengths that are useful to plants. Even in clear oceanic water there is no infrared at 10 meters and scarcely any ultraviolet. Wave lengths in the blue-green range may penetrate well beyond 100 meters. Chlorophyll is capable of using in photosynthesis just the wave lengths that penetrate farthest in clear water. In the average coastal water nearly all radiation is absorbed in the first ten meters. Generally speaking, the less clear the water, the more the shifting of "surviving" wave lengths toward the longer waves, the green and yellow.

In general, then, blue penetrates deepest in clear water, green or yellow in turbid water. There are fresh waters, at least, in which even the red goes deepest, not because the water itself is more transparent to red, but because its content of dissolved and suspended matter of particular sorts makes it much less transparent to the shorter rays.

The familiar blue color of the deep sea is due to scattering among water molecules, and it is, therefore, comparable to the blue of the sky. The less of other material there is in the water the bluer it appears. Hence, blueness in the ocean is indicative of poverty; the bluest parts of the blue sea are the "desert" areas. The green color of great coastal areas of sea water has been attributed to the presence of the water-soluble yellow substances or to combinations of yellow and the natural blue. Conspicuous greenness seems sometimes to be associated with abundance of calcareous matter, as in some coastal waters and in regions where corals are abundant.

It should, perhaps, be noted here, parenthetically, that apparent discoloration, resulting from the presence of colored bodies in the water is quite another condition from the color of sea water. Lakes and ponds are often colored by chemicals in solution or by "blooms" of algae or protozoa in suspension. For the sea, reference in this connection is to the sometimes widely extended areas of conspicuous color attributable to particulate matter. "Red seas" of great extent may be encountered where, from a slight distance, the water appears like a sea of blood; on closer examination, the color is to be found only in the bodies of millions of red shrimp. "Red" or brown seas result, here and there, from the luxuriant reproduction of copepods or of dinoflagellates. Diatoms in enormous numbers give a yellowish color.

Since the extinction coefficient is the measure of reduction of radiation in a vertical direction, the angles at which the rays enter the surface must be considered. This depends upon the altitude of the sun which, of course, varies with the latitude and the season, and even more with the time of day. The obliquity of the entering rays is greatly reduced by refraction, or the bending of light rays in passing from air into water; scattering of light rays by particles within the water also changes colors and affects penetration. When the sun is at the zenith over still water there is no refraction: the angle of refraction is zero. (But the sea is never quite still.) The lower the sun the greater the refraction until, with the sun at the horizon, the angle is as much as 48.5 degrees. Consequently, the most oblique rays that penetrate the water never form an extreme angle with the vertical: no matter how low the sun, as long as they enter at all the rays turn toward the vertical. This means that the altitude of the sun has relatively little effect on the depth of penetration of non-reflected light of given intensity; yet the *amount reflected* must increase with diminishing altitude of the sun, especially on still water.

III

LIFE IN THE SEA

CHAPTER 13

Life in the Sea: General Conditions

Modes of Living and Habitats

U NDER MANY CONDITIONS THE CASUAL OBSERVER MAY DERIVE
impressions of the richness and diversity of plant and animal
life in the sea. He may have observed the mats and streamers
on wave-beaten rocky shores of Maine or California or Peru.
Through a glass-bottom boat he may have glimpsed the luxuriant
"marine gardens" of some tropical islands. Perhaps he has made
just a slight exploration of the fauna of sand and mud flats of a
coastal bay, such as that of Beaufort, North Carolina. Anyone fortunate enough to have the opportunity to see in dry-dock a lightship
from Hatteras, or other such region, must be amazed at the dense
and heavy mat of barnacles, hydroids, Bryozoa (moss animals), and
dozens of other sorts of organic life covering every inch of bottom.
On occasion, while voyaging at sea, one may look upon enormous
areas where the surface is broken by a spatter of small fish, sardines,
anchovies, or young herring, leaping into the air to escape larger
fish predators below and diving down to avoid the birds that
threaten from above. Certainly no one can fail to be thrilled at the
abundance and variety of small organisms caught in a fine-meshed
net drawn through the coastal surface waters on a calm dark night.
Nevertheless, the sea is not everywhere crowded with life: nor is
there any uniformity in distribution. There are, indeed, areas of
"desert," so far as marine life is concerned: and these, in the waters
above, are the areas of purest blue, where there is the least of matter

other than water to scatter the entering rays of light; on the bottom, red clay is an indication of barrenness.

Obviously, life in the sea cannot be treated adequately in a few chapters: volumes are required. Discussion in this place must, then, be restricted to a brief consideration of ways of life in the sea and of how the living world has responded to the special physical conditions that have been outlined in the preceding chapters. We may want to know, too, something of the types of life characteristic particularly of oceanic rather than of interior or of coastal waters.[1]

From the pictures of marine life suggested in the first paragraph, it is apparent that marine life falls naturally into several fairly distinct categories in respect to capacity for exercise of control over positions and movements. There are animals and plants that cruise with the currents for a very brief period in early life, but, once they have landed in a particular spot, are parked in the same place for the remainder of their lives. Such are barnacles, oysters, hydroids, and ascidians, attached to rocks, wharf piles, or buoys, and kelps, anchored to rocks while streaming out in the water. Worms and clams that burrow into mud and sand or even into rocks may be nearly as localized in space as are the barnacles. Other animals that are not held back by solid barriers, yet continue to live within restricted areas, are conchs and starfishes, creeping slowly over the bottom, and crabs, running here and there at will over more or less wide ranges, but not, in respect to location, at the mercy of the moving waters. All of these are in the category called *benthos*,[2] a term proposed by the great naturalist, Ernst Haeckel, to include organisms that live on or in the bottom of other fixed objects in the water. We shall later (p. 242, below) propose a logical and seemingly necessary subdivision of the benthos, to distinguish the attached and actually fixed organisms from the creepers and crawlers.

There are other marine animals with such powers of locomotion as enable them either to roam widely by swimming against the cur-

1. The chapters by Hjort, Gran, and Appellöf in Murray and Hjort's *Depths of the Ocean*, although published more than thirty years ago still constitute a mine of exact information considered in a most discriminating manner. Of a more general and readable nature is *The Seas* by Russell and Yonge. Most recent and valuable is *The Oceans* by Sverdrup, Johnson, and Fleming; Chapters VII-X and XVI-XX deal most directly with biology.

2. Greek for depth of the sea. The adjective form is *benthonic*, to be distinguished from the term "benthic," or "benthal," applicable to zone occupied.

rents, or to remain relatively localized in spite of the movements of the water in which they find food. Without being entirely independent of currents, they are yet able to move with or against the drifts; their location at any time is, to a considerable extent, governened by their own internal energies. In this group, which Haeckel distinguished as *nekton*,[3] are found higher animals, mainly fish, whales, seals, and sea turtles, and a very few invertebrate types, such as squid and sometimes shrimp.

Although benthos and nekton include virtually all the animals that catch the eye of the casual observer, yet by far the greater bulk of life in the sea falls in a third category, which comprises the innumerable and generally small organisms that are free in the water and at the mercy of the currents. These plants and animals, because of their small size or feeble powers of locomotion, are carried hither and yon by the currents. They constitute the *plankton*,[4] a designation given by Victor Hensen of Kiel nearly sixty years ago (1887). In general the plankters are to be seen only when strained from the water by a fine-meshed net or when separated out by the use of a centrifuge. In great part these drifters vary in size from the bacteria and the minute yellowish microscopic plants called coccolithophores to copepods several millemeters in length. Yet some are quite large; for drifters also are organisms, such as the sargassum weed and jellyfishes that may be one or two meters in diameter; Salpa, too, an ascidian, fairly high in the scale of animal life and only a little below the vertebrates in bodily organization, occurs in chains several meters in length. On the whole, however, those members of the plankton that, individually, are large enough to catch the eye constitute a very small proportion of the mass. In a later chapter we shall give subdivisions of the plankton on the basis of size.

The classification of marine animals and plants by mode of life, as benthos, nekton, and plankton, is not all inclusive, and there are not absolute lines of division between the several groups so designated; but the classification has convenience and the term plankton is indispensable. For life in fresh water a fourth category is found necessary—the *neuston*,[5] comprising animals and plants that live in connection with the surface film, either on it or just beneath

---

3. Neuter of Greek *nektos*, swimming.
4. Neuter of Greek *planktos*, wandering.
5. From *naus, neus,* a boat or ship; proposed by Naumann in 1917.

it. Of these are some insects and Cladocera, the duckweeds, and, at times, great numbers of bacteria, algae, and protozoa. The surface film of the wave-ruffled sea offers no such favorable home for neuston as does that of quiet ponds; the classification neuston might, however, include the one seafaring insect, the water strider Halobates, and, too, the Portuguese man-of-war and a few other floaters at the surface.

Although sharp lines cannot be drawn between benthos, nekton, and plankton, it will doubtless appear clearly enough in later pages that the differentiation of sitters (and creepers), swimmers, and drifters is not arbitrary or technical: it is, indeed, essential for any consideration of the relations of organisms to the physical conditions of the common environment—the sea water. This much, at least, should be obvious: the currents of the sea mean one thing to an animal fixed in position and dependent upon water movement for continued feeding and breathing; the same currents mean something else to an active swimmer that may move freely through the moving water; they have still another significance to the drifters that are carried along from place to place in relative helplessness.

Again, we cannot well consider marine life without noting the diversity in conditions of life as related to proximity or remoteness from the lands. The homes or habitats of marine organisms present almost infinite diversity; but we have to recognize, in the first order of classification, several ecological domains, one of which occurs wherever sea water reaches.

The great division of the homes or habitats of marine organisms, although not sharply bounded, are yet marked by certain distinctive conditions of living and by generally characteristic associations of organisms. There is the extensive *littoral* region, bordering continents and islands and extending from the line of high tide out to the edge of the continental shelf at about 200 meters.[6] According to the very different conditions presented for living things, the bot-

6. Because of the extreme diversity of conditions along shore, in respect to gradualness or abruptness of slopes of the bottom, and, no doubt, partly because of the diversity of human minds and purposes, there is no general precise agreement in the use of the term "littoral" and its subdivisions. Some restrict "littoral" to the region in close proximity to the shore, others use it, more broadly, as stated in the text above. Sumner, Allee, and others employ the term *adlittoral*, "as designating the zone of shallow water immediately adjacent to the shore," without setting a definite lower limit of depth. Varying, doubtless, with local conditions and with species, the adlittoral would probably not extend beyond two fathoms in depth.

tom of the littoral region can be subdivided into an *intertidal* zone, above the low-water mark, a *eulittoral* zone, reaching from the line of low tide as far out as aquatic plants may grow on the bottom, or to a depth of some 50 meters, and a *sublittoral*, extending to the limits of the littoral. Beyond the littoral the bottom benthic[7] region divides itself naturally into the *archibenthic*, on the continental slope and the *abyssal benthic*, beyond a depth of some 1,000 meters; the last is, of course, a region of darkness and low temperature, *without seasonal changes* such as must play so great a role in the lives of terrestrial and coastal animals and of upper plankton. For water above the bottom, the *pelagic* region is conveniently divided into *neritic* and *oceanic* zones. The former embraces the open water affected by continental influences and extending out to the edge of the continental shelf; we may say that it includes all open water within a depth of 200 meters or less and extends shoreward over most of the littoral. The oceanic zone is the vastly greater region of "blue sea," into which comes little of the nutritive drainage from land. When, in the broad oceanic region, we wish to distinguish zones in vertical series, there is, of course, an uppermost and relatively thin illuminated zone (*epipelagic*), some 200 meters in depth. Beneath this one may recognize a twilight zone (*mesopelagic*) and a deeper zone (*bathypelagic*) of far greater volume into which no solar light may ever penetrate. Finally, and below some 2,000 fathoms, is the *abyssal pelagic* zone. It will be evident that littoral and neritic zones, receiving so much drainage from the lands, must offer conditions of nutrition very different from those of benthic and true oceanic regions.

Some Relations to Physical Conditions

In a general way the necessities of life are the same in the sea as on land: water, sunlight, heat, oxygen, carbon dioxide, food (in the forms both of the building materials of protoplasm and the fuel to supply energy), anchorage or support, and protection from enemies. We might add, among the necessities, enemies themselves or some means of keeping a particular population, with its inherent urge to reproduce, in equilibrium with the available supply of food.

Although the securing and conserving of water may be a very

7. See footnotes 2, p. 178, and 8, p. 245.

practical problem for some terrestrial animals and plants, particularly those of arid regions, the very condition of life in the sea insures an unlimited water supply. Accordingly, marine animals and plants have no need for special adaptations against desiccation, except in the cases of those that live in the extreme littoral (intertidal) region and are periodically subject to conditions of water loss.

With respect to the chemical nature of the environment, marine invertebrates (and elasmobranch fishes) have an advantage over invertebrates of fresh water in that their body fluids have very nearly the same osmotic pressure as the external medium. They do not, therefore, require such protective coverings or such expenditures of energy as are necessary to maintain the normal internal conditions against osmotic pressure from without—that is to say, against the physical tendency to equalize concentrations within and without.[8] Sea water varies in concentration from place to place and in many places, from time to time. Some physiological adjustments are necessary; and marine animals and plants differ greatly in capacity to adjust themselves to changing salinities. The Virginia oyster thrives in brackish waters where very considerable changes of salinity may occur in course of a day, or from season to season. Corals will endure only small changes and are, therefore, wanting from the vicinity of the mouths of great rivers. A few animals seem to have extremely wide ranges of tolerance—they are *euryhaline;* so that they may pass from salt to fresh water and back at will. Some, like the salmon, the shad, and the eel, are at home in salt water for certain periods of their lives and equally at home in fresh water for other periods. Most marine organisms, and particularly

8. The cell membranes of organisms are selectively permeable: they permit the passage of water with relative freedom, but are more selective with reference to dissolved substances. The permeability depends in part upon the physical and chemical nature of the particular membrane, the material in solution, and the solvent, which, in this case, is water. The flow through the membrane is governed also by the difference in concentration of dissolved substances within and without the cell, upon which depends osmotic pressure. The bony fishes of fresh water and those of sea water differ in osmotic pressure but not nearly so much as do fresh water and sea water. The body fluids of fresh-water fishes are *hypertonic* (having higher osmotic pressure) as compared with the water around them. Were there no protective effort of some kind, water would move into the body until the body fluids became *isotonic* (of like osmotic pressure) with the outside water. The fluids of bony fishes of salt water are *hypotonic*, and, but for protection, water would pass out from them into the external medium until body fluids and sea water were isotonic.

those of the open sea, have very narrow tolerances with respect to salinity; they are *stenohaline*.

Between marine organisms and the sea water around them there are many other chemical relations, some of which will be pointed out in appropriate places.[9] Water is the universal solvent and may carry in solution any chemical substance required for the maintenance and multiplication of plants and animals. So far as the substances are used, they are taken out of solution in the water—for the time. It may be remarked, then, that plants and animals, themselves, have some effect on the composition of sea water at a particular place and time. It is quite possible that with prolific growth and multiplication of some plankters, certain elements, such as silica, used in diatom shells, or phosphorus, become depleted regionally and seasonally, to a critical degree. Reproduction must then cease for a period, and a whole population largely disappear, until such time, as, by the slow processes of decomposition, the abstracted chemicals are returned to solution and made available for new use.

For the utilization of sunlight and carbon dioxide, animals in general are entirely dependent on green or yellowish plants which, through the process known as photosynthesis, form carbohydrate by combination of water and carbon dioxide with storage of the radiant energy of the sun. Virtually all the energies of animals and plants represent transformation of the energy stored by green plants; and energy is involved, not only in movement but also in growth, reproduction, and in every form of vital activity. Energy from the sun may be stored in the form of fat as well as carbohydrates (sugars and starch) and proteins, to say nothing of body warmth. Physiologically, the energy of fats is less readily available than is that of carbohydrates; but, for marine organisms, the fats, or oils, have an advantage in their relatively low specific gravity, as well as in their insolubility in water; fats favor flotation, obviating the need for excessive expenditure of energy in maintenance of level in the water. Animals are dependent upon plants, not only for the sources of energy, but also for syntheses of vitamins and of amino acids, the nitrogenous substances that are basic to the formation of proteins.

We have dealt in previous chapters with the sources and means of

9. Chapters VII, VIII, and XVII of Sverdrup, Johnson, and Fleming's *The Oceans*, and the references there cited, will be particularly helpful to those interested more particularly in the chemical relations of life in the sea.

distribution of sunlight, heat, oxygen, and carbon dioxide. Since sunlight is the ultimate source of all organic energy, including that involved in the synthesis of organic substance, it follows that original production in the sea can take place only in the superficial layers of water through which light penetrates. There are animals that spend their entire lives in the darkness of the deep, but they can live only at the expense of plants that enjoy sunlight at higher levels. Obviously, since by far the greater area of the surface of the earth is ocean, most of the radiation coming to the earth through or from the atmosphere falls upon the sea. Much of what comes to the surface of the water is reflected back and most of what is absorbed is transformed into heat. A minuscular part is used in photosynthesis (p. 169, above.) Whether the utilization of radiation for synthesis of organic substance is greater on land than in the sea is at least open to question. Terrestrial vegetation is exposed to relatively brilliant illumination, as the rays of the sun pass through the highly transparent atmosphere with relatively small scatter and absorption, and that principally by the water vapor. Yet, because of structural and other conditions, the plants on land seem to capture no more and perhaps much less of the solar radiation falling on a given area. The minute size and the unicellular form of the vast majority of plants in the sea does give them the advantage of more complete absorption and utilization of what sunlight there is to be used.

We do know that water and carbon dioxide with sunlight are the basis of all organic substance. It is obvious too that organic wastes from the land are continually carried into the sea by surface drainage. Whatever may have been the condition at the commencement of life on earth, the populations of the sea in littoral and neritic regions are now in part dependent upon the productivity of plants that live on land. If, as is supposed, life began in the ocean and later migrated out of water to reach its highest development on land, the original discovery of the land and its "colonization" must have proved in the end a stimulus to organic industry in the original briny home. In the course of geological ages the members of the terrestrial colonies attained a higher state of development than did the stay-at-homes; and now society in "the homeland" (the *home-water*, we should rather say), lives in some part at the expense of the colonies.

Temperature has much to do with the rate of chemical reactions

—which increases with rising temperature. Within limits, the chemical processes associated with life in plants and animals may be more than doubled by a rise of 10°C. Temperature, therefore, affects "rate of living," including growth, reproduction, maturing, and duration of life. Yet a notable phenomenon of distribution is the richness of life in the cold and turbid seas of the north, when these are compared with the warm and translucent waters of the tropics, where, at first thought, the conditions of temperature and light might be expected to support the richest fauna and flora. The anomaly is probably related to the difference in content of dissolved gases in cold and warm waters.

Oxygen and carbon dioxide are essential to life as we know it. Nearly all living phenomena seem to involve oxidation and the transformation of energy originally derived from the sun. But the solar energy is made available for the processes of animal life only through the use by plants of carbon dioxide and water. Cold water absorbs and carries more oxygen and carbon dioxide than does warm water. It seems a reasonable expectation then that, on the whole, there should be more prolific life in cold than in warm waters. Most of the evidence seems to point that way; but perhaps we should ask for yet more comparative data of an exact quantitative nature.[10]

It should be remarked, however, that waters may lie within the tropics, geographically, and yet not be "tropical" in respect to temperature: cool waters at low latitudes, such as those of the Humboldt Current off the west coast of Peru, may rival the waters of higher latitudes in luxuriance of animal and plant life. The warm and light waters of truly "tropical" regions may hold less oxygen and, remaining at the surface because of their relative lightness, be drained of their nutrient materials which are not replaced by ascending currents from the depths.[11] Clear blue waters are commonly associated in our minds with warm regions; but, "Pure blue is the color of desolation of the high seas."[12]

10. Allen, at least, has questioned the certainty of a generally greater productivity of plankton in high as compared with low latitudes.—Winfred E. Allen, "The Primary Food Supply of the Sea," *Quarterly Review of Biology*, IX: 161–80. Reference is to p. 175. It is possible, as Murray suggested long ago, that the turnover in tropical waters is relatively higher in warm as compared with cold waters, because of faster growth, earlier breeding, shorter lives, and more rapid decomposition, at higher temperatures.

11. See p. 86, above.

12. Schütt, quoted by Johnstone, 1908.

Thus the colder seas are richer in life than the warmer ones; or, at the very least, the amount of life in polar seas is not less than in the tropics. We are so accustomed to think of bright sunlight and high temperature as favorable to terrestrial plant life that such statements astonish us at first. "One stands," says Kjellman, "as before an insoluble problem when he makes a haul with a tow-net in the Arctic and obtains abundant and strong vegetation, and this at a time when the sea is covered with ice, the temperature is extremely low, and nocturnal gloom predominates even at noon."[13]

The density and the viscosity of sea water are conditions of real influence on life in the sea. The viscosity is not markedly different from that of fresh water, but the density is relatively high. In respect to these qualities, the atmosphere in which the higher animals live and move is hardly comparable at all. As to density, we are particularly concerned with specific gravity, which is the ratio of density to that of distilled water at a given temperature and pressure. Now, the specific gravity of the sea is not markedly different from that of the organisms that live in it. For the latter, then, there is less general need for supporting structures. Plants characteristic of the sea are without stiff trunks and stems. Relatively few of the animals have legs for walking. The four-legged amphibian frogs and salamanders do not occur in salt water. Birds, reptiles, and mammals are not at home there, except for a few that have acquired secondary modifications for excursions into the water or have become more permanently adapted, with reduction of limbs (whales for example) as means of bodily support. Of all the four-limbed animals, the fish are the only ones primarily marine in habit, and their limbs are not designed for support.[14] Of the great phylum Arthropoda, animals with externally jointed limbs, the myriapods (centipedes and millipedes) are not found in the sea, and the hexapods (insects) and arachnids (spiders and their relatives) are there represented by few species. In this division of the animal kingdom, which includes many more species of animals than all other phyla combined, only the crustacea have developed in the sea in substantial diversity of form, and with great numbers of individuals, but the majority of these (in numbers) have legs for swimming rather than for walking.

13. James Johnstone, *Conditions of Life in the Sea*, p. 205. If we should not now say that the problem is "insoluble," it can not be denied that adequate solution is yet to come.

14. Even these, or the bony fish at least, probably arose in fresh water.

Viscosity of the medium has important influences on life in water in two important respects. It impedes movement and it retards sinking. As an impediment to movement, viscosity, with density, has led to the development of streamlined bodies. Reference to this was made in an earlier chapter in connection with the consideration of viscosity, and, especially, of eddy-viscosity (p. 103). The problem of streamlining is not so much to facilitate the pushing aside of dense medium ahead as to reduce the "drag" resulting from the filling in behind with all the complex phenomena of turbulence. Streamlining expresses itself very differently in active swimmers of plankton and nekton, in relatively inactive plankton, and in attached animals; yet probably no animal or plant in the water is without some touch of streamline. The more sluggish animals in the stillness of abyssal depths, probably have least need for adaptation of form to minimize friction and turbulence.

Viscosity also retards sinking under the influence of gravity and thus facilitates maintenance of appropriate level. Both size and form affect sinking velocity. It is only as we ignore friction that we can say that a small body falls as rapidly as a large one of the same composition. Friction is on the surface and it is a recognized physical and mathematical principle that the smaller the body is, the greater the surface in proportion to weight, assuming, always, the same composition of body. Irregularities or extensions of surface also increase the area exposed to frictional "drag." Now viscosity varies little with salinity but greatly with temperature of the water. We may expect, then, in consideration of plankton and nekton, to find that bodies of organisms tend to be larger in colder waters and smaller in warmer—and also that in other ways the plants and animals of warm water often show increased extent of surface, as through spinous or plumose appendages. We may find also that, where upper waters are warm and, therefore, less viscous and deeper waters are cold and more viscous, there will sometimes be found a stratification of organisms of a species by size, the larger and older living more deeply than the smaller and younger, which have greater surfaces in proportion to bulk.

The significance of another basic condition of the environment of organisms in the sea is easily overlooked or underestimated. The fact that the water of the oceans is in continual circulation, that it is everywhere a restless dynamic medium, is in the first rank of importance to marine life. The rhythmic and the progressive movements of water affect the several types of organisms quite differently; but consideration of this aspect of the conditions of life in the sea will best be deferred to the several later chapters.

Finally, in respect to the environmental conditions, let us consider in the following section the notable absence of places of concealment in the open sea.

No Hiding Place

As regards enemies and protection, there is need to emphasize in the first line the fact that a reasonable number of enemies must generally be useful to a species. Without some control upon the increase of a species, such as is afforded by predators, multiplication in numbers must inevitably outrun the food supply and lead to starvation. At any rate, we know nothing of the existence of organisms without effective enemies and parasites. It is a recognized principle of fish culture in ponds that numbers must be controlled if one is to obtain the desired harvest of fishes of table size. Consequently, it is a practice to have mixed populations, including a small proportion of notably predatory species, such as the black bass or the pike. Of course, the same result may be obtained by annual drainage of the pond and removal of any surplus stock; just as in animal husbandry, there is at least annual removal of the surplus of pigs, cattle, or poultry. The last-mentioned practice is fully consistent with the principle of the need for enemies; only, in this case, man himself functions as the requisite "enemy" of his fish, cattle, or fowl.

On the other hand, protection or refuge from enemies, or some other means of salvation, is equally essential—both for the prey and for the enemy. The predators may serve a useful purpose to themselves and to their prey as they keep the multiplication of the prey within bounds; but, in the interest of both parties to the contract, the prey must have some means of regulating the extent, or the effect, of the depredations made upon them.

On land and in marginal and bottom waters of lakes and seas, there usually exists for animal life what is called "shelter," in the substratum or in thickets of vegetation. Such havens of retreat play a significant part in maintenance of an enduring state of equilibrium between predators and prey. In short, shelter helps greatly to preserve a balance between production and consumption—or, if we may carry over into biology a formula of economics, between "supply and demand." In the picture that has been given of the open sea, that is to say, of what is by far the greater part of the oceans, we must have been impressed with the entire lack of refuge. Where the vegetation is composed exclusively of plants of microscopic size, scattered and free floating—in this sort of diffuse and open pasture, there is no place of hiding. Survival or death for plants and for the animals of feeble powers of locomotion, which includes the vast majority of plankton animals, depends mainly upon the accidents of the presence and the state of hunger of the potential consumer. Protective coloration is undoubtedly of some help, and for many plankters transparency of body is a chief resort for concealment. Transparency is associated with high water-content and, as Ostwald remarked long ago, no organisms are so rich in water, and, generally so transparent, as the inhabitants of the open waters of lake or ocean. Fecundity offers for all species the strongest hope of survival (see also pp. 288-89, below).

Wherever shelter occurs in the sea it is availed of. Clams, worms, and crustacea burrow in the bottom, and even in rock, or find concealment among the shells of the bottom. The discarded shells of conchs become the houses of hermit crabs. Oyster beds and thickets of eelgrass harbor a rich and varied population of small plants and animals. The sargassum weed, which occurs in large floating gardens in the Gulf Stream and in the central North Atlantic, offers one of the rare refuges of the ocean proper, and the extensive masses of weed are true zoological gardens: they afford shelter to an astonishing community of fish, mollusks, crustacea, and other animals. Often these manifest the most bizarre forms, in correspondence with their peculiar habitat. Among such are the sargassum fish and a shell-less snail, both of which have colors like the weed and leaflike projections from the skin. The several kinds of animal life associated with sargassum in its diverse forms depend, according to Parr (p. 201, below), not upon place or season, but rather upon the form of the plant. Still other animals find refuge within the bells of jelly-fishes, in the empty tests of salpa or in shells of dead conchs. Many instances of the intrusion of animals into every available form of refuge could be cited; but all these will account for but a small part of the life in the sea.

The ocean generally is a place without tangible refuge. Of course we know little of the conditions of life on the abyssal bottoms; but, above the bottom, protection for the small organisms that predominate must depend upon translucency, upon other means of making their bodies inconspicuous, or upon ability to live in the darkness below the upper illuminated zones. We know of no considerable habitat on land where want of refuge prevails in a way at all comparable to that which marks the greater part of the surface of the earth, occupied, as it is, by the open sea. Perhaps the nearest approach to a shelterless area on land will be found in the open grassland prairies as a home for the great populations of hoofed animals—which, however, may resort to protective aggregation and to speed of flight. We are so accustomed to the idea that the victim of pursuit has some chance of sequestering itself that it is difficult to realize that, for the animal world as a whole, places of refuge are for the few—not for the vast majority. The copepod, the pteropod, the anchovy, and the larvae of any marine organism are almost as helpless against depredation as is the grass in the meadow.

Metabolism of the Sea

In the sea, as on land, we have a great "organic cycle" in which all organisms feed and, sooner or later, in one way or another, serve as food. The food cycle might be said to begin with the inorganic substances as utilized by green or yellow or brown plants, to run through the chain of vegetarian animals and carnivores, and to continue with the activities of bacteria and other agents of decomposition in reduction of organic wastes to inorganic substances, which are again ready for use by plants—for a new swing around the circle.

Whatever may be the actual relative productivity of land and sea, there is everywhere on land a drift of organic and inorganic materials toward the ocean, the great earthly catch basin. Much of the organic material washed into the sea from the land is utilized by the plants and animals of littoral and neritic zones, from which floating and swimming organisms, at least in some measure, pass outward into the open ocean, either traveling under their own power or conveyed by streams and eddies. Consequently, the marine organic world is not a closed system, but is continually receiving contributions of organic substance from without. To what extent some of the organic substance carried into the sea, or synthesized there, is ultimately lost to the organic cycle by sinking irretrievably into the depths remains an open question.

It may be well to look for a moment, at certain special aspects of this cycle in the sea. Plants not only need water and carbon dioxide, of which there are rich supplies (see p. 89, above) and sunlight, but they also require nutrient salts of which phosphates and nitrates are critical ones. The distribution of such salts in the sea is of interest. Certain amounts are free and available in solution; but, in times of active reproduction of diatoms or other small marine plants, the stores may be depleted to a minimal amount; growth and reproduction must cease. Always a substantial but variable proportion of the necessary nutrients is locked in the bodies of living plants and those of the animals that have been nourished by the plants. Obviously, the components of living organisms are not again available for new plant growth, at the base of the ladder of life, until the death and decay of bodies or wastes returns them to solution: only dissolution of such bodies can bring the material into circulation again. The bodies of living plants and animals hold, then, a significant reserve of nutrients for later use in new production of microscopic plants. It is well known that there may be more or less regular successions of abundant diatoms giving place to a rich animal plankton followed by great numbers of small fishes.

It is also obvious that many of the bodies and wastes holding the reserve of nutrients will sink below the upper zone of photosynthesis and thus be lost from the zone where any possible original production can occur. Such bodies can be consumed by animals of the intermediate depths, but the bodies and waste of these latter will sink deeper before decomposition. Hence there must be a gradual *drainage* of nutrient substance *from the upper water into the deep!* The downward drift of phosphorus and nitrates is well illustrated from the tables given by Harvey[15] showing the results of analyses for phosphates and nitrates at different depths. With none found either at the surface or at 50 meters, at a particular place in the Atlantic, there were 8 mg. of P_2O_5 per cu. m. at 100 meters, 74 at 1000, 78 at 2,000, and 88 at 3,000 meters. For nitrate nitrogen and ammonia nitrogen the mean value of samples taken by the "Planet" in

15. Harvey, *Biological Chemistry and Physics of Sea Water*, pp. 41, 43. See also Redfield, Alfred C., Homer P. Smith, and Bostwick Ketchum, "The Cycle of Organic Phosphorus in the Gulf of Maine," Biological Bulletin, 72, p. 421, 1937.

the open ocean was 49 at the surface, 30 at 1,000, 47 at 2,000, and 107 at 3,000.

Apparently, the salts inevitably accumulating in the deep are lost to the organic world for the time and must remain out of circulation until, through vertical movements of water masses, they are brought back into the photosynthetic zone, which is the illuminated upper water. It is a fact anyway, as is emphasized more than once in this volume, that, when deeper waters are brought up to the surface through upwelling or other upward drifts, there is notable production of microscopic plants, the small animals that feed upon them, and the fishes. Fortunately, the nutrients brought back to the surface can be used quickly and fully by the little plants, since they have bodies made of single cells exposed on every side to the fertilized medium and to the light. To illustrate how diatoms may multiply in sea water enriched with nitrate and phosphate, Harvey mentions[16] that roughly one gram of P_2O_5 will suffice for the production of nine hundred billion diatoms!

In reference to the nutrition of animals, there have been different views as to the chief basic organic food supply. It was maintained for a time, at least, that marine animals generally were able to utilize, by absorption through the integument, the abundant organic substance in solution. Neither experiment nor reason has tended to substantiate this hypothesis in any significant degree. It was another view that the chief basic food supply for animals in the sea was the detritus, or finely-divided organic matter, resulting from the partial decay and mechanical comminution of littoral plants, especially the eelgrass which grows so luxuriantly along many coasts. This theory, like the other, probably has only a small measure of truth as an answer to the problem of the source of food for animals of the plankton, nekton and benthos throughout the oceans.

In seeking the principal basic harvest in the open sea, there is, indeed, no need to look farther than the tiny photosynthetic organisms of the plankton in the upper illuminated strata. Most of the organisms taken in a fine-meshed net drawn through the water are animals; but far more numerous are the minute algae, protozoa and bacteria, the greater number of which are small enough to pass through the meshes of the net. These are best secured by killing and allowing a considerable period of time for settling, after which the water can

16. *Ibid.*, p. 40.

be drawn off, or by centrifuging at speeds that will throw down even many bacteria. Another method of sampling for bacteria is by making plate cultures from droplets of water. By whatever method the small organisms are separated out, the number of each kind can be counted, the dimensions of individuals measured under the microscope, and their volumes calculated. Further computations and observations of reproduction give results to show that the synthesizing plants of the nannoplankton, the "producers," they are called, generally exceed the net-plankton in total volume and greatly surpass them in rate of multiplication, and, therefore, in crop production. The photosynthetic algae undoubtedly afford the basic food supply for the plankton animals, which, in turn, constitute the source of nutrition for the larger swimming animals. Nothing has been learned in recent years to cause essential modification of the statement made fifty years ago by Professor W. K. Brooks:[17] "This is the fundamental conception of marine biology: the basis of all the life in the modern ocean is to be sought in the microorganisms of the surface"; by "surface" we must, of course, understand the upper illuminated zone, which may be one or two hundred meters in depth.

Presumably, animals living below the illuminated zone near the surface must depend for food largely on material falling from above. But, to utilize the food, they also need oxygen. It is not remarkable that the idea once held sway that the floor of the sea beyond the continental shelf was without life, a great desert, an *azoic* area: in this pitch-blackness, whence could come the supply of free oxygen to support animal life? In temperate and Arctic regions, wherever the surface water may at times be brought to a temperature at which it is heavier than the waters below, it will, of course, sink toward the bottom to be replaced at the surface by lighter waters from the depths. By this "overturn," the oxygen supply of abyssal waters of the region is renewed; but, over a great part of the Atlantic, Pacific, and Indian oceans, such a condition cannot occur. Animals yet thrive at the bottom; presumably they utilize oxygen brought by the slow drifts of cold and richly oxygenated waters from polar regions; cold water absorbs and carries the greatest amount of oxygen. Probably the abyssal animals are not very abundant and lead sluggish lives, involving a minimum oxygen demand.

17. W. K. Brooks, *The Genus Salpa*. Memoirs from the Biological Laboratory of the Johns Hopkins University, Baltimore, 1893.

Summary

1. In coastal regions one easily obtains an impression of luxuriant marine organic life, and this notwithstanding the dilution of nutritive material in the sea and the reduced amount of light available to photosynthetic organisms beneath the surface. Often even far out at sea, animal life may be found in profusion in the forms of fish, shrimp like crustacea, copepods or pteropods that are easily or barely visible to the unaided eye; or, if fine nets or centrifuges are used, a lush pasturage of minute plants may be revealed by the microscope. Great areas of relative desert can also be found —the regions of really "blue sea" above or those of red clay at the bottom. There is no uniformity in distribution of marine organisms throughout the oceans, either horizontally or bathymetrically.

2. According to mode of life, the plants and animals of the seas (and of lakes as well) fall into three great categories: the *benthos* comprising those dependent upon a substratum; the *nekton, includ-*ing the larger swimmers which can move somewhat independently of water movements; and the *plankton,* embracing the drifters or those organisms without or with relatively feeble powers of locomotion, whose movements from place to place are determined chiefly by the currents. A fourth category, the *neuston,* living against the surface film, is scarcely represented in the wave-ruffled ocean, although often prominent in lakes and ponds.

3. The habitats of marine organisms may be classified in a broad way. The *littoral,* for the shallow coastal regions, is subdivided into an *intertidal,* above low-water mark; the *eulittoral,* or zone of photosynthetic plants on the bottom; and the *sublittoral,* extending out to the edge of the continental shelf, the rim of the ocean basin. Beyond is the *benthic* bottom region and the *pelagic* region of the open waters above. The benthic region is conveniently subdivided into the *archibenthic* on the continental slope and the deep, dark, and cold *abyssal* zone. In the pelagic region of open water, we distinguish the *neritic* zone, which extends over the littoral, and the *oceanic* for the open sea beyond the direct influence of continental or insular drainage. The last mentioned zone has a superficial illuminated, *epipelagic,* subzone above and deeper *bathypelagic* and abyssal subzones of perpetual darkness and relative coldness.

4. Marine organisms beyond the intertidal zone are spared the requirement of coverings to protect against desiccation. They live

surrounded by a chemical medium containing in solution the materials requisite for production of organic substance. They vary widely in capacity to make adjustments to differences of salinity. In areas and times of extremely prolific multiplication, they may effect significant changes in the composition of the water with respect to some substances present in relatively minimal amounts.

5. Because of the density of sea water the need for supporting structures is diminished. Plants develop no trunks or stiff stems. Animals, other than some of the benthonts, have no need for legs to support their bodies above a substratum.

6. In adaptation to the viscosity of water the streamlining of bodies is highly but variously developed in aquatic organisms, fresh water and marine. This and the cycles of form in possible relation to viscosity were discussed in an earlier chapter. Specific gravity of many pelagic organisms is lessened by a high percentage of water in the body, giving translucency, and by the storage of food reserves in the form of light oils rather than the heavier starches. Some organisms have larger and trimmer bodies in colder waters, smaller and more elaborately formed bodies in warmer waters.

7. An indispensable basis of life is solar radiation, and most of the radiation coming to the earth falls upon the sea. The greater part of it is reflected or converted into heat and only a minute part used directly by marine photosynthetic plants. The life in the sea, particularly in the regions near the coasts, seems to depend in part upon organic production upon land. On the other hand, when the sea is compared with the land as a place of living for green plants, the much greater availability of carbon dioxide and water (basic substances for all life) and the one-celled bodies must give marine plants a distinct advantage for the use of what sunlight there is.

8. Doubtless, in part, because of the greater content of dissolved gases in colder waters, cold seas are notably rich in organic life.

9. A distinctive feature of the neritic and pelagic zones is the nearly complete lack of shelter or refuge. Survival depends upon chance more than upon individual initiative; protective coloration and translucency of body play some part with different species. Fecundity is the salvation of most species. Shelter of many sorts prevails in the smaller littoral region, but rarely in the open sea.

10. Various theorists have assumed, severally, that the basic and immediate food supply of animals in the sea is: (a) the dissolved

organic matter in solution, (b) the detritus of littoral plants, or (c) the self-reproducing organisms of the plankton. Unquestionably, for the open ocean, the last-mentioned source of food is paramount. The plankters utilize the dissolved matter resulting from decay of organic bodies and wastes in the sea or washed into the seas from the lands.

11. There is no depth of water without life. Food for abyssal animals must fall from above. The requisite oxygen is presumed to have been brought chiefly through slow drifts, over the bottom, of originally oxygen-rich water from the surface in cold regions.

12. There must be continual drainage of nutrients from the upper water into the deep. So far as they go into solution they are lost to the world of life except as in particular regions deep water is returned to the surface through upwelling or other vertical movements. Regions of upwelling are regions of richness.

CHAPTER 14

Pasturage of the Sea

Premium on Simplicity

AS COMPARED WITH SOIL WATER IN FERTILE AREAS, SEA WATER IS a dilute solution of the nutritive materials necessary for plant life. But whereas land grasses and trees have only roots in the soil, sea plants are totally immersed in the nutritive water of the sea. Food, oxygen, and carbon dioxide do not have to be reached out for by branching roots or spreading leaves. The premium is on surface exposure. The smaller the body the greater is the surface; consequently, in the oceans, there has been little tendency toward the development of complex plant bodies. In the formation of a new plant or animal body, the first step is the division of a single reproductive cell. With higher organisms the two "daughter" cells remain attached, while each divides again. With repeated divisions there is formed a mass of cells in which differentiation of form and specialization of function begin. Eventually the complex body results. But two cells, if joined together, have less surface exposure to the surrounding medium than do the same two cells when separated from each other. Capacities to absorb nutrients from the medium and the energy of sunlight are greater for each cell if it is completely separate from the other. Only under special conditions is it true that "in union there is strength." So it is found that, for most, but not quite all marine plants, union is foregone: the vast bulk of the vegetation is in the form of single cells—the diatoms, the coccolithophores, the dinoflagellates, and other small-bodied organisms. Some of these minute organisms are so clearly on the borderline between plants and animals that they are claimed both by botanists and by zoologists. Certainly, so far as they synthesize organic matter with the use of sunlight, they serve as original "producers," and are comparable to the grasses of the pasture.

In treating of plant life in the sea, it should be remembered that we deal with the greater part of the organic world: after all, vegetation is the broad base of the "pyramid of life" in the sea, as on land. Through numbers and fecundity, plants must both maintain their own populations and support the innumerable herbivores, which, in turn, support the carnivores. If we remember that always each animal, in the course of a year, must eat many times its own weight we get some glimmer of a concept of what the annual crop of vegetation must be.

We should recall, too, that, although the whole volume of the oceans, from shore to shore and from surface to bottom, is the home of animals, constituting the "consumer" group, yet the original production through photosynthesis can occur only in the upper illuminated zone. The microscopic plants of a relatively thin stratum have to support not only the animals of their own level, but also those scavengers and predators that live in the greater volume of dark waters below. Apparently this is accomplished, not so much by maintenance of excess of numbers and bulk at all times, as by rapid multiplication, insuring continual replacement of those being devoured each day and hour.

The depths to which living algae penetrate differ greatly in different waters. Gran[1] found them restricted to a very thin surface layer in Christiana Fjord, overlying a deeper infertile layer of more saline water. Out in the open sea they extended deeper, being abundant at 50 meters, and in considerable numbers at 100 meters. Others have reported algae in the open sea to be most abundant at 10 to 50 meters, with hardly a tenth as many at 100 meters. The algae are, however, much less abundant in the open sea than in coastal waters. Gran believed that the proportions of algae in coastal and typical open-sea areas would be nearer one hundred to one than two to one. The great disproportion he attributes to the fact that it is the drainage from the land that brings essential nutritive substances. Naturally the admixture of fresh water from rivers with the sea water produces

1. The references here are to H. H. Gran, Chapter VI in Murray and Hjort's *Depths of the Ocean.*

water that, as compared with the general mass of ocean water, is both more fertile and less saline. This water, lighter because it is lower in salinity, must override near the coast the more saline and less fertile oceanic water. This would account also for the relative thinness of the stratum of alga-rich waters close to the continents.

Kinds of Plants [2]

From the point of view of animal life, the producing plants of land and sea have the same basic functions to perform—to synthesize carbohydrates (sugars and starches), proteins, vitamins, and fats from inorganic salts, carbon dioxide, water, and the energy of the sun, and to liberate more oxygen than they consume. Nevertheless, as we have said, the contrast in character of vegetation in the two types of homes is marked. None of the higher plants occurs in the ocean remote from the shores. Seed plants are totally wanting there; ferns and mosses, the next lower groups, occur nowhere in the sea. Even along the coasts, the larger algae are chiefly of groups that are represented hardly at all in fresh waters. The great group of primitive blue-green algae, abundant in lakes and rivers, are prominent in the ocean only near the mouths of large rivers or in tropical regions. On an earlier page (p. 18) we have mentioned Trichodesmus, a "blue-green" in classification, but colored red by an accessory pigment, which often gives color to the Red Sea.

The *green algae* (Chlorophyceae), predominant in fresh waters, are sparsely represented in salt waters, and then chiefly where there is some admixture of fresh water. Codium, Enteromorpha, and the familiar sheets of Ulva ("sea lettuce") are restricted narrowly to coastal regions and do not occur below a depth of about 10 meters. Some of these have actively swimming reproductive bodies (zoospores), which may be so abundant as to give a distinct green color to the water. The relatively simple filamentous algae that so commonly form "blankets" on the surface of fresh-water ponds are missing from the open sea, where, as previously mentioned, the conditions have not favored cell aggregations.

On the other hand, the *brown algae* (Phaeophyceae) and the *red algae* (Rhodophyceae), richly present in the benthonic life of the ocean along and near the coast, are most sparingly represented in

2. The reader wishing more detail is referred particularly to Chapter IX of Sverdrup, Johnson, and Fleming, *The Oceans*, and to Chapter VI by Gran in Murray and Hjort, *op. cit.*

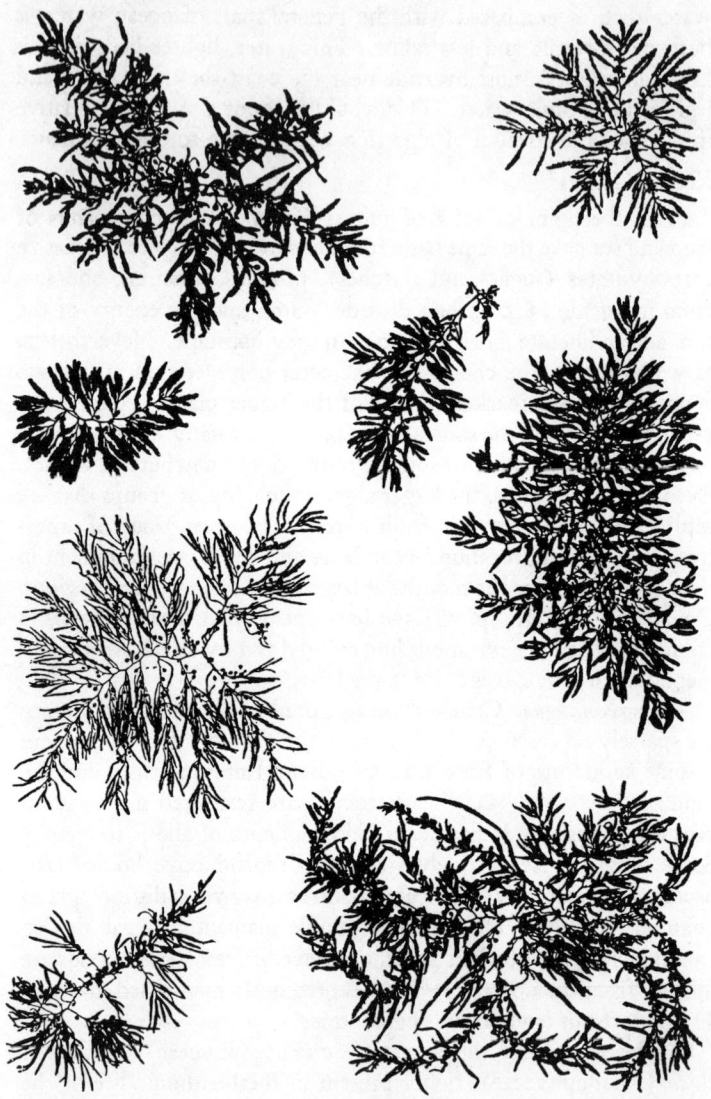

FIGURE 11. Varieties of pelagic sargassum. (After Albert Eide Parr, in *Bulletin of the Bingham Oceanographic Collection*, Vol. VI, Art. 7)

fresh water. Brown algae, including rockweeds, sargassum, and kelps, are the largest and most conspicuous of marine algae. The inherent green color is masked by yellow and brown pigments. The rockweeds are conspicuous, attached to wharf piles, jetties, and shells on the bottom. The kelps occur more commonly a little distance from shore with long "stems" (stipes) and fronds waving in the water from a base of attachment to rocks at the bottom. They may have a total length of 100 feet—and be anchored at corresponding depths; usually they are in water of less depth, and some stream out from the rocks of wave-beaten shores. Many are valuable for food and for the extraction of drugs, iodine, algin, potash, and other commercial products.[3] Sargassum is the only large seaweed that finds a prominent place in the high seas. This is a fairly large "leafy" weed. The long, branching stems bear leaflike extensions and little stalked bladders, to which it owes its name, derived from the Portuguese word for grape, *sarga*. This marine grape-weed, or "gulf weed," has been known to seafarers since the first voyage of Columbus. Originally it grows attached along tropical shores. Breaking loose, it drifts in the currents, multiplying vegetatively as it does, and accumulates in the great eddy in the Atlantic Ocean known as the Sargasso Sea.[4] Here it continues to grow. Before it dies to sink and decompose, it forms an extensive shelter for a remarkable special community of animals, many of which can live nowhere else than in the clumps of sargassum.

The more delicate *red algae* (Rhodophyceae) on the bottom extend farther out into the sea, living not only in harbors and along the shores but also in the deeper waters of the continental shelf beyond the depths of penetration of the shorter rays of sunlight necessary for the growth of truly green plants. The red algae are, therefore, presumably of special significance as "producers" or photosynthetic agents on the continental shelf. It is the red algae that are commercially valuable for the production of agar. Some have a special capacity for the precipitation of calcium carbonate, with which they

3. See "Utilization of Seaweeds," by Cheng-Kwai Tseng in *The Scientific Monthly*, LVIII, (1944) 37-46. See also "Introduction to Agar and its Uses" by Harold J. Humm and Frederich A. Wolf, Bulletin No. 3, Duke University Marine Station, 1946.

4. Perhaps some species of sargassum live permanently adrift. For much information regarding the habits of sargassum, its several species and diversity of forms, reference is made to the intensive study by A. E. Parr: "Pelagic Sargassum Vegetation of the North Atlantic," Bulletin, Bingham Oceanographic Collection, VI, 1939.

encrust themselves. They are, therefore, important geological agents.

The algae so far mentioned, being chiefly dependent upon the bottom and narrowly restricted in distribution, can not serve as principal photosynthetic agents for the oceans at large. The paramount producers, as we have already mentioned, are the single-celled chlorophyll-bearing organisms of the plankton. Some of these are indisputably plants; others have such a mixture of plant and animal qualities that both botanists and zoologists lay claim to them. Let us mention briefly the more prominent kinds: the Heterococcales (Halosphaera), the diatoms, the dinoflagellates, and the coccolithophores.

Halosphaera and a near relative are the only important algae of the open ocean that are bright green in color. Once grouped by botanists among the Chlorophyceae or true "green algae" (grass-green), they are now placed in a distinct order, and related to the yellow-greens (coccolithophores and others). *Halosphaera viridis* sometimes occurs in great numbers, particularly in the Atlantic, the Antarctic, and the Mediterranean. Although minute in size, the single-celled bodies long ago caught the eyes of Mediterranean fishermen who called them "punti verdi," or "green points."

Much more important as food for small vegetarian animals are the diatoms, whose shells of silica we have previously mentioned as the basis of a principal bottom deposit—diatomaceous ooze (see p. 114). Diatoms occur abundantly in both fresh and salt waters, free living or on the bottom where there is light, but they reach their fullest flower, so to speak, in the marine plankton. They appear in great diversity of form and size, the largest being barely visible to the naked eye. Some, Rhizosolenia at least, show notable "cyclomorphosis," or change of form with season. In winter the pointed ends of the long narrow shells (frustules) are short and blunt. Later generations in summer have long slender points, presumably in adaptation to the changed viscosity of the water; the increased surface is supposed to offer greater resistance to sinking in the warmer and "more liquid" water. Diatoms store food in the form of fine oil droplets, which lighten their bodies and facilitate floating. There is some reason to believe that they form the basic substances of vitamins which are passed on to the copepods that eat them, and, in turn, as vitamins, to the fish that eat the copepods, and so to those who eat the fish. Cold water seems particularly favorable to the development of rich populations of diatoms. Not infrequently the surface water, through areas miles in extent, may be discolored by

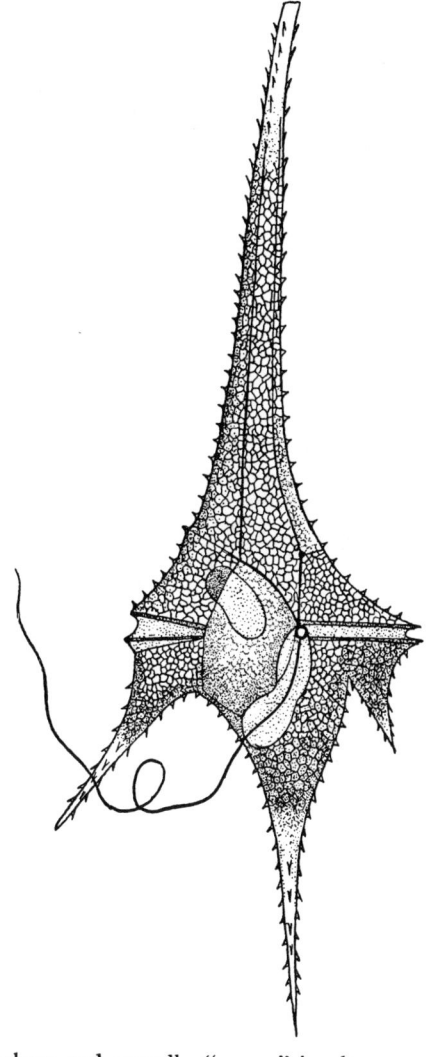

FIGURE 12. One of the minute plants of the plankton, a dinoflagellate, *Ceratium hirundinella*. (From Kudo, after Stein) Such plants, brownish in color, may occur in vast numbers causing the so-called "red seas," many square miles in extent. (See text, p. 204.)

them and actually "soupy" in character. The part diatoms play in the nutrition of animals will be mentioned in a later chapter.

The dinoflagellate algae (or protozoa to the zoologist), with shells of cellulose, or sometimes without shells, are tiny free-swimming

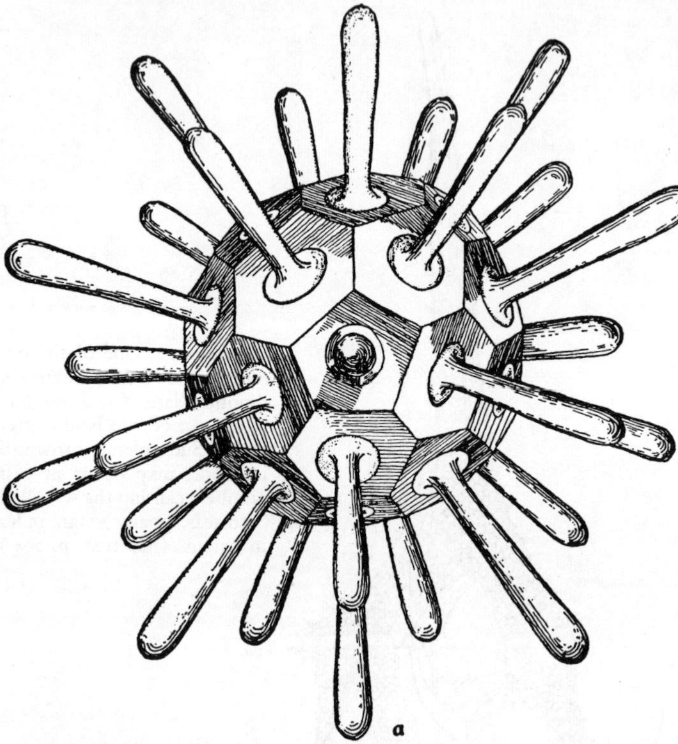

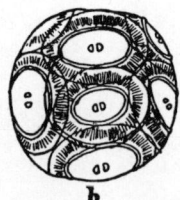

a

FIGURE 13. Coccolithophores. (a) *Rhabdosphaera claviger* (after Murray and Hjort). (b) *Coccolithus pelagicus* (from Fritsch, after Lebour). These very minute plants, whose name means "little stone bearers," constitute an important part of the pasturage of the sea, and their skeletal parts, coccoliths, form a substantial element in deposits on the bottom.

b

organisms with two flagella for locomotion. They occur in great diversity of species. They may, on occasion, be so numerous as to give the sea a muddy appearance, being one of the causes of the frequently mentioned "red seas" in the ocean. They attain greatest numbers in the warmer waters. Some kinds are highly luminescent. Because the organic shells of dinoflagellates decompose readily, they do not appear as an element in bottom deposits.

Yet smaller than the diatoms and dinoflagellates are the Cocco-lithophoridae, which are said to constitute a large proportion of the marine plankton, but which pass through the finest silk nets and must be sought by centrifuging. The name means "bearers of cocco-liths," for the minute bodies are protected by calcareous plates or spicules of the order of size of bacteria. As substantial components of deep-sea calcareous deposits, especially the globigerina ooze, coc-coliths (seed stones) were known to geologists long before it was understood that they are fragments of the shells of living organisms. These algae (or protozoa) are of the group of yellow flagellates, called chrysomonads, to which belong also Dinobryon, a fresh-water alga that sometimes occurs in such abundance as to discolor the water of lakes and ponds and give a bad flavor and odor to municipal drinking water. The coccolithophores seem to be universally dis-tributed in the oceans except in the colder waters of polar seas.

All of the plankton algae are of course restricted to the upper few hundred meters, where sunlight is available—except, as their falling bodies may invade the regions of darkness below.

We have passed over the bacteria, once thought to be not notably abundant in the sea. There is nothing in the conditions of tempera-ture and pressure at the bottom to prevent the growth of bacteria (ZoBell), and they are now known to be enormously abundant in superficial layers of the bottom. More knowledge is needed con-cerning the bacteria of the deep, where much waste organic material accumulates. In recent years, Waksman at Woods Hole and ZoBell at Scripps have been adding much to knowledge of marine bacteria. Experiments of Clarke and Gellis (1935) "indicate that bacteria and other constituents of the nannoplankton may be an important food for copepods in the sea." Bacteria may serve to some extent as syn-thetic agents in regions of the sea where green plants can not func-tion, but we still have too little information concerning the signifi-cance of bacteria in the ocean. In areas occupied by plankton, they are most abundant in the upper zone of water, are mostly attached to plankton or other objects and perhaps are not truly planktonic.[5]

5. Sverdrup, Johnson, and Fleming, *The Oceans*, p. 919.

Such small pasturage organisms as have been mentioned have much greater significance to man than is revealed by any consideration of their use as food for higher animals. Whence came a great part of the reservoirs of oil in the earth from which we derive the fuel that drives our ships and trucks and heats our homes? The bodies of organisms that settled on the sea bottom in ages past, and the action upon them of various kinds of bacteria, gave us in the end the means of transportation and of light and warmth.

Although the higher plants are completely wanting in the open sea, we should refer to a seed plant that is of considerable significance in coastal waters. The common "eelgrass," Zostera, a flowering plant of the pond-weed family, occurs on almost all ocean shores where wave action is not severe. Its abundance and general distribution are indicated by the windrows of it seen on beaches of harbor and ocean. As the annual crops of eelgrass die and the plants are broken to pieces, the fine detritus to which they are ultimately reduced may be carried well out to sea to constitute a basic food supply for many kinds of animals. Indeed, some biologists, considering the nutritive support of animal life in the ocean, have attached greater importance to the detritus formed from eelgrass grown in shallow waters than to the phytoplankton multiplying in the offshore waters. A remarkable phenomenon, and one not yet adequately accounted for, was the comparatively recent and rather sudden disappearance of eelgrass on both sides of the Atlantic and on some Pacific shores, apparently as the result, or with the accompaniment, of some sort of disease. It has been returning, to the great advantage of the scallops and other animals that find refuge in it. Apparently that disaster to eelgrass and, of course, to many of the animals associated with it, was not entirely without precedent, but why did the disease appear so suddenly and in such widespread fashion?

Summary

1. In oceanic areas the equivalent of our abundant land vegetation is to be found in the microscopic plants of the upper illuminated zone. The dilute state in sea water of many of the dissolved substances required to support life and the limited amount of light available beneath the surface have put a premium on high surface exposure in relation to volume. Increased surface is attained by reduc-

tion in size and multiplication in number. Accordingly, photosynthetic organisms in the open sea have no large and complex bodies. Marine vegetation is extremely low in the general scheme of plant classification. The higher plants with elaborate bodies and specialized parts have all developed on land.

2. Some macroscopic algae of "bushy" or platelike form and others (kelps) with long streaming fronds may be conspicuous in coastal waters; the "sargassum weed," drifts widely at sea. All these are mostly brown and red algae, low in the plant scale and characteristic of the sea. A very few seed plants have invaded the marginal waters. Undoubtedly all of these are important *regionally* as original "producers" of organic substance; but, the plants that are visible to the naked eye play a minor part in the whole "metabolism of the sea."

3. In the open sea the minute living algae are largely restricted to the upper 100 meters, where the light is sufficient for photosynthesis. Observations indicate that in coastal waters they are generally far more abundant, but more superficial, than in the open sea.

4. Bacteria are abundant in the bottom muds and oozes, and, to a lesser extent, in the upper waters.

5. The vegetation of the sea offers marked contrast to that on the land, where, with the green hills, vales, and prairie, such obvious plants as grass, weeds, shrubs, trees, and farm crops form the basic support of animal life including man. To discover in the sea the equivalent of these ultimate "producers" of organic matter, resort must be had to the centrifuge and the microscope, particularly for diatoms, dinoflagellates, and coccolithophores. The micro-pasturage of the sea is nonetheless abundant and effective in support of animal life.

CHAPTER 15

Drifting Life: The Plankton

Universality of Plankton

DRIFTING ORGANISMS OCCUR IN ALL HABITABLE NATURAL waters except shallow swift streams. On land and on the bottoms of waters the organic world constitutes a relatively thin layer, a sort of surface, whose extent is measured in two directions. In the sea and in lakes organisms adrift are to be found at all levels; the territory of occupancy is to be measured not only north-south and east-west, but also in the significant third dimension of depth. When we recall that the average depth of the seas is about two and one-third miles, the depth of terrestrial life, measured in feet or in tens of feet seems insignificant. Even in superficial extent, the waters of the earth are more than twice as great as the land. It is obvious, then, that, measured in volume, the space inhabited by plankton is incomparably greater than that occupied by terrestrial and benthonic organisms. The swimming animals, termed nekton, range through the plankton world, but they comprise only a small part of the free life in waters. Consequently, we deal in this chapter with the major part of the organic world: the great majority of plants and animals are "drifters." We have already dealt with a substantial part of the plankton in the discussion of "pasturage in the sea"; hence, in this place, we shall refer to that part of the plankton world only as incidental to the consideration of the animal plankton, or zooplankton.

It now seems somewhat curious that the great world of the plankton was hardly discovered a century ago. Ancient Greek writers

are said to have made some allusions to the drifting life; Mediterranean fishermen are known to have recognized the green alga,
Halosphaera, as "green points"; and whale fishermen have long seen
"whale feed" (copepods, pteropods, and euphausiids) as auguries
of good hunting. That great pioneer microscopist of the late seventeenth and early eighteenth centuries, Antoni van Leeuwenhoek,
who so often anticipated later scientists, saw and described a number of plankters. Yet, to the scientists, and to others generally, the
greatest of all living worlds waited for some great man to think of
using an extremely simple device—the fine-meshed net, drawn
through the water. Diatoms and some other plankters of the ocean
had been discovered by examination of small quantities of water
dipped from the surface, or by observation of skeletal remains in
samples of the bottom; but virtually nothing was known about them
and there was no real conception of the wealth of diversified populations of microorganisms living permanently or temporarily in the
water. It now seems almost incredible that, for so long, it occurred
to so few to employ a fine-straining apparatus. Charles Darwin,
sailing on the "Beagle" (1831-36) and adding immensely to biological knowledge, dragged nets of bunting, but failed to give the
method effective advertisement.

Johannes Müller, one of the great biologists of all times, (see
p. 18, above) made use of the net in 1845. Yet he did not at once
think of towing a net. He wanted to find larval stages of echinoderms, between the easily obtainable fertilized egg and the creeping
young starfish. It occurred to him to dip water and pour it through
a fine-meshed net. Then he dipped with the net on the end of a pole.
Finally he thought of towing the net with a line from a boat.[1]
Amazed at what he obtained, he wrote to Ernst Haeckel, advising
him to try the net, and added that once Haeckel had glimpsed this
world of drifting life, he would never be able to leave it. Apparently
he was right, and we owe much to Haeckel for his ecological classification of marine life. Biologists everywhere began towing "Müller nets" and examining the pelagic strainings (*pelagische mulde*).
Life histories of benthonic organisms that were hitherto unknown
were being completed by hundreds of students. Great numbers of
new animals and plants, whose existence had not previously been

1. Lohmann, 1912.

suspected, were being described. But the concept of the plankton as a coherent community of interrelated organisms was yet to come.

The tow-net was one of those rare devices that, like the microscope, opened new worlds for biological exploration. Although a real introduction to the drifting life dates from the use of the net, the word "plankton" and its definition came only some thirty years later, when Victor Hensen proposed the term, in 1887, with a somewhat broader meaning than it has today. Meantime, the first great exploration of marine plankton was made by the "Challenger" in the 'seventies. In the beginning certain misconceptions developed, and the explorations prompted by these did much to stimulate interest in plankton and to add to knowledge about it.

There were those who thought that free drifting life could exist only in the upper few hundred meters of water. The *closing nets* of Palumbo, von Peterson, Chun, and others (see p. 30, above) made possible the certain knowledge that plankton lived at all depths. It was supposed by some that plankton occurred fairly uniformly at all levels in the upper waters. The *quantitative* net, first devised by Hensen at Kiel, helped to disprove his own theory of generally uniform distribution. Quantitative studies yielded more precise knowledge of the uneven distribution of plankton and led to recognition of the significance of that basic fact in an understanding of many broad problems of oceanography.

By size, the plankton is conveniently divisible into the *net plankton* and the more minute organisms which pass through a net of finest silk and are best taken by centrifuging small samples of water at fairly high speeds. It was Hans Lohmann, at Kiel, who first used the centrifuge in the study of plankton; for the smaller organisms taken by the centrifuge he proposed (1911) the term *nannoplankton*, meaning "dwarf plankton." There can be no sharp distinction between net-plankton and nannoplankton, but the finest nets employed have meshes with diameter of about 0.05 mm. (1/500"). It may be remarked in passing that Lohmann's attention to the nannoplankton was elicited by the discovery that some marine animals that feed by filtering tiny organisms out of the water have a straining apparatus of much finer mesh than our most expensive silk nets. As the net plankton greatly exceeds the nekton in aggregate volume, so the nannoplankton often exceeds the net plankton, not only in numbers, but also in total volume and weight. This is particularly true in fresh water. It seems to be a rough general rule that, in the *aquatic* organic world, the aggregate volume of living material is in inverse proportion to size, if the rule is applied, not to particular species, but only to *sizes*.

Obviously the plankton embraces organisms of a wide range of sizes calling for various methods of capture. It is sometimes convenient to distinguish the *macroplankton*, comprising the larger organisms, like jellyfishes, small fish, salpas, and sargassum, which are easily seen, the *microplankton*, or net plankton, and the *nannoplankton* (dwarf plankton), or "centrifuge plankton"; perhaps we should add, also, the *ultraplankton* of still more minute organisms that even the centrifuge will not separate from the water. It is all one world, however, and we will not stress these subdivisions.

In the comparison of marine and fresh water plankton, two differences are noteworthy. In both there are plankters whose whole lives are spent adrift; but the diversity of these *holoplankters* is far greater in the sea than in fresh water. It is true that rotifers are prominent in fresh water and not in the sea, but this is the one exception favoring fresh water. In the denser waters of the ocean, several divisions of the animal kingdom have developed strictly planktonic kinds—such as the worms, the mollusks, and the lower chordates that never touch the bottom; these groups are not represented at all in the fresh water zooplankton.

Yet the most striking difference between fresh water and marine plankton is the presence in the latter of an almost limitless variety of larval stages of benthonic and nektonic animals. The high specific gravity of sea water, together, doubtless, with other conditions, has been favorable to the assumption of a free-swimming habit at some stage of life. Virtually all marine animals have such free larvae; practically none of the fresh water animals that are not exclusively planktonic have them. In lakes and ponds, newly-hatched snails, worms, and insect larvae crawl out of their egg shells, clams creep from the parental brood pouches to begin life on the bottom, or let fish carry them as parasites until they are prepared to burrow into the bottom.[2] On the contrary, the eggs of marine snails, oysters and worms develop into microscopic larval bodies, quite unlike the

2. The only strictly planktonic insect larvae are the "phantom larvae" of the midge commonly known as Corethra or Chaoborus. The familiar mosquito-wigglers live partly free, as planktonic, partly at rest on the bottom or at the surface, as benthonic or neustonic.

adult and provided with numbers of delicate paddles which roll them around in the water until they can undergo metamorphosis into the form of the sedentary adults. It is such free-swimming larval stages, constituting the *meroplankton* (part-plankton), that make the most conspicuous contrast between catches of marine and fresh-water plankton.

Conditions Governing Distribution by Regions and by Depth

In respect to distribution, as we must emphasize for each of the three types of major ecological communities in the sea, it is the presence of nutritive substances that chiefly determines abundance of plankton at any place. The foundation of any community is the proper assemblage of inorganic substances in conjunction with sunlight and photosynthetic organisms. The starting places for the organic cycle are the upper illuminated waters wherever they may be, and the sunlit land. Naturally, then, it is the upper waters, generally, that are most richly populated and densities of population must also show some sort of gradation with respect to distance from land. If it were all quite as simple as this sounds, the problems in the study of distribution would be easily solved. But there are many complicating factors. Currents or drifts, universally present, carry nutritive substances, algae and the animal plankton, from place to place. Nutritive materials sink into the depths for temporary loss, and much of this is brought back into illuminated waters along shore or somewhere out at sea. Among the basic nutritive substances, in a broad sense, are carbon dioxide and oxygen; and cold water absorbs more of these gases, to make them available for aquatic plants, than does warm water, while the oxygen, at least, is used more rapidly in warmer waters. This is not the whole story, but it is enough to show that the pattern of distribution is very complex.

The zone of *production* in the open sea is in the high upper waters, above a depth of 200 meters; yet it is not chiefly at the very surface. Various observers have found the maxima of minute plants (algae) at about 50 meters.[3] Since the basis of the pyramid of numbers in the sea is the community of photosynthetic organisms in the upper waters, it might be expected that the algae in these waters would vastly exceed in number and volume the animal plankton. They

3. See Chapter XIV, p. 198.

have the heavy task of maintaining themselves, the animals that live with them and feed upon them, and, in addition, all the animal life in the deeper waters below, where no original production can take place.[4] It appears, however, that generally no such conspicuous excess of plants over animals is found. The task of the algae in support both of themselves and of the animals is met, not so much by continual maintenance of a greatly predominating population, as by rapidity of reproduction. In the sea, as in the barnyard, the livestock live and grow fat, not from the food in the trough in one day, but from the regular replenishment of the manger. It is the "turnover" that counts.

For various reasons, littoral and neritic waters are generally richest in plankton. Organic and inorganic nutritive materials drain from the land; photosynthetic algae may grow on the bottom in littoral regions; and the only marine seed plants thrive on upper littoral bottoms. These die, are broken up by wave action, and form detritus that is carried by the water as food for animals of benthos and plankton. Little of this gets out into the open sea.[5] Along the coasts, and away from them as well, abundant development of plankton may be expected where ascending currents bring up nutritive material from below.[6] Where water descends from the surface into the depth, plankton in the upper depleted waters will usually be scarce. Sinking of surface water must occur where prevailing on-shore winds cause the piling up of water, or where convergence of oceanic currents occurs to produce the same effect. In the relatively dead centers of oceanic eddies, increase of specific gravity of the surface water through evaporation leads to subsidence. Thus the upper plankton of the Sargasso Sea is reported to be notably scant;[7] yet the sargassum weed decomposes to become detritus and afford nourishment for deeper-living animals,[8] so that Hjort found the waters in that sea at depths of 1,000-1,500 meters to be notably richer in deep-living plankton and fish than those east of it.

4. It has been estimated that copepods and other small animals consume something like their own weight of food in ten days (cf. Murray and Hjort, *op. cit.*, p. 727), varying, of course, with many conditions. According to other computations, plankton animals consume food materials equivalent to their own weights in two days (cf. Sverdrup, *et. al., op. cit.*, p. 901). The latter figure is probably applicable more generally to Protozoa.

5. Hjort, in Murray and Hjort, *op. cit.*, p. 386.

6. *Ibid.*, p. 368.

7. *Ibid.*, p. 371.

8. *Ibid.*, p. 718.

When warm and cold currents come together and mix, the rising temperature may promote the growth and reproduction of algae, and of their predators, to utilize more rapidly the materials carried in the cold waters: it is like the coming of spring to the previously colder waters. The mixture of Arctic currents, coastal waters carrying detritus, and the warm Atlantic Gulf Stream leads to the richness of life in the Barents Sea, the waters north and east of Iceland and those of the fishing banks off Labrador and Newfoundland.[9]

The physical conditions of temperature and viscosity have much to do with the geographic and depth distribution of particular kinds of plankton organisms, as we shall see more particularly in our brief consideration of the several groups of animals. There are species tolerant only of cold and others only of warm waters. Such animals as can endure only a narrow range in either the upper or lower part of the temperature scale are called *stenothermal*. Others are *eury-thermal*, with apparent indifference to changes of temperature. It is to be remembered, too, that cold waters are found, not only in high northern and southern latitudes, but in all latitudes, even beneath the Equator, at sufficient depths. Pressure, which increases so rapidly with depth, probably plays some part in determining the tolerable ranges of depth for particular species; but apparently of greatest significance are temperature, which changes with depth, and viscosity, which changes with temperature and, very little, with salinity.

In respect to the depths at which plankton lives, we have seen that, generally speaking, the algae are most abundant somewhat below the very top water, and live hardly at all below 200 meters. The plankton crustacea, which are the most important of all animal plankton, live mostly below 200 meters. Referring to the Atlantic, Hjort said that "the greatest volume of pelagic crustacea has never been found in the upper 100 or 200 meters, where the production of minute plants takes place, the great majority of small pelagic crustacea live everywhere in the deeper intermediate layers."[10] There is no depth at which some plankton does not occur, but, since the zone of production is in the upper 200 meters, the deeper living animals can subsist only upon each other or upon what falls from above, and those of each layer take their toll. Again, however, there are

9. *Ibid.*, p. 728.
10. *Ibid.*, p. 725.

many complicating factors. If the waters are in movement, as is the rule, the fall of material will be, not in a direct vertical direction, but obliquely; the place of consumption is not immediately below the place of production.

Falling matter may pass from a current flowing in one direction into another having a different, even an opposite course. It may pass from water of low salinity to water so much higher in salinity and, in specific gravity as to cause a retardation, or even a stoppage of descent. There will be, as Hjort suggests, a sort of "bottom" in mid-water, when food accumulates to support a relatively dense population of small pelagic animals. Such a region seems to prevail in the Sargasso Sea at 500-1,000 meters, where many more small crustacea were found than in the uppermost waters.

It is elementary knowledge now that there is great diversity in the composition of plankton, not only in different regions and at different depths, but also at different seasons, and at different hours at the same place and depth, and probably even in different years. The conditions that lead to maxima and minima, as well as to minor fluctuations of abundance of any particular plant or animal, are complex indeed in their physical, chemical and biological aspects. Just one of these conditions is the migratory habit of many plankters. The powers of locomotion of such small organisms are slight as compared with those of larger animals in respect to horizontal movements over broad areas. That is to say, a microscopic animal, however rapid may be its movement in proportion to its size, will, nevertheless, in the course of a day, travel no considerable distance under its own power. Changes in geographic location are to be accounted for chiefly by the action of currents. On the other hand, locomotion of individuals may result locally in the formation of dense schools or in scattering. Most notable are the vertical migrations, which are generally toward the surface when the light is dim and away from it when the light increases. Consequently, surface hauls taken at night will yield many times the numbers of plankters found in surface hauls in the same place taken by day. The qualitative composition of day and night collections will be different, since different species, or even different ages or sizes of the same species, may differ in migratory habit. Hjort obtained large catches of copepods in surface hauls at night, although during the day, they were taken only at 70 meters. Much greater vertical movements are reported. It is noteworthy that plankters that engage in extensive diurnal vertical migrations, undergo in a period of ten or twelve hours changes of pressure equivalent to several atmospheres.

Whether or not we deal in any particular case with plankton populations that have some powers of locomotion, we do find everywhere that communities are always in process of change. At any spot changes may occur in the kinds of plants or animals that are present and in the relative and absolute numbers of the several species. There are seasonal changes, as the spawn of crabs, worms, starfishes, mollusks, and other benthonic animals rise to constitute for a time prominent elements of the drifting populations. Finally, among the biological conditions causing changes in plankton populations, is the work of predators. Increase of algae promotes the growth and reproduction of small animal plankters, which, in turn, are devoured by larger predators. Whole populations of particular organisms may be greatly depleted or nearly wiped out in succession. Hence there are notable cyclical changes in the plankton picture in any one region.

A distinctive feature of the conditions of life for marine plankton derives from the dynamic nature of the environment. Marine plankters live generally in a moving home, whether the movements are the rhythmic and reversible tidal currents of harbors or the progressive currents, drifts, and eddies of the wide ocean. The immediate home environment is without fixed geographic location: the several populations are "on the move" but without ability in themselves to govern their geographic distribution. Only at first glance can this difference seem insignificant. Assuming that a copepod were carried all the way across Lake Superior, it would have travelled several hundred miles, but it would have encountered no notable change of conditions of life. Imagine, on the other hand, a copepod in the Gulf Stream, making 24 miles, more or less, each day, some 700 miles a month, and perhaps several thousand miles in the course of its whole life. If not devoured on the way, it could have passed from one set of conditions of light, temperature, and salinity to another and significantly different environment. It might, of course, have been thrown out into an eddy, or it might have lived only so long as conditions were not greatly changed; but at least, the hazards of change were there.

Since not only the copepod, but also nearly everything surrounding the copepod would be traveling at the same rate, the change in geographic location could not be perceived if the copepod had perception. We do not feel the daily movement of rotation of ourselves, our homes, and our animal and plant associates around the axis of the earth at a rate something less than 1,000 miles per hour or our even more rapid movement in the orbit of the earth around the sun. As we go on our diurnal and annual pilgrimages we encounter changes in conditions of light and temperature, if not of chemical environment, but we are regularly returned to the old positions relative to the sun. This brings up the question, to what extent does the return occur with ccpepods, diatoms, pteropods, and worms; and, if it does, by what paths are the circuits completed?

Let us trace our touring copepod a little farther, with the clear understanding that the story is hypothetical, although having a logical basis, and that we follow it only for the purpose of raising a question. If, after 3,000 miles of travel, this copepod had offspring, the members of the next generation, fortunate enough to complete a life span of six months might well, at the end, be over 7,000 miles from the parental natal spot. So, from generation to generation, the log of travel would grow in mileage at various rates but mounting eventually to astronomical figures, under any assumption as to rate of movement. Conceivably, there might be a return to the original home; yet, if this were the case, the successive generations would have endured gradual but presumably significant changes in the conditions of life as regards temperature, light, and salinity. If there should be no return, then the question arises: How is the original stock of a Gulf Stream or a Peru Current maintained? If everyone in Florida moved to the Carolinas, then on to Virginia, New Jersey, etc., who would start the new migrant populations in Florida?

Exactly the same problem arises if we assume a drift of only a fraction of a mile an hour. There seems to be nothing seriously wrong with our assumptions, except that they lead to questions that may not now be definitely answerable. A hypothetical answer would be that at least a "nest egg" of all such planktonic species occurs practically universally and has only to encounter the right set of conditions to propagate actively enough to make the large populations that are observed in particular regions.[11] Another possible

11. But Schütt, from the Plankton Expedition, concluded that different ocean currents are inhabited by different types of floating plants (Sverdrup, *et. al.*, *op. cit.*, p. 791).

answer, and a more likely one, would put the enduring brood stock, for plankton species of oceanic currents, in lateral eddies relatively fixed geographically. The populations conveyed to other regions in far-reaching streams would then represent loss by drainage from the original brood stock in a relatively fixed home, upon which always the perpetuation of the species would depend. It is well known indeed that eddies adjacent to oceanic currents receive animate contributions from the currents, some of which are incapable of continuing life indefinitely under the new conditions, while others reproduce an endemic stock. The reverse may be equally true—that the populations of currents are dependent upon the eddies, some of which are small and some of oceanic proportions. There are many significant unsolved problems of plankton geography, and many of these have to do with the fact that marine plankters inhabit a moving rather than a stationary medium—that the sea is a dynamic body of water, not a static one.

CHAPTER 16

Composition of the Plankton

S INCE ALL OF THE GENERAL TYPES OF LIFE ARE REPRESENTED IN
the ocean and some only there, and since virtually all animals in the sea enter into the composition of the plankton
at some stage of life, any complete account of the plankton[1] could
only be compassed in a shelf of volumes. Some suggestion of the
diversity and nature of plankters and of their significance to the
larger animals may be gained from a brief review of the several
groups of animals.

Many representatives of the *Protozoa* have already been mentioned in the consideration of algae. The microorganisms that form
a bridge between plant and animal kingdoms make impossible any
sharp line of division. The Foraminifera, typified by *Globigerina
bulloides* with external shells composed chiefly of carbonate of lime,
have already been mentioned as agents in the formation of globigerina ooze. This occupies a large part of the bottom of the ocean
and, in places, at least, forms a rich feeding ground for benthonic
animals. In a calm sea globigerina may be found at the surface, the
larger ones barely visible to the naked eye. Since the calcareous
shells are relatively soluble, the deposits in which they predominate
are found only at moderate depths. The richest and most diverse
populations are said to be found in warmer waters; the number of
individuals and of species diminishes as one goes away from the
tropics. This is in partial contrast to the distribution of some other

1. Those particularly interested should read such books as Steuer's *Planktonkunde* or Ekman's *Tiergeographie des Meeres* or the pertinent chapters in Murray
and Hjort, Sverdrup, Johnson, and Fleming, and other general works on oceanography.

organisms, for the more general rule is: many more kinds in tropical regions, but denser populations in colder waters.

Silicious shells of the Radiolaria (internal shells it may be recalled,

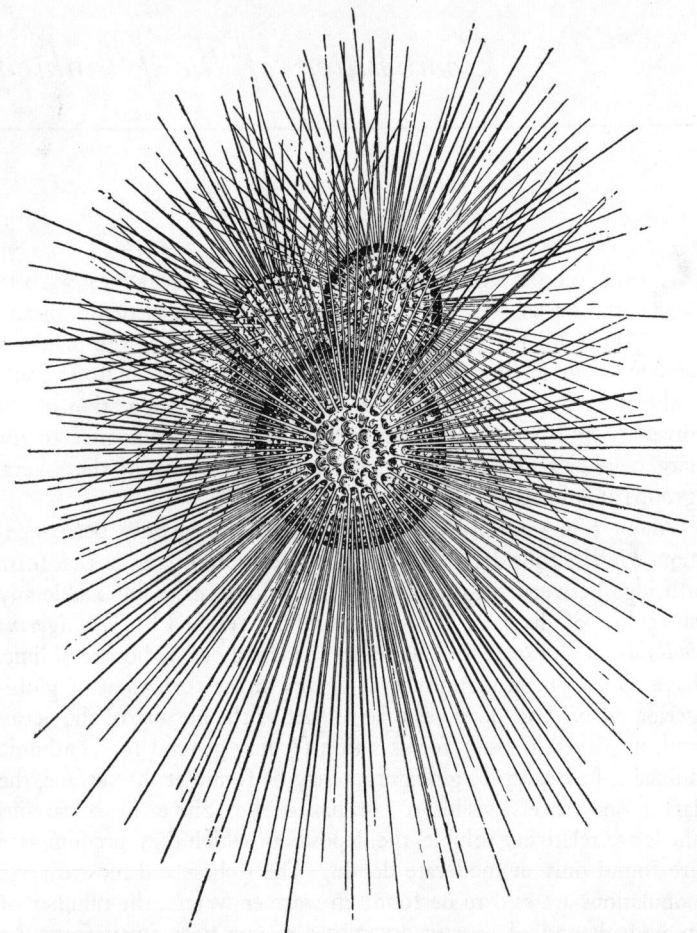

FIGURE 14. The protozoan, *Globigerina bulloides* D'Orbigny. (from Murray and Hjort). This minute animal with house of calcareous and organic matter and fine spicules is important in the plankton, and its skeleton gives the name to the type of bottom deposits called globigerina ooze.

p. 117) are less soluble than those of Foraminifera and are therefore characteristic of oozes that underlie deeper waters. Among the Radiolaria, with their strikingly beautiful shells, there is great diversity of form and of distribution by depth and latitude. Some species have been found only in abyssal depths under the equator, others only in the Antarctic. Those taken by the "Valdivia" expedition, were found to fall into groups distinguished by the depths at which the species lived. There were species of the uppermost layer of water, species of a higher intermediate layer, 50-400 meters, and others of a lower intermediate layer, 400-1,000 meters; there were also abyssal species living chiefly at 1,500-5,000 meters.

The flagellate Peridineae, with shells of organic material, have been mentioned before as occurring sometimes in such enormous numbers as to cause "red seas." They are most important as food of salpas and other plankters that feed by filtering water. Their shells decompose too readily to figure in the formation of bottom deposits. The ciliate protozoa are sometimes represented abundantly in the plankton, particularly in coastal waters, by the tintinnoids, which also have shells secreted about their bodies and often carry, attached to the shells, minute solid objects such as parts of the shells of other protozoa and algae. The highly important flagellate coccolithophores have already been discussed (p. 205).

The large cystoflagellate Noctiluca of coastal waters should be mentioned, if only for its brilliant luminescence. In certain inshore waters, as at Beaufort, North Carolina, Noctiluca may at times occur in such density of population that any moving body in the water, whether fish, boat, or human bather, is brilliantly outlined in light by the flashes of the protozoa with which all parts of the body-surface are making continuous contact. Most impressive testimony to the capacity of some organisms for multiplication and concentration in the sea is that of Allen[2], who found *Noctiluca scintillans* in a concentration of three million to a liter in water as dipped from the surface in the Gulf of California. Since this well-named "scintillating night light" is macroscopic rather than microscopic in size (it may attain a diameter of one millimeter), three million of them in one million cubic millimeters would seem to leave little room for water!

2. Winfred E. Allen "The Primary Food Supply of the Sea," *Quarterly Review of Biology*, IX, 161-180.

The sponges (*Porifera*) are not significant in the plankton. The colonial masses live attached on the bottom or other solid objects and grow vegetatively. Yet they do form eggs that, when fertilized, develop into free-swimming planktonic larvae.

The *Coelenterata*, on the other hand, are very prominent and some are among the largest animals of the macroplankton. In this group of jellyfishes, polyps, corals, sea anemones, and siphonophores, there is remarkable diversity of form and habit. Typically, a coelenterate is a small elongate sack with a single opening surrounded by a circlet of slender tentacles provided with minute stingers. This is the *polyp* form. Attached to solid objects, they grow vegetatively by budding and also sexually by fertilized eggs that develop into free-swimming ciliated larvae. Commonly the eggs and sperm are not produced by a polyp itself but by a *medusa*, or jelly fish, which has arisen as a specialized bud that becomes free to swim in the water. The bulk of the body of the jellyfish has the form of a bell margined by the tentacles; suspended from the center of the bell is a clapper-like portion having the mouth at its free end. Nearly the whole of the body, bell and clapper, is a non-living, translucent, gelatinous supporting material, sandwiched between very thin layers of living cells covering the outside and lining the internal chambers. Swimming with apparent aimlessness by rhythmic contractions of the bell, the medusa makes a prominent part of the plankton. Some are of immense size—as much as 2 meters in diameter, and with tentacles 35 meters or more in length (much more than 100 feet.)

We have, then, in many coelenterates, an "alternation of generations," with a sedentary polyp form, reproducing by budding, and a free-swimming medusa form, originating as a particular sort of bud, and reproducing through fertilized eggs that grow into new polyps. In different groups there are various modifications of this cycle: in some the medusa never separates from the attached colony, but simply liberates the fertilized eggs; in others the eggs set free from the free-living medusa develop directly into medusae, and there is no sedentary asexual stage; and there are other modifications. Hence we have medusae that are temporary members of the plankton—meroplankters; (see p. 212) appearing seasonally as stages in the life history of benthonic hydroids, and medusae whose immediate ancestors and descendants live always adrift—holoplankters. Not only

Pl. 16. The Clarke quantitative plankton sampler ready to be hauled.

Coit M. Coker   Coit M. Coker

Upper left, Pl. 17. Attaching a meter net to the towing cable for collecting plankton. *Upper right,* Pl. 18. Towing a plankton net near the surface. *Lower left,* Pl. 19. Hauling in the quantitative plankton net. *Lower right,* Pl. 20. A heavy catch in the plankton net.

U.S. Fish and Wild Life Service   Carnegie Institution of Washington

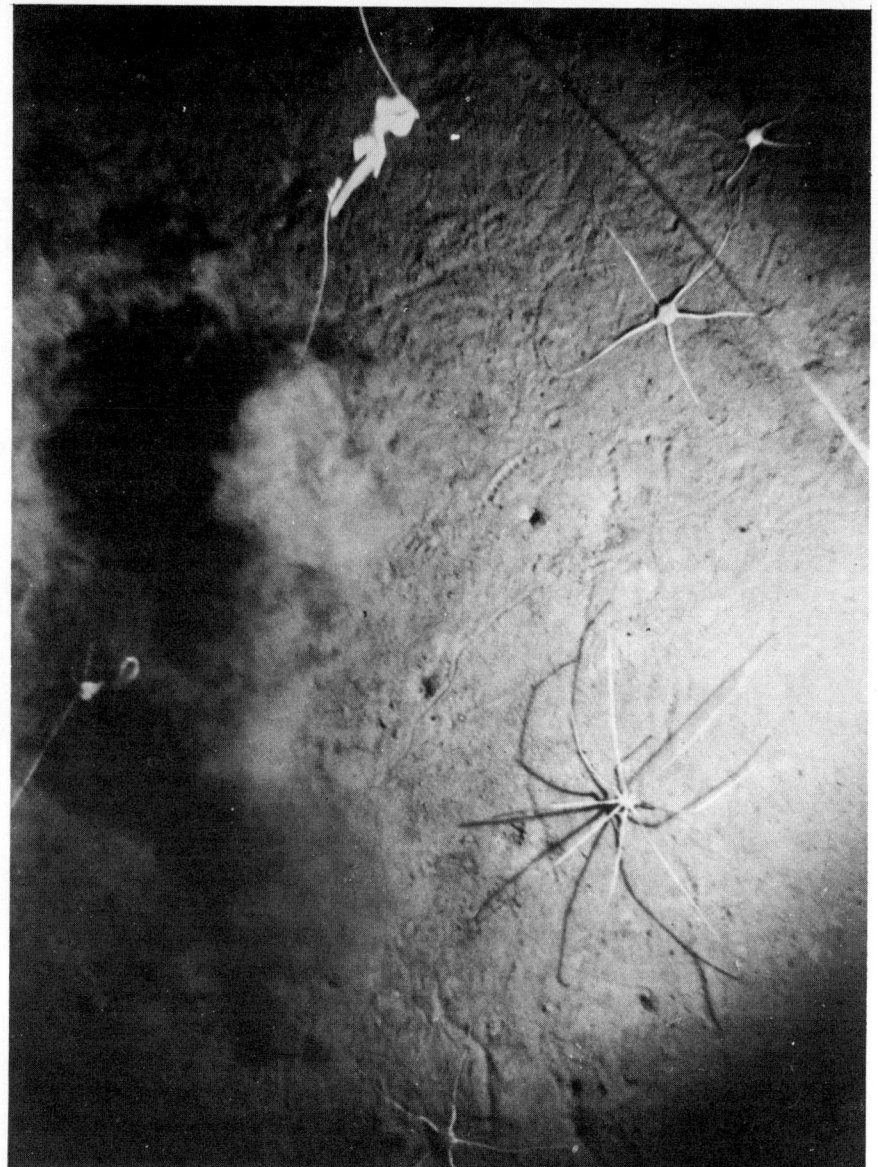

Pl. 21. Sea Spider, three brittle-stars and various tracks on sea floor. Photo by D. M. Owen, south of Cape Cod in 1,000 fathoms.

Above, Pl. 22. Living coral, *Acropora muricata* L. *Below,* Pl. 23. Its cleaned skeleton.

Dr. Waldo Schmitt and U.S. National Museum

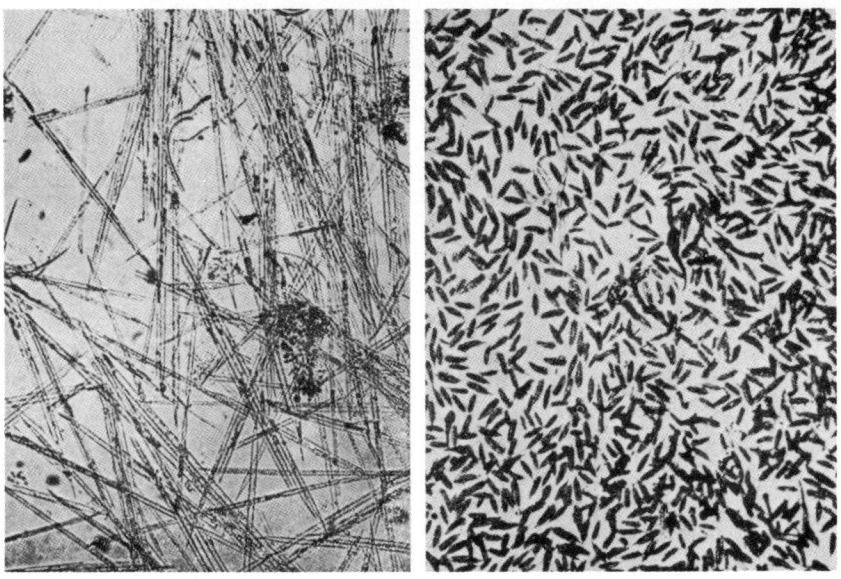

Varieties of plankton catch. *Upper left,* Pl. 24. Chiefly diatoms. *Upper right,* Pl. 25. Almost exclusively one species of copepod, *Calanus finmarchicus.* *Lower left,* Pl. 26. Chiefly a dinoflagellate, *Ceratium tripos.* *Lower right,* Pl. 27. Chiefly a radiolarian protozoan.

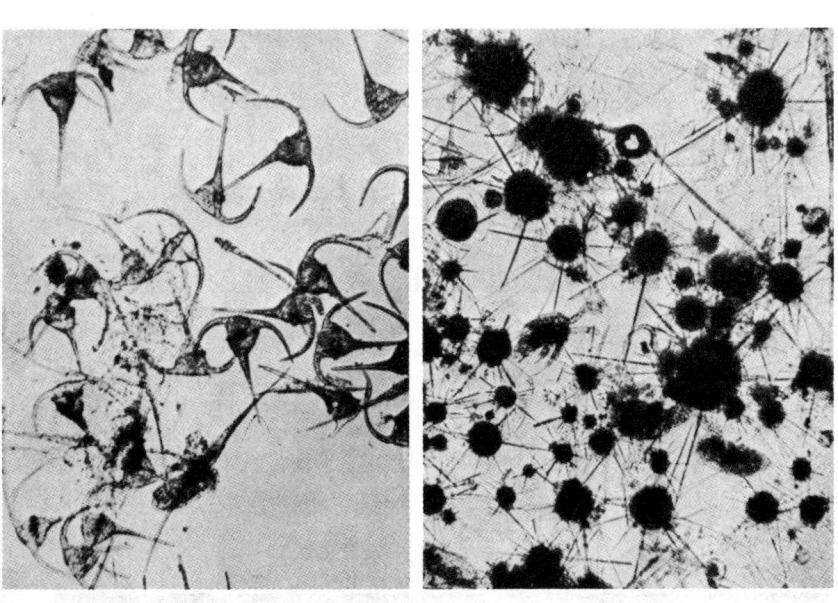

Pl. 28. The development of self-contained underwater breathing apparatus (SCUBA) has opened up a new world to the marine scientists. A diver on Capricorn Expedition examines coral beds of the tropical Pacific. The two-ship expedition was carried out by The University of California's Scripps Institution of Oceanography in 1952-53.

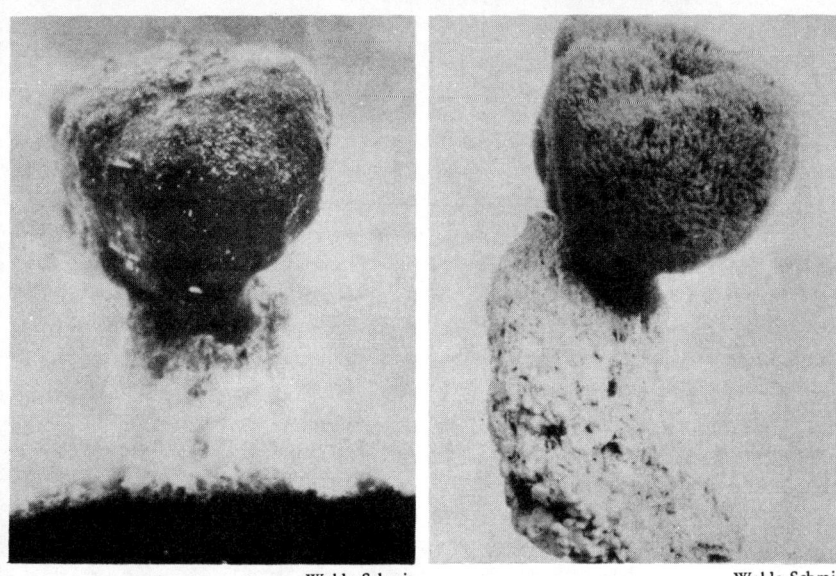

Waldo Schmit

Waldo Schmit

Left, Pl. 29. Living sponge attached to a shell. *Right,* Pl. 30. The cleaned skeleton of same.

Pl. 31. Spider crab, *Peralithodes camtschica* (Tilesins).

U.S. National Museum

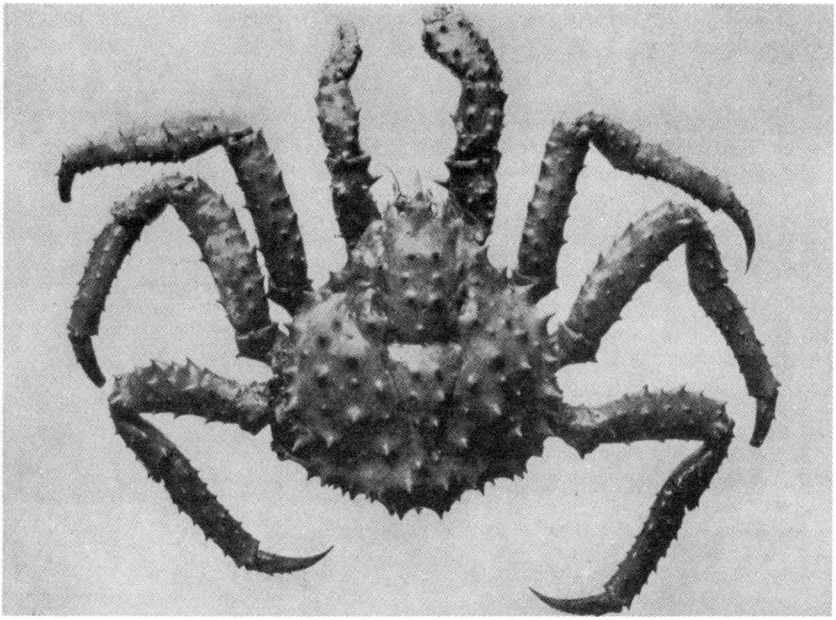

Pl. 32. Towed rapidly behind a moving ship, the Isaacs-Kidd midwater trawl collects the marine creatures who live in waters a mile or more deep. The wide metal vane keeps the trawl level and at the required depth during towing. The wide use of the trawl has revealed many new species of fishes in the mid-depths and has caught large quantities of other fishes once thought very rare. The trawl has been adapted for use in scientific studies throughout the world.

The University of California, La Jolla

in waters along the coasts, but also in the central areas of the great oceans, medusae often display themselves in such numbers as to arrest the attention of the most casual observer.

In some coelenterates the colonial polyps secrete about their bodies a calcareous exoskeleton to form the elaborate coral masses, a few of which are beautifully colored and commercially valuable. Certain kinds of coral grow vegetatively to such an extent that whole islands and reefs are built by them. Thus the tiny living polyps of coral are actually geologic agents of no little significance. Corals, too, liberate fertilized eggs which swim freely for a period of days or even weeks; hence corals also enter into the plankton, before settling to the bottom to make the beginnings of new colonies. The same is true of the sea anemones which, likewise, have no medusa stage. Hence we have, as important elements in the plankton, not only the large and small jellyfishes, but also the minute larvae of all kinds of coelenterates.

There is yet another type of coelenterate in which the polypoid forms are attached, not to foreign objects, but to large gas-filled floats of their own manufacture. These are the siphonophores, of which the "Portuguese man-of-war," Physalia, and the "by-the-wind sailor," Velella, are representatives. The large floats of Physalia, several inches in length, and half as high, display beautiful translucent iridescent tints, but they are to be dreaded by the swimmer, because the long dangling streamers, which may be 30 or 40 feet in length, carry quantities of the pernicious stinging organs. Both Physalia and Velella are surface animals and restricted, except for strays, to the warmer waters. Other and deep-sea kinds, of which Physophora is an example, are provided with numerous swimming-bells.

The comb jellies or sea walnuts, *Ctenophora*, with jellylike bodies and no sessile stage, were once classed with the Coelenterates, but they are fundamentally distinct. They may be quite prominent in the plankton of both the surface and the deep water. Their young are also free swimming, of course.

The flatworms, or *Platyhelminthes*, are not generally planktonic as adults; yet, if the nemerteans, or ribbon worms, are to be classed with them, they have many planktonic species. One of the ribbon worms (not planktonic) has the distinction of being the longest of

all invertebrate animals—about 75 feet, nearly equalling in length
the longest of all animals (a whale), but only a thread in diameter.
A nemertean of leaflike form and pelagic habit has been found at
1,800 fathoms.

Although the round worms, or *Nemathelminthes*, are predominantly parasitic or benthonic, there are planktonic species. The
wheelworms or rotifers (wheel-bearers), or *Trochelminthes*, as
we have said, are almost exclusively inhabitants of fresh water, yet
a few marine species may appear in great numbers in neritic plankton. The moss animalicules, *Bryozoa*, chiefly conspicuous as brushy
tufts on solid objects, have larvae in the plankton, as do the peculiar
"worms" of the small phylum *Phoronidea*, and the *Brachiopoda*,
those now fairly rare or localized, sedentary, shelled animals, which,
paleontologists tell us, were in ancient times the dominant animals of
the bottom communities.

The *Chaetognatha* (seta-jaws) make another very small phylum,
comprising the arrow-worms or glass-worms, which are highly important elements in the plankton. They are peculiarly dainty, translucent, swift-moving animals of slender arrow form. Sagitta is found
in all oceans: some species are widely distributed, some occur only in
warm waters, others in cold Arctic and boreal waters. They are most
conspicuous in surface catches, but certain species are taken only in
deep hauls, and are bright red in color. Generally rather small, the
maximum length is about 3 inches. The distribution of sagittae has
been the subject of a good deal of study, since they serve sometimes as indicators of the origin of water masses, where mixing
occurs.

The segmented worms, *Annelida*, are mostly of bottom-living
habit, some free, some in burrows, and some in calcareous or fibrous
tubes of various forms. The pear-shaped larval stages, or trocho-
phores, may be very prominent in the plankton of coastal waters at
the breeding times of the several abundant species. Remarkable
among all zoological phenomena is the breeding behavior of the
palolo worm. The adults live on the bottom, until the time of breeding approaches; then a part of the body, carrying the reproductive
cells, is thrown off from the remainder. These breeding segments
of the body rise to the surface in countless numbers to swim while
the eggs are in process of liberation. Most remarkable of all is the

fact that the appearance of the palolos occurs each year with almost clock-like regularity. The very day may be anticipated and the natives of the Samoan, Fiji, and other islands, go out to net them in quantities, for they are highly esteemed as food. The genus Tomopteris comprises annelids of general planktonic habit, including some beautiful species of the warm surface waters, others of cold surface waters and some from deep water. Examples taken in deep water óf the Antarctic are described as being "as long as the finger, transparent and with rose-colored feet" (platelike appendages on the sides of the body).

In the phylum *Echinodermata* are the starfishes, sea urchins, brittle stars, sea cucumbers, and sea lilies. All are benthonic as adults, creeping, burrowing, or anchored in the bottom; but their larval stages are often prominent in the coastal plankton, and very different in appearance from the adults. To the student of the plankton, the group has this special interest: it was the search for possible free-swimming stages of echinoderms that led to the use of the plankton net and to the real discovery of the plankton world.

The *Mollusca* command special attention whether we deal with benthos, nekton, or plankton. Most prominent in the bottom fauna are oysters, clams, scallops, limpets, conchs, snails, tusk shells, devil-fishes, and others. In the division of swimming animals, we find the squids playing a great part in surface and deep waters. In the plankton we have the larvae of all of these, and, in addition, the pteropods and heteropods, which are relatives of the snails (gastropods). The solid fleshy or muscular part of a mollusk, the so-called "foot," is capable of most diverse modifications for crawling, seizing, or swimming. In the snails it is a serviceable foot for creeping; in most bivalves it has become a hatchet-shaped blade for burrowing; in the squid and devilfish, the nautilus and the argonaut, it has the form of a head with eight or ten long sucker-equipped arms used for seizing prey or for walking; in the pteropods and heteropods it is hardly more than a pair of light paddles for swimming.

The free-swimming mollusca may have light, small, spiral shells of pinhead size or long, slender, conical shells. They live more generally in warmer waters and, therefore, at no great depth. Pteropod ooze, characterized by the abundance of pteropod shells, is "limited to the tropical and subtropical regions." Certain kinds, however, occur in vast numbers in Arctic waters, even around Greenland and Spitsbergen. Some species are reported from the Atlantic, Pacific, and Indian oceans. Of chief interest is one known as whale's feed, *Clione limacina*, which is found in polar waters, "swimming among the ice floes." Individually quite small (or something over an inch in length), they occur in such numbers, that, strained from the water by the whalebone sieves of the right whales, they afford rich nourishment for these largest of all animals.

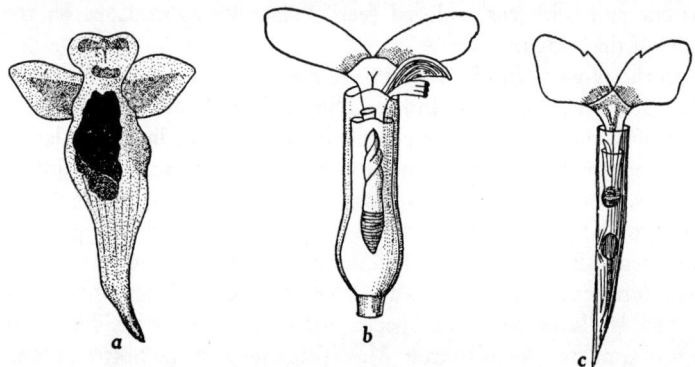

FIGURE 15. Free-swimming pteropod mollusks. (a) *Clione limacina* Phipps (from Murray and Hjort, after Vanhöffen). (b) *Cuvierina columnella* Rang (from *Cambridge Natural History*, after Souleyet). (c) *Cresis virgula* Rang (from *Cambridge Natural History*, after Souleyet).

Among the mollusks we have also the largest of the animals without backbones. The class *Cephalopoda*[3] comprises devilfishes, paper nautilus, squid, and pearly nautilus. Except for the squid, these live mainly on the bottom. The eight-armed "devilfishes" may attain a length of 16 feet. Lurking in grottoes or other retreats, the mouths of which may be littered with the skeletons of their victims, these animals have excited the imagination of several writers, notably Victor Hugo. The thrill of the titanic struggles between man and octopus narrated in "Toilers of the Sea" need not be greatly lessened by knowledge that the story is fiction and not well-founded natural history. Nevertheless, a sizable octopus does not offer a pleasant encounter for a diver. The female argonaut, paper-sailor or paper-

3. Cephalopoda, head-foot; that is to say, the "foot" (of other mollusks) forms the head of these.

nautilus, has a beautiful, delicate shell which is formed as an "egg-nest" by two of its eight arms, and is not at all comparable to the shells of other mollusks. They come to the surface at spawning time, but, contrary to old beliefs, they do not use the shell as a sail. They swim, like other cephalopods by pumping water out of the mantle cavity (see p. 290, below). Thus they are benthonic and, at times, nektonic or planktonic. The males are tiny "about an inch in length, being sometimes scarce a tenth of the size of a female."[4]

Far more numerous than any other cephalopods are the ten-armed squids, which include the largest of invertebrates—up to 50 feet or more in length. These will best be considered in a following chapter on nekton.

The pearly nautilus or chambered nautilus, which creeps over the bottom in relatively shallow water, and also swims by jet propulsion, is generally best known for its beautiful chambered shells and the novelties made from it and for its established place in literature. The "tentacles" of the pearly nautilus are without suckers and are numerous—about ninety.

Finally among the invertebrates, we have the most important of all plankters in the phylum *Arthropoda*, or animals with externally-jointed limbs. The joints of limbs and body are external because the whole body is encased in a continuous outside skeleton to which the muscles of movement have their attachments. This integument is not interrupted for joints, which occur only where, in rings around the body or limbs, the skeletal armor remains flexible enough to permit freedom of movement. In this great branch of the animal kingdom are the insects, spiders, and centipedes, which, together, provide many more kinds of animals than are found in all the other branches of the animal kingdom combined. The insects are almost wanting in the sea, although some midge and caddis larvae occur on the bottom in coastal waters, and a single kind of water strider, Halobates, runs over the surface in tropical regions of the Atlantic and the Pacific, ranging even far from land. The spider and mites keep to land and fresh water, but some mites are marine, and distant relatives, such as the king crab, or horse shoe crab (Limulus), and the small lanky pycnogonids, live on the bottom or among the gardens of plants or animals in waters near the shores.

4. *Riverside Natural History*, I, sec. 2, 370.

The jointed-limbed animals of the class Crustacea, on the other hand, are primarily marine. A good many (crayfish, copepods, cladocera, and others) have become adapted to life in fresh waters, and a very few to life on land (land crabs and pill bugs). The great majority live only in the sea. "No class of multicellular animals in the ocean," says Hjort, "is represented by anything like such countless forms and individuals as that of the Crustaceans." Haeckel compared the part played by crustacea in the sea to that of the insects on land. We may conveniently distinguish the smaller Entomostraca, mostly holoplanktonic, and the generally larger Malacostraca. Most of the latter subclass live on the bottom as adults, but a few kinds are important permanently free-swimming crustacea. Of the Malacostraca we are concerned particularly with the Mysida, the euphausiids, the amphipods, and the decapods.

Everyone is familiar with some of the larger decapods (tenlegged)—crabs, lobsters, crayfish, and shrimp. Most of these crawl on the bottom, but the shrimp are active swimmers, especially the larger ones, and will call for some attention in the chapter on nekton. The larvae of all, which may be entirely unlike the parent form, appear abundantly, but seasonally and briefly, in the neritic plankton. Some pelagic amphipods may occur abundantly in the upper waters of warm regions, but others are found in deep water and at least two species are important in very cold, even icy, waters. A particularly interesting group of species taken in plankton catches makes homes in the translucent empty barrellike coats of salpas (see p. 235, below.) The primitive mysids live in cold water near or on the bottom.

Most noteworthy for us are the somewhat shrimp like euphausiids,[5] the "kril" of fishermen, which are highly important in the plankton of colder northern and southern waters; they sometimes constitute nearly the whole catch in the plankton nets. They may be an inch or two in length. Generally they are colorless and transparent, but some are conspicuously red in color. Brilliant light organs are characteristic. They may live near the bottom but rise to the surface for spawning in great swarms. Sometimes one may see the surface of the ocean blood-red with the dense shoals of small shrimp, affording rich nourishment for fish and birds. They are a favorite food of whalebone whales. It was found that in the cold

5. Once grouped with some other families in the order Schizopoda, but now regarded as more closely related to the Decapoda.

waters of Davis Strait, the maximum number of whales occured in just the regions where the greatest number of euphausiid crustacea were found.

The Entomostraca comprises the cladocera, the copepods, the ostracods and the cirripedes or barnacles. The cladocera are nearly always prominent in fresh-water plankton but only a very few genera occur in the sea, being important in neritic waters. The ostracods have a comparatively small number of species in fresh water, chiefly along the bottom, but are highly developed in the oceans, where they rank next to the copepods, and occur from the surface to great depths. Some are highly luminescent. There are Arctic and Antarctic species, and at least one that occurs in upper waters "all the way from the Norwegian Sea to the Antarctic." A notable abyssal species is the giant ostracod that may have a length of one centimeter and is found in the Atlantic, Pacific, and Indian oceans.

FIGURE 16. Giant ostracod, *Gigantocypris agassizii* G. W. Müller (from Murray and Hjort).

Barnacles are the only crustacea (other than parasitic species) that, as adults, give up all freedom of movement from place to place and live attached to solid objects.[6] The immobility of a "barnacle" is proverbial. Barnacles are, of course, well known as pests on the

6. The burrowing isopods, Limnoria and others, so destructive to unprotected wood structures, live relatively sedentary lives in the narrow self-made homes; but they are not attached or incapable of some locomotion.

bottoms of ships. In development they go through a remarkable metamorphosis from the fertilized egg to the sedentary adult, and mostly while drifting or swimming aimlessly in the plankton. When liberated from the eggshell, they have minute triangular bodies with a long "tail" and three pairs of limbs: this is the *nauplius*. With successive molts they acquire more appendages through several stages of nauplius and metanauplius. At the same time they undergo change of form until they appear like small ostracods with body enclosed in a bivalved shell. After swimming in this form for a short while, they attach "head-to" on some favorable object, cement themselves firmly, and undergo further metamorphosis into the adult barnacle. Some have long flexible "necks," bearing at the free end the body enclosed in a white shell; these are the well-known "goose barnacles." Others, the "acorn barnacles," are strictly sessile, the body enclosed in a cup-shaped shell, with its flat base cemented to the substratum. Barnacles are among the most numerous of benthonic animals. Prominence of larval stages in the plankton depends upon breeding seasons, since the duration of free-swimming life is short. Some species of warm-water barnacles are widely distributed in the several oceans.

It is the copepods, that almost everywhere and all the time, are important in the plankton. In their elongate bodies, two parts are readily recognized—a long oval forward part and a tail-like hinder portion. On the fore body are various paired limbs, including long antennae and several mouth parts, and usually there is a single eye. *Monoculus* was the first scientific name applied to copepods. Ancient Italian fishermen are said to have known some of the larger copepods as "occiussi" or eye-bearers. They are all small, generally one to three or four millimeters in length, although there are species much less than a millimeter long and a very few that are substantially larger: *Calanus hyperboreus* attains a length of 9 millimeters. Probably no other group of animals of corresponding rank has such a wide distribution and is of like importance as affording food for other animals. They occur in virtually all fresh waters, small or large, temporary or permanent. They are at all depths in lakes or oceans. Some are in subterranean waters, some in debris or wet moss above water, some in the wet sand of beaches a short distance landward from the line of high tide.

With such multiplicity of habitats, it is natural that copepods should be notably diversified in modes of locomotion, in feeding habit, and in structure of mouth parts. Some (harpacticoids) with more or less worm-like bodies are formed for creeping amidst debris or sand grains, and have appendages around the mouth adapted for

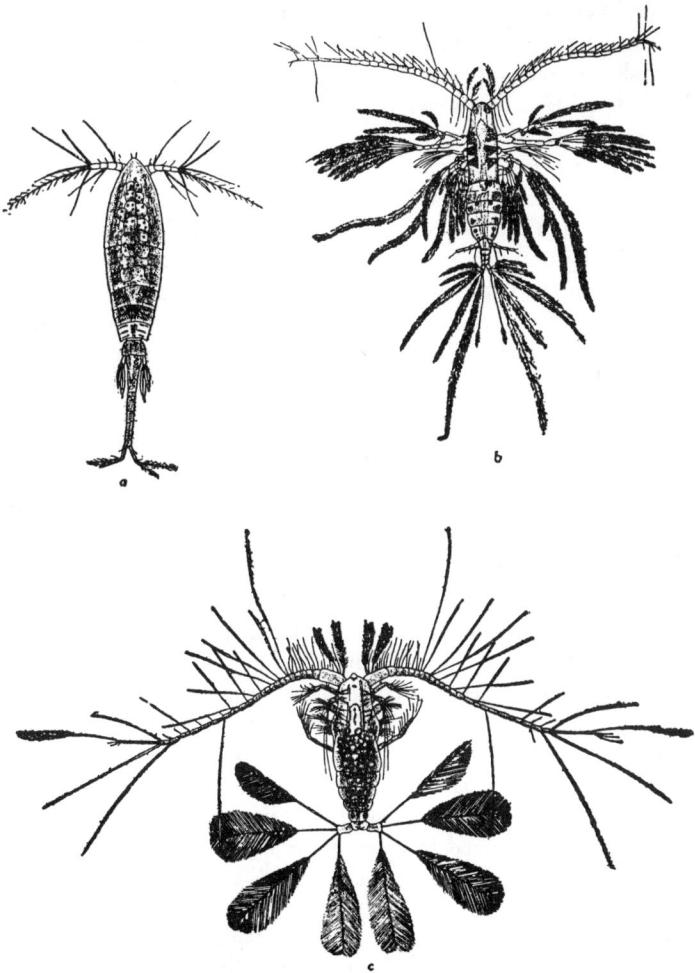

FIGURE 17. Copepods. (a) *Lubbockia squillimana*. (b) *Augaptilus filig-erus*. (c) *Calocalanus pavo*. (All after Giesbrecht). In (b) and (c) are seen the extreme development of plumose setae as so-called "flotation processes."

scraping up food. Others (cyclopoids) are active leapers in the water and have mouth parts formed for seizing small objects of prey as they come upon such victims. Still others (calanoids), although capable of strong swimming movements, habitually "tread water," keeping fanlike appendages about the mouth moving with almost incredible frequency of movement, up to sixty strokes per second: the lively activity of these limbs keeps the body at a fixed level, or raises it to a favored level; at the same time, it draws the water toward the copepod in a "feeding vortex" and passes it through an extremely fine sieve to screen out minute algae, fine debris, and even bacteria. When a mass of these fine particles has accumulated in the food chamber between the appendages, another specialized part pushes the ball of food into the mouth. It is the copepods of the last mentioned group, the "filterers," that play the leading part in the economy of the open sea. There are thousands of species of copepods in the sea, and hundreds are planktonic, but a comparatively few account for the great prominence of the group in the plankton, and certain species of Calanus are most noteworthy.

Various oceanographers have testified to the significance of copepods in the ecology of the sea. Hjort says: "It may safely be asserted that they are the chief consumers of these minute plants and in turn serve as food for larger animals."[7] Gran remarks that "The chief consumers of plants in the sea are undoubtedly copepods.[8] "It is an undoubted fact," says F. S. Russell,[9] "that the Copepods are the most numerous components of the animal plankton community." Sverdrup, Johnson, and Fleming conclude that "the planktonic copepods are doubtless the chief diatom grazers";[10] and, they add, "The greatest number of adult herring are caught in calanus-rich waters."[11] Obviously, however, the deep-living copepods cannot feed upon living algae; presumably their food is the bacteria and the fine detritus, resulting from the breaking up of the dead bodies of organisms that lived in upper waters.

The natural history of marine copepods is obviously too broad a

7. Murray and Hjort, *Depths of the Ocean*, p. 579.
8. *Ibid.*, p. 382.
9. F. S. Russell, "The study of Copepods as a factor in oceanic economy," *Proc. Fifth Pan-Pacific Science Congress*, Canada, III, 2025.
10. Sverdrup, Johnson, and Fleming, *The Oceans*, p. 772.
11. *Ibid.*, p. 907.

subject to be summarized satisfactorily in a few pages. Only a few general comments can be made. Apparently temperature has much to do with the horizontal and vertical distribution of copepods, and with their form, as well. Since viscosity changes notably in correlation with temperature, one cannot readily tell, of course, whether the response is to temperature or viscosity. There are copepods in cold waters, of fairly large size and trim bodies; and there are copepods in warmer waters, smaller in size and armed with the most strikingly plumose appendages, as is shown in fig. 17, p. 231. There are those that have large vertical ranges in northern and southern waters; others are bathypelagic, occurring only in deep water.

Most fresh water and some marine copepods carry the fertilized eggs in paired or unpaired sacs attached to the body of the female, but most of the pelagic marine copepods cast the eggs out in the water. The females, after one mating, are more or less independent of males. The sperm carried in pockets will suffice for successive hatches of eggs—and perhaps serve for the remainder of the spawning life of the female. The young emerging from the egg is a nauplius much like that of a barnacle but without the long tail-like appendage. By successive molts with change of form the young pass through a definite number of five (or six) nauplial and six copepodid stages, the sixth copepodid being the last or adult stage in which mating and spawning occur.

Calanus finmarchicus is one of the most important of all plankton organisms. It is a fairly large copepod (up to 5 millimeters in length), and is particularly prominent in the colder waters, as in the Norwegian and Greenland seas. With oil-rich body, it may occur in such vast numbers as to discolor the surface of the sea and to afford rich nourishment to whalebone whales. In colder waters it plays a great part in the surface plankton, but it also has a large vertical range. In southern regions this copepod appears only in deep, cold water. In the north it spends the winter, as late immature stages, in deeper waters, but rises to the surface in the spring for spawning; three or more broods of young are liberated during the spring and summer.

One of the largest of all copepods is *Calanus hyperboreus*, which attains a length of 9 millimeters, or more (more than one-third of an inch). It is reported as being a purely surface plankter in Arctic waters where it lives at 5 to 10 meters.[12] In the somewhat warmer waters of the Norwegian Sea it is found at various depths from the upper waters to 1,000 meters. Off the Newfoundland Banks, it was taken by Hjort only in hauls below 200 meters, where the water was 5 to 6 degrees in temperature. Beneath the warm surface waters of the Sargasso Sea it was caught in numbers in the colder waters at 1,000 meters.

The collection of the "Carnegie" as reported by Wilson[13] revealed no such great aggregations of copepods in the Pacific as are known in the North Atlantic; yet the Pacific seemed much richer in numbers of species and probably in total numbers of individual copepods. The pattern of distribution seems to be different for the great oceans. His observations on vertical stratification and on vertical migrations of copepods are also of much interest.

No better or more concise summary of the service of copepods in the organization of life in the sea could be given than that phrased, more than fifty years ago, by Professor W. K. Brooks.[14]

"We have already seen that the eucopepods[15] are the chief intermediaries between the microorganisms of the ocean and the larger and higher marine animals; that they prey upon the protophytes and protozoa, and in their turn supply either directly or indirectly most of the food for the large inhabitants of the water; that most pelagic larvae feed upon them; that they are the food of the great pelagic banks of pteropods and heteropods (mollusks), of many coelenterates, of the young of most fishes, and of some of the most abundant and important adult fishes, like the herring; and that the sea-birds, the cetacea [whales] and in fact almost all the larger pelagic animals, prey upon animals which in their turn prey upon copepods."

In general, the abundance of copepods in the surface waters of northern regions seems to be more seasonal than in southern waters, where breeding may occur all the year and the catches be fairly

12. "The wealth of animal life in the Arctic is largely due to the enormous abundance of this species. [*C. hyperboreus*], which constitute the food of the Arctic whales."—Hjort, p. 639, 40.

13. Wilson, Charles B. Copepods of the Plankton Gathered During the Last Cruise of the Carnegie. Carnegie Institution of Washington, Publication 536. Washington, 1942.

14. Brooks, *The Genus Salpa. loc. cit.*

15. Eucopepods, or true copepods, in distinction from certain parasitic crustacea, classed with the copepods.

uniform regardless of season. The dense populations are, however, those of cold waters, while the sparser communities of tropical regions are more diversified in respect to species.

This concludes consideration of the "invertebrates" proper; but, between invertebrates and the vertebrates of the phylum chordata, there is a transition group of *Protochordata*, which have special interest to the student of animal evolution. Many of the protochordates are sedentary or burrowing in habit, but the group is of particular concern to us here because one division of the protochordates, the tunicates, is of great importance in the plankton. The name tunicate implies that the bodies of adults are enclosed in a tunic, or mantle, which is generally of a resistant material related to cellulose. As adults most of them are entirely unlike vertebrates, and many kinds may reproduce by budding; yet all have, at least in larval stages, gill slits and the rudiment of a skeletal axis called notochord. The chordate young, indeed, bear a rough resemblance to young tadpoles. There are three classes of tunicates. Those that undergo a radical metamorphosis, to become, externally, rather formless, sack-like adults that live sedentary lives, are the ascidians, "sea squirts" or "seed peaches," so often seen in crowded formations on wharf piles. Their young are planktonic before metamorphosis, but only for a brief period. Another group is the Larvacea, in which the tadpole form and the free-swimming habit persist; they are exclusively planktonic, sometimes abundant, but small in size, or about half an inch in length. Generally they are in the upper 200 meters, but some are found in deeper tropical waters; a few live in cold northern waters.

The third group includes larger tunicates which are also independent of the bottom. The salpas live in barrel-shaped tunics, which may be beautifully colored and irridescent, and are often united in chains up to 20 feet in length. Individual "barrels" may be an inch or more in length. Because of their number and size the salpas are generally familiar to those who observe the surface of the sea in warmer regions. When carried by warm currents they may be found rather far north. A century ago the famous Norwegian scientist, Michael Sars, recognized Salpa as "a portent of successful herring fishery"! Hjort mentions that some species common in warm surface waters have been found at depths below 1,000 meters in the

Antarctic. Salpa and Doliolum are the most common genera. Their translucent tunics have a high percentage of water. Species of Pyrosoma (fire body), found in both surface and deep water have most attracted the interest of seafarers, because of their brilliant luminosity. The bodies are sometimes aggregated in great masses several feet in length and nearly a foot in diameter. They give a brilliant phosphorescent light, both in the water and, as captured specimens, when touched with the finger.

Salpa and its relatives have an extremely fine filtering apparatus which enables them to screen out from water passing through the pharyngeal pores the most minute marine algae, coccolithophores, peridinians, etc. which can rarely be captured in the man-made nets. Salpa, in turn, seems to furnish food to turtles and other larger animals.

The feeding mechanism of tunicates is particularly to be mentioned. These little plankton animals and microplankton feeders have placed oceanographers greatly in their debt by serving as collectors. Water drawn in through the mouth and passed through the micro-fine pores in the wall of the pharynx, acting for gill slits, is so effectively strained that the catch of the living filter proves "a peculiar gold mine" for rare pelagic algae whose bodies pass through the meshes of finest silk and, therefore, could not be captured by plankton nets; "In fact," says Hjort, "Stein, the well-known specialist on Protozoa who had no plankton-catcher to aid him in his researches, got the best part of his material from the stomachs of Salpae, and was thus able to write his valuable initiatory monograph on peridinieae."[16] "And this too," he adds, "was the plan adopted at first for studying diatoms, so that our knowledge of pelagic genera like *Asteromphalus* and *Asterolampra* is largely due to the examination of the stomachs of Salpae."[17] Furthermore, it was the catches of minute algae made by small tunicates that seem to have prompted Lohmann to try a new appliance, the centrifuge, for separating the finer organisms from the water and concentrating them for study. This, in turn, led to the concept of the nannoplankton. Hydrobiologists owe a monument to the tunicates!

16. Murray and Hjort, *op. cit.*, p. 308.
17. *Ibid.*, p. 381.

Summary (for chapters 15 and 16)

1. The space on earth inhabited by drifting and swimming life vastly exceeds that occupied by all other kinds of life in water and on land. The great part of the organic world lives adrift as plankton.

2. Practically speaking, the plankton world as such was revealed to science only a century ago, when Müller's "fine pelagic net" was brought into use as a mode of collecting.

3. The use of the centrifuge for collecting plankton, begun less than forty years ago, made possible the effective exploration of the open waters for the more minute algae comprising the dwarf plankton. Since many drifters (medusae and salpa-chains, for example) are quite large, even a meter or two in diameter, or many feet in length, and since some are too small or differ too little from water in specific gravity, for capture by nets or centrifuge, we can differentiate plankton into four groups by size: macroplankton, microplankton, nannoplankton, and ultraplankton.

4. Marine plankton differs markedly from fresh water plankton in the greater variety of organisms that spend their entire lives adrift (holoplankters), and, as to neritic plankton, in the occurrence, seasonally at least, of the larvae of virtually all animals that mature and breed on the bottom (meroplankters).

5. A distinctive feature of the conditions of life of marine plankton is that their homes are always moving, because of the circulation of sea water through currents, drifts, and other shifts of position. Interchange of organisms between progressive currents and eddies probably plays a great part in maintenance of populations.

6. The zone of original production in the sea is the uppermost 200 meters; but, through drainage from the lands, the terrestrial photosynthetic plants contribute to the nutrition of the sea; requisite inorganic materials come in part also from the land. Waters near the coasts and currents carrying such waters are particularly prolific in plankton.

7. Much nutritive material, subsiding into the deeper waters, is lost for the time. Upwelling and other upward displacements of deeper waters are favorable to the local development of plankton. The warming of the waters of cold currents by admixture of warm waters of other currents makes for plankton growth and reproduction. Areas of subsidence of surface waters are generally areas of

poverty in surface plankton. The deeper waters of such regions may be richer.

8. In the sea remote from land, the animals of all depths are dependent upon the photosynthetic organisms of the uppermost 200 meters. The rain of falling bodies and wastes is consumed at all levels while successions of bodies and wastes descend farther and farther. Plankton occurs at all depths. There must be a generally diminishing density of populations with depth; but the rule is not simple or regular. The greatest abundance of plant life is not in the extreme upper waters but at a depth of some 50 meters. The greatest numbers of small crustacea have been reported as prevailing below 200 meters.

9. Because of oceanic currents, the fall of materials from the surface is generally not in a vertical but in an oblique direction. It may change angular direction in falling because of conflicting currents, or it may be retarded by the intervention of cold waters of high salinity at intermediate levels.

10. The excess of green pasturage in the upper waters is not as great as might be expected. Apparently it is the rate of reproduction of these organisms, the "turn-over," that maintains an adequate basic food supply.

11. Temperature and viscosity have much to do with distribution, geographic and bathymetric. Some organisms are broadly tolerant in respect to these conditions; these may have wide distribution in surface waters. Most plankters are incapable of withstanding considerable changes in temperature and viscosity and, therefore, have restricted ranges in surface water; but some of these may thrive both in upper waters of cold regions and in deep cold waters beneath warm surface areas. Pressure seems a secondary factor.

12. Various kinds of organisms, even many of only microscopic size, may at times occur in such countless numbers and in such closeness of association as to cause conspicuous discolorations of the surface waters over very great areas.

13. Many kinds of marine plankters, including protozoans, jellyfishes, worms, euphausiids, tunicates, and others, are highly luminescent.

14. The catches in plankton nets at different times and places may include almost every kind of organism that lives anywhere

in the sea (eggs, young, or adult), but, on the whole, with collecting at all seasons and places, the bulk of the catch will be made up of radiolarians, arrowworms, pteropods, copepods, and tunicates.

15. As a general rule, individual plankters are larger in size and much more numerous in colder waters; but by far the greater number of species are to be found in the warmer waters.

16. The organisms of colder and therefore, more viscous waters are generally simpler or trimmer in form. Extensions of the body surface, through plumose appendages and otherwise, are common in copepods and other plankters of warmer and less viscous waters. Smallness of size and proliferations from body and appendages give greater surface in proportion to weight and greater "resistance to sinking" in the more fluid water.

17. Much remains to be learned about the natural history of plankton, the distribution of particular plankters, and its relations to the conditions of the environment.

CHAPTER 17

Life on the Bottom: The Benthos

Sitters and Creepers

IN THE FIRST PARAGRAPH OF CHAPTER XIII THERE WERE SUGGES-
tions of the richness of organic life on wave-beaten rocks, at
the bottom in coastal regions, and, at least here or there, in the
open waters. In other sections we have emphasized the dilution of nutritive material and oxygen. The apparent incongruity between the
pictures of lush organic communities and the statements about environmental conditions disappears in great measure when we reflect
on certain physical conditions of the environment, particularly on
the dynamics of the sea as described in the chapters entitled "Sea
Water in Motion." In whatever concentration the requisite materials exist, the fact that the sea water is virtually always moving
means that an animal may remain in one position and have a constant
service of water carrying food in suspension and oxygen in solution.
On land an animal must either roam or starve. In quiet lakes and
ponds the aquatic animal must be able to move itself or to keep the
water about it in movement; most sedentary animals of still water,
such as fresh water mussels and Vorticella, have both capacities:
not only do they have means of drawing water toward them, but
they also retain some ability to move from one place to another as
conditions may require. Only in streams, or where water is kept
in motion by outside forces, can there be a substantial population
of animals permanently fixed in position: fresh-water sponges and
Bryozoa are examples; but the irregular fluctuations of level of
brooks and rivers introduce special hazards, and, besides, the condi-

tions of turbulence in flowing streams are generally unfavorable for the development of plankton to serve as food for sessile animals. The sedentary animals of streams, snails, insect larvae, hydra, are generally not sessile, or fixed in positions, but merely slow to move. It is notable, indeed, that the actually sessile colonies of sponges and moss animalcules (Bryozoa) are just those animals that have developed a system of "internal buds" (gemmules and statoblasts, respectively), which may survive unfavorable conditions and drift away to start new colonies. In contrast to fresh waters of all types, the continually moving but relatively unchanging sea water offers a very different picture of life.

At any rate, a notable and distinctive feature of the organic world in the sea is the high development of populations of fixed animals of many types. On reefs between the tide lines, we sometimes see solid beds of oysters,[1] in which the several individuals, barring accident or interference by man, will never change their abiding places. On buoys, boat bottoms, or rocks we see thick blankets of fixed tunicates, hydroids, Bryozoa, and barnacles. Through the glass-bottom boat there are revealed on the bottom elaborate and colorful gardens of fixed corals, sea anemones, gorgonias, and sponges. There are also large and diversified populations of worms, echinoderms, and mollusks, with relatively fixed homes in the bottom, often with permanent houses constructed of organic and inorganic materials, or excavated in rock or wood. Sedentary animals, without powers of locomotion, may thrive in the sea.

Again, there are in the sea many animals of the bottom and shores that move about, regularly or irregularly, showing all degrees of capacity for locomotion: there are snails and conchs that creep slowly; there are crabs and lobsters that may dart rapidly from place to place within a more or less restricted range. With bodies or shells of such weight as to keep them from being independent of the bottom, these animals do not properly constitute a part of the nekton or free-swimming life. All animals associated with the bottom are grouped in the benthos, but, quite obviously, the benthos includes animals of two very distinct types as distinguished by habits of life: the sitters, on the one hand, and the walkers or creepers, on the other. For these two categories I would propose the terms:

1. Other kinds of animals, fixed or crawling, are always mixed in with the oysters, however continuous the bed of oysters may be.

edreobenthos,[2] for the strictly sedentary, fixed organisms, plant or animal; and *herpetobenthos*,[3] for those that may walk or crawl, the peripatetic benthonts, whether slow or rapid in movement. Edreobenthos, most prominent in the sea, is but scantily represented in fresh water, and there chiefly by plants and, among animals, by sponges and Bryozoa, with their characteristic means of self-preservation previously mentioned. Herpetobenthos, on the other hand, occurs abundantly and in great diversity in both fresh and salt water: there are snails, crustacea, and worms in both, there are many kinds of insect larvae in fresh water, and there are starfishes and their diverse relatives in the sea; other types could be mentioned for either medium.

Sessile (edreobenthonic) animals without capacity for locomotion can abound in the sea, not merely because the surrounding water is in motion, but also because the environment offers a peculiar combination of constant or periodic change and relative stability. Unlike the moving rivers and brooks, the sea presents nearly everywhere relatively stable conditions of depth, light, and chemicals in solution. There may be marked changes in these environmental conditions, as in the intertidal zone; but these changes are more or less *dependable*—and dependable through long periods of time, so that adaptations to them have been acquired by the slow processes of evolutionary change.

Life Near the Shores—the Littoral

Richest in number of individual animals visible to the naked eye, and in diversity of kinds, is the *littoral* zone, which, as previously defined, extends from the upper tide line to a depth of some 100-200 fathoms—or as far out as there is light enough at the bottom to permit the growth of benthonic plants. There are several reasons for the relative populousness of this region. The shallowness and the illumination of the bottom favor the growth of photosynthetic organisms, the "producers," from top to bottom. Mixing by waves and tides is here more active and complete. Better vertical circulation promotes turnover of the nutritive substances, bringing them back from the less well lighted bottom into the uppermost and better

2. The prefix is from Greek—*edraios*, stationary.
3. The prefix is from Greek—*herpetos*, walking or crawling. Acknowledgement is made to Professor P. H. Epps for help in devising these terms from the Greek.

illuminated waters, where they are most effectively used. Drainage from the land comes first into the littoral region. In respect to the photosynthetic organisms, it is almost exclusively in this region that we find the homes of the larger algae—the greens, browns, and reds —and of the few seed plants that have invaded the margins of the oceans. Of microalgae, the diatoms are particularly important on the bottom in shallow water. Bottoms exposed between tides may often have a distinctly yellowish color given by the diatoms in dense populations.

It is true that in littoral regions waves and tides cause conditions of turbulence, sometimes quite extreme; the benthonic animals must have become adapted to withstand this turbulence. Kelps and other seaweeds may have "hold-fasts" of some kind; mussels attach themselves by brushes of small but strong threads; oysters and barnacles are able to cement themselves to firm surfaces; worms live in tubes cemented to rock or rooted in the bottom; some crustacea burrow into the sand or mud; the mollusks that are known as "shipworms," Teredo and others, readily burrow into wharf piles, boat bottoms, or driftwood. The rock-inhabiting clam even burrows into solid rock that is not too hard. These are only examples of the many successful adaptations for maintenance of fixed residence in strongly or even violently moving water, which, in turn, brings food and oxygen to animals without capacity or need to travel in search for the necessities of life.

Animals of the littoral must also be adapted to periodic or, sometimes, irregular changes in conditions of salinity, pressure, and light. The extent of vertical mixing in waters close to the coasts offers a contrast to the conditions in oceanic regions, where falling bodies and wastes have a long way to go to the bottom and the materials carried down by them can be restored to circulation above only by slow, round-about, and time-consuming movements of water masses. We have seen in another place (p. 141) that much of the "upwelling" that brings back to the surface nutritive substance from some distance below occurs near the coasts on western sides of continents; but the material brought up may have originated offshore.

As the tides and the waves introduce hazards in coastal waters, so does the drainage from the land. There must be wide fluctuations in salinity, and other chemical conditions, with the irregular distribution of outflow channels (rivers and creeks) and with the fluctuations in volume and composition of the discharges. Seasonal and diurnal changes of temperature are far greater along shore than in true oceanic waters; changes with latitude are also more marked near the coasts. Drainage from lands is not all nutritive material: much inorganic sand and mud is carried to sea, where great deltas are built by the larger rivers, and "flats" with various mixtures of sand and mud appear in bays and harbors. The littoral region itself forms deposits in which organic wastes constitute a major element.[4]

It is not surprising that, with the almost infinite variety of home surroundings in littoral regions, the greatest number of species is found there.[5] In the restless coastal waters Nature presents us with a marvelous multiplicity of solutions to the problems arising from the special vicissitudes of life.

The allusions to vicissitudes and the previous suggestion of dependability in changes may seem, at first thought, to be in conflict. The contradiction is more apparent than real. The worm called Chaetopterus lives with its little guest crab in a U-shaped tube almost entirely buried in the sand flat lying between the lines of high and low tide. Only the narrow openings at each end of the tube, a little above the sand and several inches apart, give evidence on the exposed flat of the presence of the concealed animals. The greater buried portion of the tube enlarges from each end to a fairly capacious chamber between the bends of the U. There worm and crab lie bathed in stored sea water while the flat above bakes in the direct rays of the sun. But the tide gone out will turn back: the salinity that went down as the tide ebbed, will rise with the flood.[6] Worm and crab could have achieved this mode of living only because the tide is regular enough to insure that, twice each day, the mud-flat and the small openings of the house will be submerged to permit circulation through the sack of new water laden with food and oxygen. So, also, the thick-shelled barnacles can live on the rocks between tides, because they have "learned" to close on the ebb and open as the water comes back on the dependable flood. Oysters may

4. Reference may be made to the brief discussion of terrigenous deposits in Chapter VIII, (p. 114, above).

5. The larger divisions of the animal kingdom are reviewed in the chapter on plankton. All of these, except the Chaetognaths, are represented in the littoral benthos.

6. Referring to conditions at Beaufort, N. C., where salinity is lowered with the ebb tide and raised with the high tide.

clamp shut when the ebb tide brings water of intolerably low salinity, but open to feed again when the flood tide restores favorable conditions.

There are, of course, restricted regions where at times the changes are more extreme or enduring. In such cases, whole populations of many kinds of animals are destroyed; only the most tolerant, if there are such, will survive; but, with restoration of measurable dependability of conditions of life, invaders from more fortunate regions will wander in to re-establish a living community.

Deep-Sea Life—Benthic Life

What has been said applies more particularly to the *intertidal* and *eulittoral* divisions of the littoral.[7] The deeper *sublittoral* shades imperceptibly at some 200-400 meters (roughly, one-eighth to one-fourth of a mile, varying with conditions) of depth into the *archibenthic*, or continental deep-sea fauna, and the *abyssal*, or true deep-sea fauna. Since the one-thousand fathom line marks generally the base of the continental slope, the abyssal fauna is well below a mile in depth. In the continuous absence of effective sunlight, there can be no green plants—no synthesis of organic matter. Obviously, then, the benthic animals must depend for nutrition upon what drifts out from the littoral or falls from the illuminated superficial layers of water. It is equally plain that life could not have originated here; the ancestors of the present benthic organisms must have wandered out from the littoral, and could have become established in the deep only after the development of prolific life in the lighted littoral and upper pelagic zones.

Nevertheless, there is a characteristic abyssal fauna; for the species that "discovered" the depths of the ocean could have done so only as, in the long course of evolutionary history, they developed the special adaptations for the new and peculiar conditions of the abyss. Among characteristic animals of the great depths are the glass sponges (Hexactinellidae) and the long-stalked echinoderms—the

7. See p. 180 and footnote 6.
8. For good diagrammatic indications of the zones and discussions of them, see Sverdrup et al., 1942, p. 275, fig. 67, or W. C. Allee and Karl P. Schmidt, *Ecological Animal Geography*, New York: Wiley, p. 218, fig. 18.

sea-lilies or crinoids—animals with stems rooted in the bottom to hold them above the soft ooze. Some of these are very large: Murray[9] tells of "glass sponges" (hexactinellids) from the deep sea, three or four feet in diameter and of hydroids (Monocanthus) three feet in height—gigantic sizes for these groups. There are shrimp of the abyss with extremely long limbs, and there are special groups of deep-sea fishes. These, like the glass sponges and the deep-sea holothuroids (sea cucumbers), are not found at all in the more turbulent waters of the littoral. Many animals of the deep have "developed special apparatus for catching the minute shells and particles of food that fall from the surface water."[10]

Conditions of life in the depths are notably different from those in shallow coastal regions. Here there is stillness—no violent wave movements, no strong tidal currents. Even the slow drifts, horizontal or vertical, that are traceable to conditions of wind, temperature, or salinity elsewhere, can scarcely be felt. We know now, of course, that there can be "internal waves" and turbulence phenomena of some sorts (see p. 154, above). Streamlining of bodies is less necessary, and some deep-sea animals have bodies that would ill adapt them for life in more turbulent waters. The temperature is always low, the supplies of oxygen (in the absence of green plants) only what was brought down with surface waters at some place of subsidence, perhaps far away and long ago (in months or years). It is also a region of great pressure, equivalent to hundreds of atmospheres, or even a thousand; but this is probably of least biological significance, since the pressure is within the body as well as without. Perhaps most notable of the conditions of existence is their *evenness*. There is no diurnal or seasonal change of light or temperature; there are no storms or perceptible currents. From place to place in the large there will be differences in pressure, slight differences in temperature, changes in character of bottom and in amount of food supply; but doubtless these changes, over considerable distances, are beyond the experiences of individual animals.

In such circumstances, it is natural both that the number of abyssal species should be relatively small and that those which are peculiar to the deep bottom should have comparatively wide distribution.

9. John Murray, "The General Conditions of Existence and Distribution of Marine Organisms," *Annual Report of the Smithsonian Institution* (1896).
10. Murray and Hjort, *The Depth of the Ocean*, p. 426.

Although many kinds of animals of the bottom live in the deep, and certain families, and even orders, are peculiar to it, yet the number of known abyssal genera is not nearly comparable to the number of genera in littoral regions, and the number of species per genus is also relatively small. Within the species, the populations are also sparse, in adjustment to the limited food supply. It is, indeed, a general rule in animal geography that the number of bottom animals per given area is in inverse ratio to the distance from shore—not, primarily, to the depth. The lack of marked diversity in physical conditions must have influenced the diversification in species, the scarcity of food and oxygen undoubtedly underlies the paucity of individuals. Benthic animals must of necessity be carnivores or scavengers, and the food that falls from above or drifts from the littoral has to support all the animal life of intermediate as well as terminal zones.

The distribution of life in the deep can not be expected to be uniform, since, naturally, there must be some relation between the density or sparsity of animals on the dark bottom and the amount of food descending from above.[11] This means some sort of relation between density of bottom populations on the one hand, and, on the other, density of surface population and depth, or the number of strata of scavengers and carnivores ready to devour the falling material; of course the animals of each level send their own dead bodies and wastes toward the bottom. Another factor influencing the abundance of falling food is the amount of destruction of life in the upper waters where convergence of currents contrasting in temperature and salinity creates conditions incompatible with the survival of the current-borne organisms. Although not all the ocean floor has been surveyed as to its fauna, explorations indicate that no extensive part of the floor is without benthic animals.

Coastward, we find that terrigenous bottoms (see p. 114, above) are richest in food substance—and these extend much farther out in some regions than in others. In the North Atlantic, for example, land-affected bottom extends very much farther out from the North American coast than from the coasts of Europe and North Africa.[12]

11. Bearing in mind that, because particularly of currents and drifts, organic materials may not accumulate on the bottom *directly beneath* the place of their original formation in the upper waters.

12. See Map IV in Murray and Hjort, *op. cit.*

The bottom beyond the mud line at about 100 fathoms has been termed by Murray "the great feeding ground" for bottom animals.[13] The surface layers of the deep-sea oozes (see p. 114, above) farther out yield a good deal of nutritive material to the bottom animals that may engorge themselves with it. Globigerina ooze seems particularly rich in food material. "In the eastern Atlantic, at any rate," says Hjort,[14] *"most of the fauna of the continental slope live on globigerina ooze."* At the other extreme is the red clay bottom: it is red clay because, at great depths, so little other than insoluble and indigestible mineral matter (including iron oxide which gives the red color) can ever reach the bottom. Areas of red clay, such as are found in the central South Pacific, are relatively barren regions.

It should be remarked finally that not all species of animals are restricted to either littoral or benthic zones. There are what are called *eurybathic* types—those that seem equally at home in depths covering a wide range. According to Ekman, a polychaete worm, Amphictera, is found from the littoral to 5,000 meters and a brittle star from 5 to 4,500 meters, not to mention others of very wide ranges.[15]

How the Bottom Fauna is Taken

For collecting attached or creeping animals near the shores, various sorts of dipping, scraping, and raking apparatus may be employed. The simplest is the baglike net on a ring attached to the end of a pole: the ring may be modified to have a section of the circumference made straight and beveled to form a scraper; or the scraping part may be provided with sharp teeth to make a rake. Seines and other sorts of nets will take crawlers but are used chiefly for swimming animals. In deeper water other kinds of apparatus must be used. The *dredge* was perhaps the first mechanical collector employed for taking animals from the deeper bottom. A deep net of suitable mesh is attached to the rear of a rectangular or triangular steel frame. To the front part of the frame a bridle is linked, while the free end of the bridle is connected by a swivel to the end of the

13. *Ibid.,* p. 427.
14. *Ibid.,* p. 430.
15. See Sverdrup, Johnson, and Fleming, *The Oceans,* p. 806, where ten species are listed as occurring from the littoral out to depths of much more than one mile.

hauling line. The two long sides of the rectangular frame, or all sides of a triangular frame, are given such a form as will cause them to slide over the bottom, or, if preferred, to dig into the bottom. If the bottom is rough enough to cause much wear on the net trailing behind the frame, an apron of canvas on each side will give it protection. Behind the net there may be trailed a bar with masses of shredded rope to serve as *tangles,* which are very effective in catching starfishes and such other animals as will adhere to the threads.

The several forms of trawls are also very effective in taking animals free on the bottom, as well as swimmers living close to the bottom. In the Sigsbee and the improved Tanner *beam trawls,* there are U-shaped runners, held apart by a beam of steel, 3 to 10 feet long. A deep net, widely open at the front, is attached to the rear of the

FIGURE 18. Old-type Blake trawl with double lead-line to serve whichever side is down. Note the free cork-line within. (Courtesy U. S. Fish and Wild Life Service).

runners. Around the free front lips of the net are attached small lead sinkers to ensure that whichever lip is down will keep close on the bottom. Corks on a free cross line within the mouth of the net will swing upward, whichever face of the net is up, and so help to keep the net open. Well back inside the long net, and attached to it all around, is another funnel-shaped net. The fish, crabs, and other animals that pass through the small rear opening of the funnel are securely trapped in the hinder part of the main net. When the trawl is hauled aboard, the trap is opened by unlashing the bottom end. Fine plankton nets, to be described later, may be attached to the frame of the trawl to capture the minute animals that would pass through the coarse-meshed bag of the trawls. The much larger *otter trawl* will best be described in the next chapter.

The trawl is not intended to take animals which live in the bottom, but rather those on or a little above the bottom. The dredge, especially one of the plowing type, actually digs out many burrowing animals, and can be dragged for as long a distance as is desired, depending on the presumed density of population. Minute organisms pass through it, of course, unless the bag is of canvas, as in a *mud dredge*, which fills quickly with the superficial mud or ooze.

A better device for taking moderate-sized portions of the bottom with the contained organisms is the *bottom sampler*, originally designed by the Dane, C. G. J. Petersen (1911). This is a brass cylinder, a foot long and split in half, with the two parts hinged together at the top. While the mechanism is being lowered the half-cylinders are spread widely apart below, like two great jaws. When the sampler rests on the bottom and the suspensory apparatus is relieved of the weight of the cylinder, the bar holding the jaws apart against the action of strong springs drops out of place; the springs and the weight of the apparatus cause the jaws to come together, biting out a chunk of substratum a foot square and several inches deep. The depth of the bite varies with the softness of the bottom. In a modified form of bottom-sampler, the catches that hold the jaws apart may be released by a mechanical "messenger," sent down the line from above after the grab is on the bottom. The messenger is a brass cylinder of sufficient weight; it is split lengthwise and the two parts are hinged together, so that it can readily be clamped around the line at any time, and allowed to glide down, however long the line may be. The bottom sampler, taking a measured area of surface material, has the obvious advantage of making possible quantitative studies of the density of population of the kinds of organisms that it takes. It also gives a better idea than does the dredge of the character of the non-living bottom material. It must, however, be heavy and be provided with strong springs to enable it to bite into hard bottoms.

When bottom-working apparatus is used at great depths the kind of line used is of great significance. It must be strong enough to withstand the strain of the load to be pulled in—several miles of line paid out is a load in itself. The strain is heightened by the jerking resulting from the roll of the ship. Miles of line have not only weight but also bulk, involving storage space on deck, and space for spare lines; occasionally a line is lost, and reserves must be available. For dredging and trawling the "Challenger" used hemp lines up to nearly an inch in diameter with a greatest length of nearly five miles. They were bulky and, even in the water, their weight was considerable. Furthermore, so that the dredge or trawl might run smoothly on the bottom, a heavy weight was usually attached some hundreds of fathoms above the appliance. The weight would drag on the bottom, while the dredge would trail a considerable distance behind.

It was mentioned on an earlier page (p. 42) that Alexander Agassiz and Captain Sigsbee, on the U. S. Coast Survey steamer "Blake," were successful in substituting wire rope for hemp. The wire rope was made of forty-two fine wires wound about a small tarred hemp line in the middle. As compared with hemp, such lines, of the order of one-third of an inch in diameter, were heavier in water, but they were much stronger and more capable of withstanding sharp strains. They slipped through water more easily and, aboard vessels, required much less space for storage. Before the stout steel rope was introduced, a most important part of the hauling apparatus on the ship, was the large rubber "accumulator," or other elastic device, to compensate for the jerks resulting from the lurching of the vessel in a heavy sea.

Needless to say, important parts of the ship's equipment are drums about which the lines are coiled, strong booms reaching out over the side and, between these, the several pulleys, power winches, and devices for recording the amount of line paid out. For handling such apparatus at great depths, there are required no end of experience and skill in design, manipulation, and seamanship.

Benthonic Animals Useful to Man

Animals that live strictly sedentary lives and those that creep over the bottom or burrow into it are not of mere scientific interest. Among all the commercial products of the sea quite a number of these have high rank in monetary value. Considering only the fisheries of the United States, the oysters of the Atlantic Coast, harvested both from natural "rocks" and private "farms," are second in value only to the salmons of the Pacific Northwest. Other familiar mollusks of the market are the common clams (long-neck clams), quahogs (little-neck clams), and escallops. Here and there over the world many others are used as food: one thinks at once of mussels, abalones, conchs, periwinkles, and octopus. Pearl "oysters" of the Orient—they are not really oysters—yield both pearls of value and, with other mollusks, shells for the manufacture of the better grade of pearl buttons.

Among jointed-leg animals the shrimp seems to take first place, with crabs and lobsters following not far behind. In tables of fishery products the value of each is measured in millions of dollars per annum.

Invertebrates other than mollusks and arthropods must be listed in lower ranks when measured in commercial value. Yet some of these are of substantial importance in particular regions—sponges, for example, in the Mediterranean and in the Gulf of Mexico. Probably no Coelenterates are eaten by man but fine corals are a market product for other reasons. As we have seen (p. 225) some marine worms are esteemed as food in particular regions. Among the echinoderms (starfishes and their relatives), the sea cucumbers, under the name of *trepang* or *bêche-de-mer*, are highly esteemed as food in some parts of the world. The roe of the spiny sea urchins appears as a delicacy in the markets of Peru.

Finally, although a complete list is not attempted, mention should be made of the seaweeds harvested and processed for food, for the preparation of agar, or for extraction of rare chemicals.

Summary

(1) The fact that sea water is everywhere in motion, because of waves, tides, currents, surface and deep drifts, convection currents, upwelling, and internal waves, makes possible a notably high development of more or less fixed populations and crawlers—all commonly and conveniently grouped as "benthos."

(2) Because of marked differences in habits and adaptations, and for the sake of comparison with fauna of fresh water, the benthos should be subdivided into the actually sessile animals without capacity for locomotion and those that move about over the bottom. For these subdivisions, the terms proposed are edreobenthos, for the sessile animals, and herpetobenthos, for the creepers and crawlers. Sharp lines can not be drawn between any groups classified by habit, such as nekton and plankton or nekton and benthos, but the distinction here recognized is at least as definite as that between any of the other groups based on habit of life. Sessile animal life is characteristic of coastal regions, although not entirely restricted to such waters.

(3) Organic production and the turnover of nutritive materials are greatest in littoral or narrowly coastal regions, because hori-

zontal and vertical circulation is more complete, light penetrates to the bottom, and drainage from the land is first received in coastal waters. Only the littoral is the home of the larger algae, the true greens, the browns (except sargassum, in part), and the reds.

(4) Diversity of physical and nutritive conditions and periodic or irregular changes are greatest in true littoral regions. The problems of adaptation for animal life, and the solutions to the problems in the forms of distinct species have there been most diverse. Numbers of individuals and diversity of species have been found by animal geographers to be, broadly speaking, in inverse ratio to distance from shore.

(5) Although the vicissitudes of life in the littoral are greatest because of tides, waves, and land drainage, with its effects on salinity, temperature, and bottom, the fluctuations in physical and nutritive conditions are, by and large, relatively dependable.

(6) Benthic animals live in a dark region, where there can be no original production of organic matter. They may feed upon each other to some extent, but, basically, they are dependent upon what comes from the outside by falling from above or drifting in from the direction of the shore.

(7) In consequence, organic life could not have originated in the deep. Life is presumed to have arisen in littoral regions, from whence the bottom of the sea and the open oceans were "discovered." These great regions became populated as primitive animals developed the adaptations appropriate to the special conditions. There is now a characteristic abyssal fauna, comprising species and larger groups which have no adaptation for life under other conditions.

(8) The deep-sea bottom is a place of relative stillness, darkness, and coldness where life may be presumed to move at a slow pace, the streamline form is not at such a premium, and bodies may have forms that would be disadvantageous in the more turbulent coastal waters.

(9) In really abyssal depths, presumably, there can be no sharp changes of conditions from locality to locality: marked changes in temperature, salinity, and nutrition can be encountered only between places far apart. Truly abyssal species have wide ranges of distribution.

(10) Animal life occurs everywhere over the bottom of the sea. Apparently it is sparse. The distribution is uneven, being governed, it is to be assumed, by the availability of nutritive material, and, therefore, by conditions that prevail in the upper waters. Areas of red clay are most nearly barren.

(11) A few animals are widely tolerant to conditions of depth, being found from the littoral out to depths of several miles.

(12) The bottom-living animals and plants of coastal regions are more easily studied. Animals of the deep are taken only with special apparatus and by laborious manipulations; this fact together with the sparseness of life in the abyss, makes it difficult to gain a quantitative understanding of the populations or a satisfactory knowledge of the natural history of abyssal animals.

CHAPTER 18

Life at Large: The Nekton

Barriers to Distribution

ANIMALS THAT SWIM AND THOSE THAT DRIFT, THE NEKTON AND the plankton, are not separable by an absolute line of division. Non-motile algae must, of course, be carried by the currents. Almost equally at the mercy of outside forces for position in space. are those algae and protozoa with feeble powers of locomotion by microscopic paddles and with insignificant capacities to govern direction of movement. Copepods and other small crustacea swim with greater powers, but even if their movements are rapid for their sizes, they are yet slow moving in comparison with most oceanic currents. Larger shrimp or prawn, several inches in length, are on the border line: where currents are not particularly strong they have, no doubt, substantial capacity to determine their places of habitation. Among the mollusks, the adult squid move backward under considerable power by "jet propulsion"; they are usually regarded as important elements of the nekton. Adult fish in general are definitely swimmers and capable of opposing any current in the ocean with some success; yet eggs and larvae of fish are planktonic. The very young fish must follow the movements of the water, until, at some hardly definable stage of early life, it becomes capable of swimming where it will; having graduated from a planktonic career, it enters into the more or less self-governing nekton; eventually, it may have the task of traveling hundreds of miles back to a proper place for breeding and the launching of new generations for the same old circuit. Turtles, whales, and other marine mammals are definitely nektonic. In this and the following chapter we restrict attention to the marine mammals, adult or well-grown fish, and cephalopods (mainly squid), with some references to the larger crustacea, and to reptiles and birds. All of these animals, comprising the nekton, are relatively high in the scale of life.

In Chapter V we emphasized the continuity of the several oceans that form the one great "ocean-sea," which embraces the earth. We dwelt upon the absence of visible barriers other than continents and islands which may readily be by-passed by the circulating waters. It is all one great system; yet, when we give attention to the life in the sea, we find that broad geographic ranges for particular kinds of organisms are the exception rather than the rule. Even for most fishes that are structurally and functionally equipped for rapid and extensive travel, the respective areas of occupation have definite, if not always sharp, boundaries. There are barriers, almost as effective as stone walls, that serve to keep each kind within more or less clearly definable ranges in both horizontal and vertical directions. These barriers are chemical (salinity, for example), chemico-biological (nutritive conditions), and physical (oxygen supply, temperature, and conditions associated with temperature). By way of illustration, it has been said that, in passing southward from Labrador to a place off the northeastern part of the United States, one may go in succession through Arctic, boreal, and subtropical Atlantic waters, each with characteristic faunas. Actually, the changes of temperature encountered are not greater than most land animals in temperate regions will often and repeatedly endure in twenty-four-hour periods. But changes of a few degrees, with corresponding changes in viscosity, are highly significant to fishes adapted for life in the sea, where the temperature varies hardly at all with day and night, little with the season, and only gradually in space, except where cold and warm water masses adjoin.

It happens sometimes that a cold current, or a warm one, strays from its regular course, and the effect upon fish and other forms of life that cannot or do not escape may be devastating. We have mentioned in Chapter IX (p. 132) the disastrous conditions attending the occasional southward wandering of a warm current along the coast of Peru. In the spring of 1882, millions of dead tilefish (Lopholatilus), an important commercial species of the time, were found floating over an area several thousand square miles in extent off the northeastern part of the United States. Many fishing vessels recorded them and one schooner reported sailing "for about 150 miles through waters dotted as far as the eye could reach with dying fishes." The mortality was presumed to be due to the intrusion of a current from the Arctic over a relatively warm-water bottom.[1] In the Barents Sea, where sudden changes of temperature occur, notable mortalities of the boreo-arctic capelin (Mallotus) have occasionally been reported.

Further evidence of the existence of invisible barriers may be found in the common knowledge that the commercial fishes of our northeastern states (cod, haddock, herring, halibut) are notably different from those of the South Atlantic states (mullet, sea bass, weakfish, drums, Spanish mackerel). The common mackerel, chiefly northern, extends farther south, particularly in winter. With Florida and the Gulf states, yet other kinds of fish come into prominence. Across the continent, on the one hand, and across the Atlantic, on the other, still different species engage the attentions of commercial fishermen, although there is continuity of sea water, indirectly around the American continents in the one case, and directly across the ocean in the other.

It should not be inferred that the limitation of ranges of fish is all a matter of temperature. Changes in density and in viscosity go along with changes in temperature; changes in viscosity mean much to animals that need to keep at certain levels in the water, because viscosity has so much effect upon ease of movement in the water and upon tendency to sink. Differences in conditions of nutrition will be found to play a great part in respect to distribution of fish and whales. Variation in salinity between water masses must have some physiological influence. Differences of pressure in a vertical direction will be felt by fish, especially those provided with a swim-bladder. The distribution of fishes is known also to be correlated with character of bottom: the commercial fisherman knows "cod bottom." Finally, let it be remembered that, for any water mass, salinity, temperature, and nutritive conditions depend in great part upon the origin, or past history, of that particular water.

We may be prepared, then, to find that the several species of fish

1. Generally too high a temperature is more likely to kill fish than too low a temperature. Cod and haddock albumen is coagulated (cooked) at the temperature of the Gulf Stream off the coast of Florida (coagulation point 31°C).—Communication from Dr. H. F. Taylor.

in the sea have their respective territories, some much broader than others, and that these territories are distinguishable, as far as we know them, both horizontally and vertically. The rule is not weakened by the fact that, as is true on land, no two species have precisely the same range. In the sea, changes in environmental conditions from place to place are generally gradual. A particular stage in transition presents itself as a barrier to one species, a different stage to another: species differ in tolerance or preference by all shades. All this is so much a part of the general order that we may well reserve a reasonable doubt, subject to the most exactingly critical analysis of the evidence, when we are told that a particular fish, or other higher organism, seems as much at home on one side of a great ocean as on the other or that a fish occurs in both the Atlantic and the Pacific.

A fish may occur in the depths of all the great oceans and still have a range that is strictly bounded—but bounded in a vertical direction. There is little difference between the abyssal conditions of life in the Atlantic, the Pacific, the Indian, and the Antarctic oceans, respectively; but in each ocean there are marked contrasts between life in the abyss and life in the surface waters. Within each ocean, too, there are differences in character of bottom, as we have seen in Chapter VIII.

Zones of Life

Preliminary to any discussion of the swimming life in the sea, we need to recall the several zones of life as distinguished by depth or relation to continents and islands. These, in the first order, are *littoral*, *neritic* and *oceanic* (see p. 181). We must have in mind also certain great zoogeographic zones, distinguished primarily by temperature, between the poles and the equator. The *Arctic* and *Antarctic* faunal zones will concern us little. There is said to be no strictly pelagic Arctic species of fish, although the capelin is at least close to being one. The *Atlantic Boreal* and the *Pacific Temperate* zones include a large part of the commercial fisheries; for great fisheries and cold water seem to go together. The Atlantic boreal extends well down along the coasts of North America and Europe, embracing, to the east, the Norwegian and North Seas and the region around the British Isles, and, to the west, the waters about Newfoundland and off New England and the Middle Atlantic states. There are *Antiboreal* zones in the southern hemisphere, and *Tropical* faunas in the Atlantic, Pacific, and Indian oceans, with various subdivisions, and with *transition* zones between these and the boreal or temperate faunas. The whole system is too complex for discussion in a limited space. It should be mentioned, however, that the great continuous *oceanic* area of the North and South Atlantic and that of the eastern Pacific, extending through North and South Pacific, constitute effective barriers between the *neritic* regions of the two sides of each ocean, which are the regions of commercial fisheries.

Finally we must remember the general types of bottoms: terrigenous, reflecting continental influences; and oceanic, with several kinds of oozes and the relatively barren red-clay bottom. The great commercial fisheries are mainly in the littoral and neritic regions, in boreal or temperate zones, over terrigenous bottoms, and over shallow "banks."

Kinds of Fishes [2]

The bony fishes are presumed to have originated in fresh water and thence to have invaded the seas with great diversification of species. The body fluids of bony fishes are hypotonic, or low in osmotic pressure, as compared with sea water. To put it very roughly, the blood is less saline than the water about them. They must take this saltier water in no little quantity along with their food; but they have means of excreting chloride through the gills. The several species of bony fishes—and there are thousands of species—vary much in capacity to endure changing salinities. A few, like the jumping mullet, along the coast, may pass from salt to fresh or almost fresh water and back. During different stages of their lives, shad, salmon, eel, and many other fishes live in fresh and in salt waters. Other fishes are intolerant of very small differences. The blood of elasmobranchs (sharks, rays, and chimaeras), in contrast to that of the bony fishes, is isotonic with sea water, although

2. In this chapter substantial use has been made of Hjort's Chapters VII and IX in Murray and Hjort, *The Depth of the Ocean*, with some changes in respect to classification suggested by Dr. L. P. Schultz. For much invaluable information the reader is referred to Hjort's chapters, to several chapters in Sverdrup, Johnson, and Fleming, *The Oceans*, and to Schultz, *The Way of Fishes*.

the higher osmotic pressure is attributable both to salts and to the content of urea.

The elasmobranchs, most primitive of all fishes, include the largest fish of the sea, as well as many of moderately small adult size. All are active and predaceous. Some sharks approach the larger whales in size, with a length of at least 45 feet. Let us mention three sub-orders—the sharks, the rays, and the chimaeras. Fishermen, generally, know and dislike such fish, the sharks because some are dangerous to man under certain conditions, the rays because of the pernicious barbed spine, or "sting," on the tail of the stingray, or "stingaree," and both because of the serious damage they may do to fish and nets. Nevertheless, in some places the sharks and rays are highly valued as food. Most common of small sharks in the Atlantic are the several species of "dogfish"—so called, it is said, because they trail the schools of herring, like dogs following their prey. The familiar sharks are those of littoral waters; but there are also species of the deep waters of the continental slope. Some of the rays, the mantas, or "dining tables," are of very large size, with "wing-spread" up to 20 feet, at least. One of the chimaeras is notable not only for its highly bizarre appearance, which suggested the scientific name, *Chimaera monstrosa*, but also for its extremely wide distribution. This chimaera has been taken near the extreme north of Norway, in various parts of the Atlantic down to the Cape of Good Hope, and from the Pacific near Sumatra and Japan. The chimaeras are presumed to be deep-water fishes generally, but at least one species is known to swim at the surface. Many elasmobranchs bring forth their young "alive." An unborn manta, taken from the body of the mother, had a spread from side to side of 5 feet.

The more primitive of the higher fishes, the *ganoids*, are largely restricted to fresh waters—paddlefish, sturgeons, garpikes (of fresh water), and bowfin; but some of the larger sturgeons live most of their lives in the sea, although returning to fresh water for spawning. Sturgeon more than 26 feet in length and weighing more than a ton and a half have been taken in Russian rivers.[8]

Among the bony fishes, the salmonlike and herringlike fishes (*Malacopterygii*, or soft-rayed fishes) command special attention. We shall mention six sub-groups: the salmonoids, clupeoids, ale-

3. E. W. Gudger, "Giant Freshwater Fish of Europe," *The Field* (Aug. 4, 1945).

pocephs, elopids, stomiatids, and sternoptychids. Of the salmonoids, the several species of Pacific Coast salmons are hatched in fresh water, hundreds of miles or a thousand miles inland. The young make their way downstream to the ocean, where they spend the greater part of their lives. When fully mature they return to fresh water, invading the mouths of rivers, ascending, once for all, the swift mountain streams, battling rapids and surmounting low waterfalls, only to reach the proper spawning grounds. There they mate, spawn, and, their life work over, die. Since the grown fish do not habitually feed in fresh waters, where they expend so much energy, the depletion, not only of food reserves, but even of normal body tissues, leaves them no alternative but death. The Atlantic salmon is also hatched in fresh water to mature in the sea; but, since it feeds in the rivers on the way up to the spawning grounds, the adults remain virile and may return to the ocean to feed again on marine life and to grow and replenish their stores of ova and sperm. Consequently, these salmon may return again and again to the interior spawning grounds. Some varieties, indeed, may spend their whole lives in fresh water. Relatives of the salmon, like the brook trout and the whitefish of the Great Lakes, never enter the sea, while still others never leave salt water. The common smelts are marine fishes of anadromous[4] habit like the salmon; but there are smeltlike fishes that live only on the deepest parts of coastal banks.

Among the clupeoids, or herringlike fishes, are the herring, sprat, sardine (pilchard), anchovy, white shad, and menhaden, economically the most important of all commercial fishes. Herring and sprat are more northern in distribution, and of immense economic importance in the fisheries industries of Northwest Europe and the British Isles. Everyone knows herring, if not as a fresh fish, at least as salt, smoked, and kippered. On the American side the herring is the basis of a large industry in the northeastern states and Canada. The young herring are also packed as sardines in Maine. Pacific herring are important to our northwestern states and Alaska, although rather overshadowed there by the salmon. The sardine or pilchard is the most important pelagic fish off the Atlantic coast of Europe. The Pacific pilchard supports the great sardine-packing industry of southern California.

4. *Anadromous*, ascending rivers to spawn.

The white shad, or river shad, and the river herring, like the salmon, start their individual lives in fresh water, but grow and mature at sea; young herring and sprat like brackish water and invade estuaries; pilchard and anchovies are more strictly marine. Herring, sardines, anchovy, and menhaden have particular biological significance for their numbers and feeding habits. With large mouths, poorly developed teeth, and good straining apparatus, they are specially adapted to feed on the small plankton organisms. The fish, in turn, are of convenient size and numbers to serve as food for larger fish, for sea fowl, and even for some of the whalebone whales. Off the coast of Peru, for example, one may see enormous shoals of small "anchobetas," pursued from below by bonitos and other large pelagic fish: the surface is literally spattered with anchovies leaping through the surface to escape the fish, while cormorants, pelicans, and gannets are diving at them from above. Indirectly, through the birds, the anchobetas are the principal basis of the highly valuable deposits of guano on the Peruvian islands.

The family Alepocephalidae includes true deep-sea fishes approaching the salmon in form and size, but black in color and known only from the greatest depths of the ocean. Even the young, which are also black in color, seem not to invade the upper waters above a depth of 500 meters. The Elopidae merit mention for the large Tarpon of the western subtropical Atlantic and the smaller, beautiful, silvery "ten-pounder" or "John Mariggle," *Elops saurus* of warm and tropical seas, Atlantic and Pacific.

The last two families of the great group of soft-rayed fishes lead us far from shore into oceanic waters. Of the Stomiatidae, *Stomias boa* and *Chauliodes sloanei* are notable for their full equipment of light organs and for their odd forms, with relatively huge fierce-looking mouths provided with great numbers of teeth, at the end of long slender bodies. They are also noteworthy for their wide distribution: both species are said to occur in all oceans. In the related family of Sternoptychidae are pelagic fishes that occur in "vast numbers," being among the most abundant of all pelagic fishes, and occurring in all oceans. Some have notably compressed silvery bodies. Many are provided with luminous organs. Certain species of Cyclothone are of special interest. The "Michael Sars" found them all over the North Atlantic, wherever a fishing appliance was hauled below 500 meters. The differential distribution of two species was noteworthy. *C. signata*, light in color and abundantly provided with light-emitting organs, was most numerous at 500 meters or less; in the Atlantic and Indian oceans it lived where the waters were 10° to 15°C. *C. microdon* was darker in color and less well equipped with light organs; its colder and darker habitat was chiefly below 1,000 meters, where temperatures of 3 to 6°C. prevailed.

In the second great group[5] of bony fishes, the *Apodes* (meaning "without legs" or "no hind limbs"), is the eel, Anguilla, which has a habit just the reverse of that of the salmon. Its place of birth was long a complete mystery. Although it is one of the most familiar fishes in the fresh waters of Europe and America, no one had ever found anywhere an eel in breeding conditions; nor had eggs or early larvae been known as such. Meantime, a small translucent bandlike fish had been known and described under the generic name of Leptocephalus. By the mere process of elimination, and because fully grown eels were known to head downstream and to undergo a gradual change to a silvery color, it came to be inferred that the common river and pond eel must actually be an oceanic deep-sea fish, as far as individual origin was concerned. Next it was learned that the thin transparent Leptocephalus of the sea approached the coast and the mouths of rivers, while undergoing reduction in length and change in form to metamorphose into an elver, or "glass eel"; and this was the young Anguilla, which entered fresh water. Still, the question where the silvery eels spawned and the young leptocephalid larva began life remained unanswered. Finally, the Danish ichthyologist and oceanographer, Dr. Johannes Schmidt, succeeded in tracing the leptocephalid larva back to its remote place of origin, which, remarkably enough, was halfway across the Atlantic Ocean.

The breeding ground of the eel is now known to be in a broad area of the Central Atlantic, southeastward of the Bermuda Islands. The spawning grounds of American and European eels adjoin and overlap to some extent. The maturing adult eels of both continents leave their fresh-water homes at the age of eight years or more,[6] and,

---

5. We pass over a major group comprising the minnows, characins, carp, catfishes, the so-called "electric eel," and the dangerous *piranha* of the Amazon—a group but slightly represented in salt water.

6. As contrasted with the *anadromous* salmon and shad, eels are *catadromous*, descending rivers to spawn in the sea. The *Leptocephalus* shown in plate 77 is that of a conger eel, described by D. P. Costello in *The Anatomical Record* 96, p. 68.

while sexual maturity approaches, travel over unmarked trails for thousands of miles through the Atlantic to reach the place of mating and spawning. Presumably they, like the Pacific salmon, die after launching a new generation, for they are never seen again. The eggs or larvae rise gradually to the upper waters and commence the slow trek back towards the mouths of rivers in America or Europe. Larvae of European eels seem to go invariably to Europe, so far as they escape death on the way, and those of the American eels to America; but they are faced with journeys of very different lengths in space and time. The two kinds travel a long way in the same current, which first takes them toward America; but the leptocephalid larvae from eggs of American eels turn in to the American continent to complete their one-year travel through the ocean. Those from European eels continue on with the ocean current, to arrive at the mouths of rivers in Europe only after a journey of about three years in all. Yet each kind approaches the end of marine travel at the proper stage of development: the America larvae require one year to develop to the elver stage, the European three years, in remarkable correlation with the distances between birthplace and parental homes!

Eels that mature in fresh water are not the only members of the Apodes, or fish without hind limbs. Some, the Muraenidae, are coastal fishes that are taken for the market. A few are dangerous to swimmers and divers. The large Muraena of the eastern Atlantic, Mediterranean, and Indian oceans, was reared for the table in coastal reservoirs and fed by the ancient Romans, it is said, upon the corpses of slaves. Another, a deep sea bottom-living eel, *Synaphobranchus prinnatus*, with body like a long slender tapering band, "is known from all the oceans of the world."[7] Its depth range, according to Hjort, is from around 200 meters to 3,250 meters (nearly two miles). It too has a leptocephalid larva. Quite different in appearance is the bizarre *Gastrostomus bairdii*, of pelagic habit; it appears like little more than a great mouth with a slender tapering tail behind (fig. 21e, p. 271).

The group of pikelike fishes (*Haplomi*) includes mostly fishes of fresh water (pike, pickerel) and others of the deep sea; yet it embraces also the scopelids of the open sea, fishes of small or mod-

---

7. Murray and Hjort, 1912, p. 389, and fig., p. 80.

erate size, which "play a greater part in the surface fauna of the ocean than all other pelagic fishes." The "Michael Sars" took them by thousands and in great diversity of species. The genus Mycto-phum is particularly prominent, and some may be found at consider-able depths. They show well-developed organs for the emission of light.

The spiny eel, the *Heteromi*, have long slender bodies and taper-ing tails but are not closely related to true eels. They include true deep-sea fishes, some of which have world-wide distribution.

Rather queer fishes are some of the Solenichthoidea, including the pipefishes, much like slender tapering cylinders, and the strikingly bizarre "sea horse" (Hippocampus). The males of pipefishes and sea horses have pouches on the underside of the hinder part of the body in which the female deposits the eggs to be incubated by the male. Some are extremely littoral, living in the eelgrass of shallow coastal waters. Others are characteristic of the community of life in the Sargasso Sea where they live midst the weed. One of the sea horses has long and elaborate leaf-like outgrowths from the skin in imita-tion of the weed in which it lives. Some pipefishes are pelagic in the Northeast Atlantic, being taken in "all the hauls of the surface net." In a related group are the little stickle-backs of freshwater and the flute-mouths, or giant marine stickle-backs, up to 6 feet in length, of shore waters of tropical Atlantic and Indo-Pacific regions.

Remarkable are the flying fishes of the Synentognathoidea, which, of course, do not actually fly but leap and glide through the air for considerable distances. There are more than forty species of flying fishes (*Exocoetus*) in tropical and subtropical waters of all oceans. Flying fishes have a "fishery" value, in so far as masses of their eggs appear on the market in some places and are highly esteemed as food.[8] The grapelike eggs, each with long slender fila-ments, may become so thoroughly entangled as to make a closely woven mat, a double handful, or more, in size. The mats may float at the surface or be entangled in seaweed. They were long mistaken for the eggs of the sargassum fish, Pterophryne. Dried in the sun, the egg masses may be kept for months to be softened by soaking in water in preparation for the pan and the table. In this group also we have the ferocious, long-jawed, green-boned marine garpike

8. Robert E. Coker, "The Fisheries and the Guano Industry of Peru," *Bulletin of the United States Bureau of Fisheries*, XXVIII (1910), 333-65.

(Belone) and the halfbeak (Hemirhamphus) with only the lower jaw prolonged.

The *Anacanthini,* or fish without spines in the fins and (generally) of bottom-living habit, command special attention, because of their great importance in the food supply of man. They are almost exclusively marine, although the large burbot (*Lota*) lives in fresh water. In one family (Gadidae) are the cod, haddock, pollack, and related species, which are among the most important food fishes in northern waters. Some are distinctly northern in distribution. Others live on the upper part of the continental slope. Some species of whiting (*Merlucciidae*) are also of some importance as food fish from coastal grounds. Another family the Macruridae, includes "the most important and numerous bottom fishes on the continental slopes and over the abyssal areas of the ocean."[9] Their short body region is continued by an elongate tail that tapers to a point and is without the usual caudal fin. Of this family, *Macrurus armatus* is of special interest for its "immense geographic range" in the Atlantic, Pacific, and Antarctic oceans, but only where the temperature is from 10° to 3°C. In truth, it has a *limited* range, but the limits are not geographical; they are to be found in physical conditions which happen to prevail widely in a geographic sense.

We come now to a group of most highly developed, diversified, and important fishes, the "perch-form fishes," *Percomorphoidea;* such are the basses, perches, sea breams, sheepshead, drums, mackerel, and flounders, many kinds of which are most familiar to the coastal fishermen and the frequenters of markets. Characteristically, they have hard scales, and stiff spines in the fins, and they are often brightly colored. The species in this group are extremely numerous and highly diversified in form and habit. In general, the spiny-rayed fishes are more diverse in species but less numerous in individuals than are the soft-rayed fishes.

Without considering all general types, we may conveniently deal with three broad divisions, which may be distinguished, in a rough but practical way, as, respectively, the perchlike, the mackerel-like and the flounderlike fishes. Many of the perchlike fishes occur only in fresh water: this division comprises nearly all the interior game-fishes (perches, sunfishes, basses, and others) not included in the Salmonidae and the Haplomi (pikes). Of the much greater number

---

9. Murray and Hjort, *op. cit.,* p. 389.

of marine species, most are fishes of the shallower and warmer waters—the sea basses, drums, sheepshead, sea bream, snappers, and others; but some are found on or amidst coral rocks in deeper or shallow waters. Still others live out on the coastal banks. The rockfishes of the Pacific coast at North America and the redfish or rosefish (*Sebastes marinus*) are important commercially. More than a hundred million pounds of redfish are brought into one eastern port each year. The rockfishes have special scientific interest because, instead of passing eggs out into the water they hatch them within the body and bring forth the young all ready to swim.

Some fishes of this group that we need mention only by name are the tilefish (see p. 256 above), the well-known shark's pilot (remora) that, with a sucker on its back, gains free rides through attachment to sharks and other fishes, the flying gurnards, which do not fly but have broad, winglike pectoral fins, the small marine and brackish-water red mullets (or surmullet, Mullus)[10] of tropical waters, the striking bandfish (Cepola) with species in all oceans, and the cusk eels of all oceans, of which the "congrio" of Peruvian waters is a particular table delicacy.

More pelagic are the numerous species in several families constituting the scombriform, or mackerel-like fishes—mackerels, horse mackerel, pilot fishes, pompano, bluefish, and many others. They are mostly surface fishes with a good deal of range; but all probably seek the coasts in time of spawning. Dr. Hjort mentioned that the only commercial fishery known to him "in the open ocean over deep water and away from the coast banks" was one for bonito and tunny, in the Atlantic 150 miles off the coast of France. They are now taken in quantities at great distances from the coast. The common mackerel (*Scomber scombrus*), which is more northern in distribution than many others of the family, is, of course, one of the most important of all food-fishes. In Peru the much larger bonito (Sarda) is most important on the market. The southern Spanish mackerel and the kingfish or cero (species of *Scomberomorus*) and the sailfish (*Istiophorus*) are highly favored sport-fishes. So also are the tunny (*Thunnus thynnus*) and the swordfish (*Xiphias gladius*), which range very widely, with virtually world-wide distribution. Of the Carangidae, the horse mackerel (*Caranx trachurus*) and the

10. Not to be confused with the jumping mullets (Mugil) previously mentioned (p. 268).

pilot fish (*Naucrates ductor*—not the "shark's pilot" or *Remora*) are noteworthy for their broad ranges. Naucrates is said to lead the sharks to their prey and then to feed upon the fragments wasted by the shark or upon the latters excrement. Caranx, at least, is widespread and probably spawns in the open ocean, as do, perhaps, some other species of fish. The young of Caranx have a wide oceanic distribution, being found "even at the greatest possible distance from the coast." The dolphin (Coryphaena), which pursues flying fishes, is notable for its large size, deep head, short snout and long hind body; it attains a length of 6 feet.

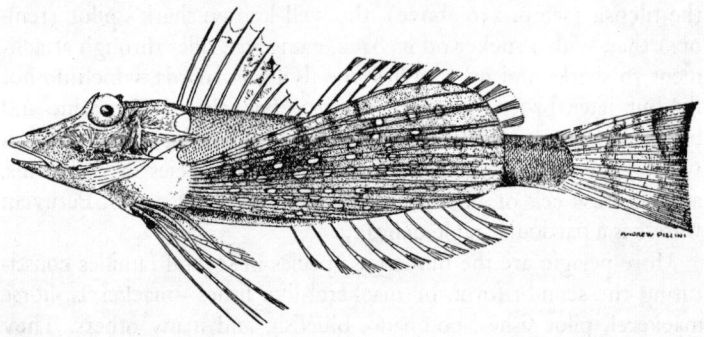

FIGURE 19. Sea Robin (Courtesy Carnegie Institution of Washington)

Others are the sand eels or sand launces (Ammodytes) of the coasts; the small but numerous silversides (Atherinidae), of which the small and slender, but highly delectable, peje-rey (royal fish) of Peru is a good example; the gray or jumping mullet (Mugil) found, in several species, on both sides of the Atlantic, most important as food, and at home in both fresh and salt coastal waters; the climbing perch of India and the Malay region; and the ferocious barracuda (Sphyraena) which may attain a length of 8 feet and is often dangerous to bathers.

Tetragonurus in the Mediterranean, Atlantic, and South Pacific, has poisonous flesh; it is said to feed on medusae and to descend to great depths. Another (Nomeus) has the strange habit of living for protection beneath the "Portuguese man of war," feeding on remains of fishes caught by the Physalia, and immune, apparently, to the poison darts of the host. Equally remarkable in another way is another fish of this group, *Chiasmodus niger,* which can ingest fish very much larger than itself. This it can do because not only its stomach but also the ventral wall of the body is extraordinarily distensible. When a large fish has been swallowed, even one of its own species, the stomach and body wall protrude far downward, appearing as a great rounded sack, hanging from the underside of a normal fish body. In contrast to the flying fish of highly superficial habit, Chiasmodus was found at great depths in the Sargasso Sea. It is known from various parts of the Atlantic and from the Indian Ocean.

Lastly, among the perch-form fishes mention may be made of the very slender naked bodied Carapus (formerly called Fierasfer), which lives as a lodger, or possibly a parasite, in the interior of some echinoderms, pearl oysters, and clams.

Among the most specialized of all our fishes is the order Pleuronectoidea, including the flounders, the halibut, and the soles. Besides being highly important in the commercial fishery, flounders have special interest in oceanography because, among fishes, they make one of the closest approaches to the benthonic modes of life. Anyone who, for business or pleasure, has gone "floundering," in the light of a flare of pine knots blazing in an iron basket swung out from the prow of a skiff, knows that flounders may be found almost completely buried in the bottom, with their forms outlined in the mud or sand, and only a part of the back and the eyes exposed. The extreme benthonic habit has been acquired only at the expense of normal body form. When very young the flounder has the shape of an ordinary fish, with eyes symmetrically placed on the sides. In the course of early development the body becomes much compressed from side to side. At the same time it loses bilateral symmetry, even to the extent that one eye gradually migrates across the top of the head, until both are on the same side. While still relatively small, the fish turns on its side, which meantime has lost its pigment. The right (or left) side is white and blind, the other, having both eyes, is normally kept upward in swimming or resting, and is colored with characteristic pattern. In some species, at least, the flounder has the capacity to change its colors to a marked extent, without complete loss of pattern, in adaptation to the colors of the background upon which it lies. The eggs of flounders are said to float at some depth. Somewhat related to the flounders, but hardly flounderlike, are the zeids of Atlantic and Pacific oceans, including the "John Dory" (*Zeus faber*), valued as a table fish.

Finally, we mention two groups of peculiarly specialized fishes. The pedicel fishes (*Pediculati*) include, among others, the weird angler fish or goosefish, *Lophius piscatorius*, a large bottom fish, with all sorts of leafy camouflaging projections from the integu-

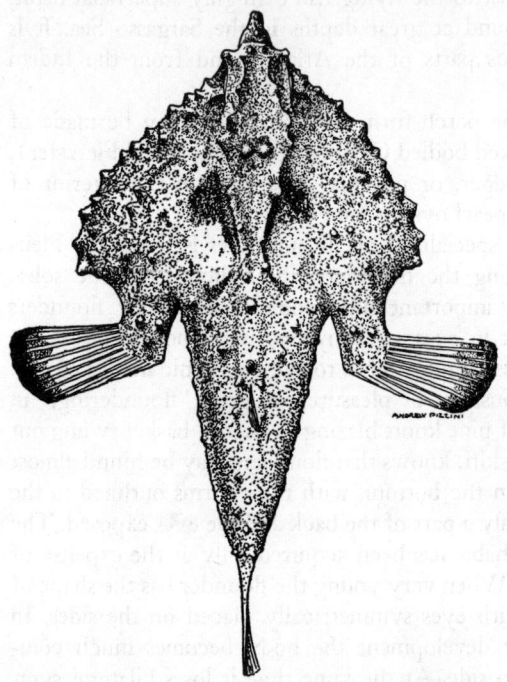

FIG. 20. Batfish (courtesy Carnegie Institution of Washington) The small tentacle does not show, being retracted into a cavity, under the long prominence on the head. Length about 12 inches.

ment, an enormous mouth, and on top of the head, a long slender stalk, bearing near the end a small fleshy lure, which can be dangled out well in front of the mouth. It lives on coastal banks and down to a depth of over 600 meters. For an obvious reason, it is known to many fishermen as the "all-mouth". Other angler fishes are small deep-sea species, black in color, with relatively enormous mouths and powerful teeth and provided with the same type of lure. The batfish lives in shallow tropical waters.

Incidentally, the analogy of the rod, line, and lure of the goosefish to the rod, line, and bait of the human angler is not mere play of scientific imagination. There are well-authenticated observations of the angling operations of one or another of the several species of

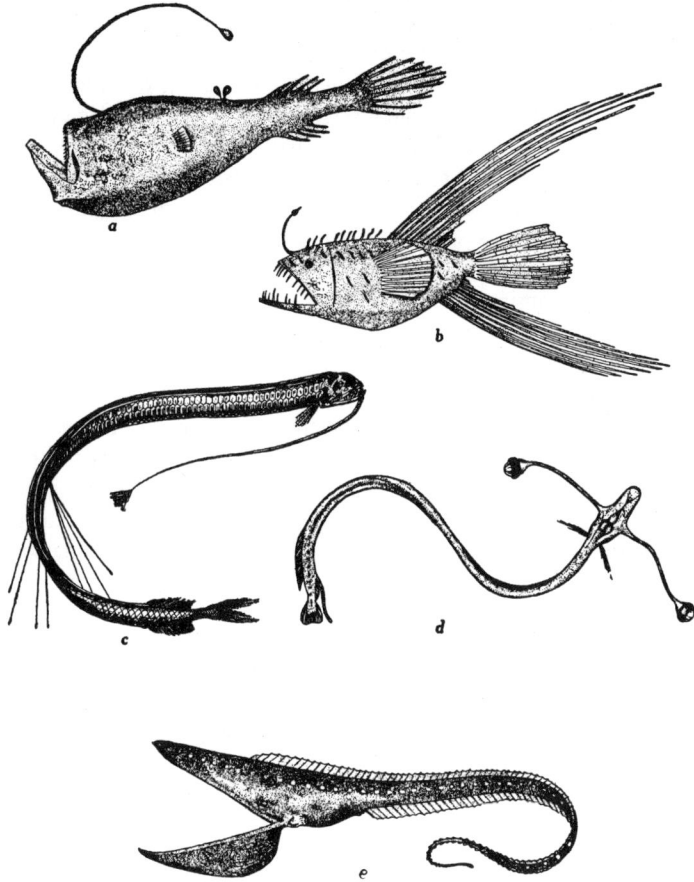

FIGURE 21. Oceanic fishes. *Mancalias shufeldtii Gill.* (b) *Caulophryne setosus* Goode and Bean. (c) *Macrostomias longibarbatus* Brauer. (d) *Stylophthalmus sp.* Brauer (young). (e) *Gastrostomus bairdii* Gill and Ryder. (c and d after Chun; others after Goode and Bean)

pediculate fishes. Aristotle's reports, made more than 2,000 years ago, were regarded with skepticism until checked by repeated observations during recent decades.

Two of the anterior dorsal spines, which in most fishes are located well back over the body, have in these fishes become strongly modified and displaced. Long, slender, and flexible, they have been moved forward in the anglers to be anchored just above the upper jaw. The front one, serving as combination rod and line, has a worm-like fleshy attachment at its tip. When not in use, the rod is laid back on the head and the bait coiled in a small hollow. When employed in fishing, the "bait" is dangled forward or above the mouth or it may be actively jerked to and fro. Small fishes obviously attracted to it are easily seen by the angler fish whose eyes are on top of its head. When suitable prey approaches closely enough, and apparently before it actually seizes the lure, the fish suddenly opens its large mouth, causing a strong current by which the prey is sucked into the mouth even more rapidly than can be followed by the eye. Aristotle remarked that "fishing frogs" that had lost their lures through accident were found to be unusually thin! [11]

In this group are, too, the many species of frog-fishes, some of which are also called mouse-fishes, marbled anglers or sargasso-fishes. These have been variously known under the generic names of Antennarius (with antenna), Histrio (a harlequin), Pterophryne (wing toad), and Chaunax (gaper). Some can fill their capacious stomachs with air to sustain them at the surface; thus they may drift widely. There are species that live in groves of coral, with bright and protective coloration. The small sargassum fish or gulfweed fish, *Histrio gibba*, is remarkable for its camouflage in color and form, for its predaceousness and voracity. The large head is capable of so enormous a gape that Histrio may take in fish almost as large as itself. Common in masses of floating gulfweed, it is streaked and mottled with brown and white and yellow, "all of the precise hues which prevail in the masses of algae to which the species is practically confined." Tints and patterns are subject to quick changes when the fish is disturbed or when it changes its environment. Leaflike protrusions from the skin serve as further camouflage. Like other fishes of the group it bears on its head a "fishing rod," tipped with fleshy "bait." Longley describes its eggs as "a single gelatinous mass, which floats like a raft, monstrous in proportion to the size of the

11. See E. W. Gudger, "The Angler-Fishes, *Lophius Piscatorius et Americanus,* Use the Lure in Fishing," *American Naturalist*, LXXIX, 542-48.

fish which produces it. Before its discharge the egg mass lies close packed in the ovaries like a bank note tightly rolled up from its two ends."[12]

Fishes of the next group, the *Plectognathi*,[13] and the last to be considered, are of queer appearance in other ways. The triggerfish has very stout spines on the back, which it can "set" like hammer and trigger, making it difficult for a larger predator to take this fish into its mouth. The flesh of some triggerfish is poisonous to men; something in the meat seems to act on the nerves, causing violent spasms of stomach and body muscles which may lead to death with extreme suffering. Here also are the filefishes and puffers, or globefishes, with inflatable bodies and generally with poisonous flesh. Others of the group are the porcupine fishes, with reputedly poisonous flesh and the well-armoured trunkfishes, with boxed-in bodies. One of the most aberrant fishes in respect to external appearance and behaviour is the headfish or giant sunfish, *Mola mola*, often seen sunning itself at the surface of warm seas. It attains a length of over 10 feet and a width of over 13 feet. Its powers of locomotion are weak. As shown in plate 79, it is notably different in form from the familiar market fishes. Its appearance is more that of a huge rough leather sack (not inflatable), compressed from side to side, with high dorsal fin, deep anal fin, and with a short scalloped tail fin which is rather wide in a vertical direction. It is frequently seen floating sluggishly at the surface of the ocean and sometimes occurs in abundance locally. The tough skin protects Mola against enemies. Its mouth is small, and its chief food seems to be coelenterates of various kinds. Closely related is the more elongated sharp-tailed ocean sunfish, *Ranzania*, occurring in all warm seas. It does not grow to giant size; sometimes, but inappropriately, this species has been called "king of the mackerels."

Useful fishes

The preceding pages have offered only a general and sketchy review of the types of fishes that have found means, and sometimes most remarkable ones, of adapting themselves to a great diversity of

12. William H. Longley, and Samuel F. Hildebrand, *Systematic Catalogue of the Fishes of Tortugas, Florida.* Carnegie Institution of Washington, Publication 535 (1941). Pp. xiii, 331. 34 plates.
13. Meaning "joined jaws."

conditions, as they are found in the sea—in the open waters at various depths, on the bottoms, and along the shores. To some of us many of these types are mere curiosities. To others they are intriguing evidences of nature's extreme versatility in adapting form to special conditions of living. To the more practical minded, and to all of us in our practical moods, the question arises: Which of these fishes are directly useful to man; which of them offer a substantial amount of subsistence or otherwise give employment to fishermen, processors, transporters, and marketers?

The ocean fishes that we eat have been reared by nature without expense to us for feed or fertilizer or for protection against enemies or disease. Unlike farm animals they require no nursing by man. They have grown in a medium that has in solution every mineral or other chemical necessary for the production of animal substance. They are not reared on mineral-deficient soils. It has been well said that "for all-around dietetic quality and value, per unit of effort or cost to produce, no food product known to man excels or even equals the fatter varieties of ocean fish."[14] The fisheries yield many other products than food for the table. Vitamins extracted from the livers or other parts are sold in the drug stores. The coatings of the silvery scales of fish go into the manufacture of artificial pearls and fire-fighting foams. Commercial oils, fertilizer, animal feed, and glue are made from fishes and fish wastes. It is doubtful if in agricultural fertilizing practice we have ever improved much, except as to convenience, on the old American Indian practice of putting a fish under each hill of planted corn.

The number of kinds of fishes runs well into the thousands and the number of families into hundreds. Looking the world over and considering all kinds of uses to which fish may be put, a great number of kinds have some industrial value. It is a fact, however, that the bulk of merchantable fish from the sea, perhaps three-fourths of the total catch, are in five small groups or families. These may be listed in order of abundance.[15] (1) The herringlike fishes (Clupeidae) include herring, sprat, sardines, shad, and menhaden, valued for food, fertilizer, and oil. (2) Of the codlike fishes we have primarily the

14. Harden F. Taylor, "Research in the Fisheries for the Betterment of the South," *Research and Regional Welfare* (University of North Carolina Press, Chapel Hill, 1946).

15. With acknowledgements to Dr. Harden F. Taylor, recently President of the Atlantic Coast Fisheries Company.

cod, haddock, and pollack, valuable not only as food but as commercial sources of vitamins A and D; important in this group of spineless fishes, but not in the first rank, are the hakes or whitings (Merluccius) and ling (Molva), not to be confused with vitamin A-rich Alaska ling (Ophiodon). (3) The salmons give five species of the west coast of North America and the Atlantic salmon, not to

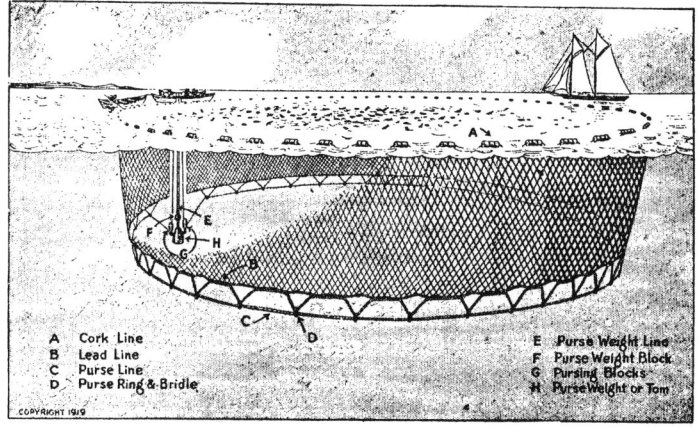

A	Cork Line	E	Purse Weight Line
B	Lead Line	F	Purse Weight Block
C	Purse Line	G	Pursing Blocks
D	Purse Ring & Bridle	H	Purse Weight or Tom

COPYRIGHT 1919

FIGURE 22. Diagram of a purse seine such as is employed in capture at sea of food-fishes and menhaden. (Courtesy Linen Thread Co.)

mention some in other parts of the world. (4) The flounderlike fishes embrace the halibut, flounders, soles, plaices, and dabs, the halibut being another important source of vitamin A. (5) Among the mackerel-like fishes are the common mackerel, Spanish mackerel, kingfish or cero, the tunas, bonitos, and albacores, with the swordfish taking a rank of some importance. "The tunas are the richest and most valuable sources known for natural vitamin D."

Of these families the first and third, the herringlike fishes and the salmons, are among the soft-rayed fishes (Malacopterygii) discussed above (p. 260). The fourth and fifth, the flounders and the mackerels, are spiny-rayed fishes. But none of these ranking fishes are among what may be called the perchlike spiny-rayed fishes which embrace most of the families of spiny-rayed fishes. Nevertheless, many such fishes are very important commercially, without ranking in quantity taken with those of the top five families. We have already mentioned the redfish or rosefish of the family of rock-fishes (Scorpaenidae) of which much more than one hundred million pounds are regularly marketed each year in America, as is true also in Europe. The so-called "black cod" (which is not a cod), sable-fish or coalfish (*Anoplopoma fimbria*), of Alaska and the North Pacific coast, is of a nearly related family. The red snapper and the jumping mullets in other families are important, as are the consider-able number of drumfishes (Sciaenidae, including squeteagues, or "sea trout," surf whitings, spots, drums, sheepshead, and croakers) and the sea basses (Serranidae), with some others. Eels (Apodes), too, are not insignificant in the world fish markets. Several bony fishes have been mentioned as potent producers of the important vitamin A; so also are some of the sharks, especially the soup-fin shark, for which there is avid fishery on the Pacific coast of North America.

In this summary statement we have had particular reference to the fisheries of North America. Looking the world over, the whole pic-ture would probably not be greatly different. Were we dealing with the marine fisheries of Peru, which are not large as compared with those of North America and northwest Europe, or with those of some more distant country, we should have to place emphasis on some of the same families, but also, perhaps on a few others. The fact remains, however, that of the thousands of kinds of fishes, a very few kinds in an even more limited number of groups give the great bulk of the fisheries product.

Capture of Fish in the Depths

The problem of securing exact information about the distribution of fish in depth is naturally a difficult one. Seines and traps, by which fish are taken in coastal waters, cannot be employed in the open sea. Where fish are large enough and populations sufficiently dense, the set line or trawl line is useful for fish near the bottom; a very long line, with numerous short side lines bearing baited hooks, is run out, anchored and buoyed. After a reasonable waiting period, the line is hauled in and the captured fish removed from the hooks. This trawl line serves only in reasonable depths and for certain kinds of fish. Drift nets, in which the fish become "gilled" may be useful in the upper waters for particular sizes of fish. The closing nets, so use-ful for studies of bathypelagic plankton, even in the largest practicable sizes, unfortunately, take few large adult fish; they capture young and small fish dependably only where these occur in considerable abundance. The beam trawl described in a preceding chapter takes only those fish living in close proximity to the bottom.

One method of collecting from the depths has been by use of the *vertical,* or vertically-hauled, net. A large deep conical net of desired mesh is suspended from a metal ring of a diameter of 2 or 3 meters. It is lowered successively to various depths and then hauled straight up. Several nets may be hauled simultaneously from different depths. Comparison of the catches from the several hauls gives valuable information as to the depth distribution of the organisms taken. The *purse seine* for surface fishes is shown in an illustration.

The most effective appliance for taking fish in the deep is the *otter trawl,* employed in some of the great commercial fisheries. In the commercial otter trawl, an enormous net with very wide mouth (50-100 feet) and considerable depth, is kept open by wide sheerboards, or "doors" attached at each side. The lines by which the trawl is towed are attached to these boards, not at the ends, but on the faces and outward from the center. The boards may go down face to face, with the collapsed net hanging below. When the vessel steams ahead, pulling on the boards from off center, the two boards, drawn partially broadside against the water, veer off in opposite directions, until the mouth of the net is stretched wide. The haul is made from the stern of the vessel, a "trawler," especially designed for the purpose. The success of the haul depends in part upon the speed of the vessel and the skill of the steerer.

Naturally a vessel designed for general oceanographic research can not be especially designed for the use of the large trawls; nor could they carry conveniently the amount of twin heavy steel lines requisite for the use of so large an appliance at the great depths that must be explored for scientific purposes. Nevertheless, modifications of the otter trawl for oceanographic collecting have proved most effective. The boards in this case are attached by short steel lines to a single line, or "warp," which is hauled by coiling on a winch-driven drum of particularly sturdy construction: The "Michael Sars" used 9,000 fathoms, or more than 5 miles of such steel line and the trawl was hauled at a maximum depth (vertically) of nearly 3 miles. For the haul at such a depth it required a little more than five and one-half hours to lower the apparatus; after three and one-half hours of trawling it was hauled aboard in a little over six hours. Thus, the total period of time required for a single haul was fifteen hours. It is, of course, possible to attach more than one trawl to a line for simultaneous hauls at different depths; other appliances, such as plankton nets, may also be attached at intervals as the line is paid out; so that the whole day and all the effort are not expended for a single set of observations. The "pelagic trawl" used by the Prince of Monaco and the "young-fish trawl" of C. G. Johannes

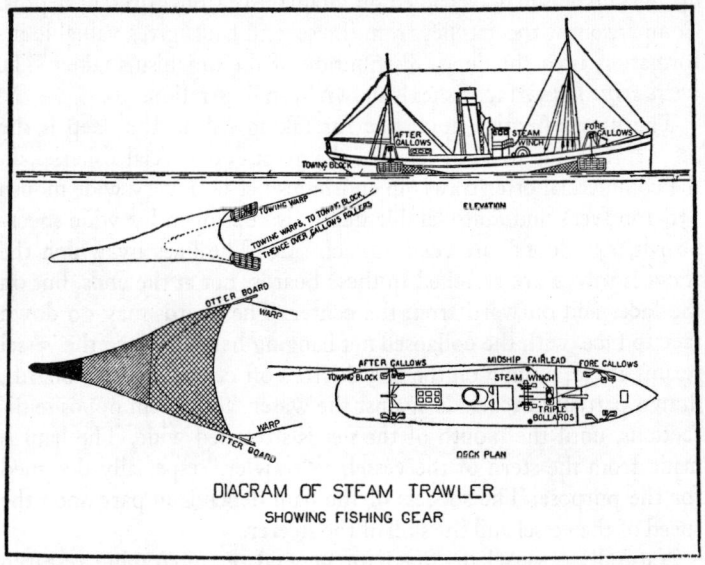

FIGURE 23. Diagram of steam-trawler with otter trawl. (Courtesy U. S. Fish and Wild Life Service)

Petersen were based in part upon the same principle of employing sheer boards to keep the net spread widely open by the pull on the lines.

Of course such nets capture fish, not only while they are being towed at a particular depth, but also as they are being hauled to the surface; so that it will not be known for a particular fish, taken in a particular haul, at what depth it entered the net. On the other hand, if a particular species is never or rarely caught at 300 fathoms and is taken in numbers when the net is hauled at 500 fathoms, it is a fair presumption that the habitat of the species in that place is well below 300 fathoms. If only a few of the same kind of fish are found in a net hauled at the same place, but at 750 fathoms it is quite likely that they could have been taken as the trawl was hauled in through the 500 meter level. With a sufficient number of hauls at different levels, and an adequate number of individuals of a species, it is possible to draw fairly safe conclusions as to the depth at which the species chiefly lives. Fishes that are rarely taken offer a greater problem. Day and night hauls must also be compared for evidences of vertical migrations. Catches at different seasons are also desirable.

In this connection it is proper to recall the echo sounder, or sonic sounder. This is the instrument by means of which an observer on a moving ship makes a continuous record of depth through measurement of the small interval of time required for rebound of supersonic waves between ship and bottom (p. 70, above). The echo sounder has also proved useful in locating schools of herring and other fishes as far down as 50 to 90 fathoms.[16] It can be used effectively for this purpose with the ship going at full speed, in the day or in the night, and even in bad weather. Not only does the echo sounder give practical information as to the depth at which the fish are moving, but also it affords indications of the size of the school, its density, and its upper and lower limits, or "thickness."

Summary.

1. The nekton comprises chiefly fishes, whales, seals, turtles, squid, and sometimes, the larger crustacea.

2. Although visible barriers present no obstacle to movement of any swimmer from ocean to ocean or from one side of an ocean to the other, there are, everywhere, nevertheless, effective barriers of temperature, salinity, viscosity, pressure, nutrition, and character of bottom, so that each species has a limited range. Great mortalities of fishes have been caused by temporary shifts of masses of ocean water.

3. Species that occur in all oceans are not an exception to the rule just stated. They, too, are limited in *vertical* distribution.

4. Fishes of some kinds seem to occur nearly everywhere, but they are most abundant and support great commercial fisheries mainly near continents and islands and in cold or temperate waters.

16. Albert L. Tester, *Use of the Echo Sounder to Locate Herring in British Columbia Waters.* Fisheries Research Board of Canada, Bulletin No. 43 (1943).

5. Some fishes that spend most of their lives in the sea ascend rivers to spawn. The eel, on the contrary, grows nearly to maturity in fresh water, then descends the streams to breed in the depths far out in the ocean. European and American eels breed in adjoining and even overlapping areas of the central Atlantic, but the young find their way back in two or three years to the proper continent.

6. Probably most numerous and important of all marine fishes are the relatives of the herring (including sardines and anchovies), the cod and its relatives, the salmons, the flounders including halibut and sole, the mackerel-like and many of the spiny-rayed fishes, notably the redfish.

7. The otter trawl, described, and its modifications, the pelagic trawl, and young-fish trawl are the most effective implements of capture for deep-sea fish.

8. Of particularly wide and interoceanic distributions are the Chimaera, some stomiatids and sternoptychids (relatives of the salmon), Macrurus, a relative of the cod, the swordfish, the tunny, the horse mackerel, the pilot fish, and perhaps, the ocean sunfish (Mola).

CHAPTER 19

More about Life at Large: The Nekton

Some Features of Natural History of Fishes

I T MUST NOW BE APPARENT THAT ALL THE FISHES OF THE SEA ARE limited in distribution—either horizontally or vertically. The boundaries of the several ranges, although not physically impassable, are none the less effective. The boundaries are to be found in the chemical and physical conditions, such as salinity, temperature, nutrition, oxygen supply, depth, and character of bottom. Apparently they center about temperature and nutritive conditions, which vary so much, according to distance from land, depth, currents, and vertical movements of the water.

In general, as we have seen, the great commercial fisheries are not far removed from the coasts—in neritic waters. This is not just because such waters are more accessible, but primarily because the waters of the coastal regions and the off-shore banks are richest in nutritive materials. The more important fisheries are in the colder waters, which absorb more oxygen and carbon dioxide. Students of marine algae, of the plankton, and of the benthos have found the coastal waters more fertile. (Reference may be made to pages 198, 213, and 247, above.) The great reserves of nutritive substances, however, are not all upon land, to be brought into the ocean with the surface drainage. Other reserves are in the deeper waters of the ocean, wherever dead bodies of organisms and organic wastes have suffered decomposition below the depths at which there is light enough for photosynthesis and prompt reconversion. In consequence, wherever the conditions of oceanic circulation bring about upwelling of deeper waters, as on the west coasts of North and South America and Africa, there is likely to be a great stimulation of algal reproduction, accompanied, of course, by a large development both of the smaller organisms that feed upon algae and of the fish and other larger animals that devour the smaller; the commercial fisheries follow. Again, where great currents diverge from one another, causing a condition of low pressure at the surface and a rise of deeper waters, there may be expected to be a region of fertility and prolific organic growth. Where warm and cold currents come together, too, there may occur a springlike outburst of pelagic algae to support prolific animal life in the upper waters and on the bottoms beneath. Such regions as the Barents Sea north of Norway and Russia and the off-coast banks of Labrador and Newfoundland are seats of great commercial fisheries.

For fishes that live on the bottom, the character of the substratum is often of vital importance; but, so often in the ocean, the character of the bottom is a reflection of conditions in the waters above. Terrigenous deposits extend out from the shore to a considerable distance and include a variety of fairly deep muds, known as blue, red, green, volcanic, and coral muds. Beyond are the oceanic oozes—pteropod, globigerina, diatom, and radiolarian—and, in the greatest depths, the relatively barren red clay. Terrigenous deposits are made up of detritus from land and the remains of the organisms of littoral and neritic waters.[1] Pelagic deposits are formed mainly of the remains of pelagic organisms, which are much fewer in number per unit of area than are corresponding organisms in waters closer to land. Where the sea is very deep, the rainfall of bodies and wastes from the surface waters, the "fall of manna" for deep-living animals, must supply the fish and other animals of all levels, intermediate as well as bottom. The amount available at any level must vary according to some diminishing scale. It is to be expected, and all the evidence indicates, that the oceanic abyss is poorly populated with fish, as with other organisms. Referring to fishes living near the bottom, Hjort comments that in the Atlantic the fauna at depths of 3,000 meters (nearly 2 miles) or less is "infinitely richer in numbers of

1. These extend broadly out from northwest Europe and from the North American shores, but are narrow off the coast of southern Europe and North Africa. They underlie the greater part of the Gulf of Mexico and virtually all of the Mediterranean.

species, as well as in individuals" than is that of the abyssal plain, which lies below 2,000 fathoms (or nearly 4,000 meters).

Conditions in the abyss are probably not widely different in the several great oceans. It is the less surprising, then, that fish of the same species, *Macrurus armatus* for example (see p. 267, above) have been taken in Atlantic, Pacific, and Antarctic oceans, but only where the temperature was from 10° to 3°C. Another species, *M. filicauda*, with known bathymetric range of 2,500 to nearly 5,000 meters has been found in the same three oceans. "The deepest living forms have a wide distribution."

Many kinds of fish are peculiar to the continental slopes, and the faunas of the slopes on east and west sides of the Atlantic are very different, although the deepest-living fish are about the same on both sides. On the American side the slopes are farther out than on the European side. Off the coasts of Europe there is much less change of temperature, from depth to depth and from north to south; correspondingly, faunal changes are more gradual—from a mingled community of boreal and southern forms west of the British Isles to a strictly southern fauna off the west coast of Africa. On the western, or American, side of the Atlantic, the currents and drifts are such that the changes from north to south and, generally, with depths are more drastic.

It is of interest in this connection that the abyssal plain of the Norwegian Sea, at a depth of around and exceeding 2 miles and with bottom temperature below minus 1°C., does not have a single species of fish in common with the Atlantic deep; yet the pelagic species above are common to sea and ocean. Here is the great significance of the Wyville Thomson Ridge (mentioned on p. 29, above), which bars the passage of warmer waters from the oceans into the sea. The ridge is a solid obstruction—not to the movement of fish but to the passage of water and the continuity of temperature in the deep. It is noteworthy that in the depths of the Norwegian Sea fish spend their lives in water below the freezing point of fresh water![2] Beyond the ridge in the Atlantic, conditions are relatively uniform all the way south to the Canaries off the coast of Africa, and the fishes of the slope and the waters above have correspondingly wide

2. We may well wonder at the efficiency of the enzymes that keep the biochemical processes going in the bodies of the fishes at this low temperature.

distribution. Hjort has commented that "In the history of oceanic research nothing has contributed so much to the awakening of this interest [in the influence of environmental conditions on the structure and distribution of animals] as the discovery of entirely different animal-communities living on either side of the Wyville Thomson Ridge. Atlantic forms occur to the South and Arctic forms to the North of the ridge, corresponding to the very different thermal conditions on either side."

In true oceanic areas fish are found in less density or concentration of populations and, as we have seen in discussions of the kinds of fishes, there are fishes of the uppermost waters, fishes of intermediate depths, and abyssal fishes. Where the waters are uniformly cold from surface to bottom, the fish of one species may be found at all depths; but where warm water overlies colder waters, as in the greater parts of the open oceans, the fish of colder waters may never approach the surface. Certain species found at relatively high levels in northern waters may be found at decidedly greater depths in more southern water. Even beneath the warm Sargasso Sea, some boreal (cold-water) species are found at 1,000 meters. There has been observed, too, some correlation of size with depth and temperature. In the case of *Cyclothone signata*, living mostly at 500 meters and higher, the younger and smaller fish were found at upper levels, and the same sizes of fish lived in deeper water in southern as compared with northern regions. In respect to *Cyclothone microdon*, Hjort concluded that smaller and younger individuals lived a thousand meters higher in the water than the largest and oldest—and also that the average size was much less in southern than in northern waters. Comparison may be made of the findings with respect to plankton organisms (see pp. 105, 233, above). With certain prawns, the larvae were taken at 50 to 100 meters, the medium-sized individuals at 500 to 700 meters, and the largest and oldest at 1,000 to 1,500 meters.

The surface waters of the extensive Sargasso Sea have a characteristic fish fauna in association with the sargassum weed: the pipefishes and seahorses of the Solenichthoidea, the file fish of the Plectognathi, and, *par excellence*, the sargasso fish of the Pediculati (see pp. 201, and 272, above).

Some characteristic differences in color have been noted in correlation with vertical distribution and illumination and with background. It seems impossible to believe that the coloring does not have some adaptive significance in affording a measure of protection from enemies. Fish of the uppermost strata in the brightly illuminated tropical waters are sky blue, in more northern waters they are darker. We have mentioned above the changes of color in flounders on different backgrounds. The bright and even gaudy colors of fishes in tropical coastal waters, among the gaily colored gorgonias, sea fans, and sea anemones, are well known. We have noted, too, the concealing coloration of the Sargasso fish. The dark backs of herring and other fishes make them almost invisible at a little depth when looked at from above, while their lighter undersides give concealment from below. In strictly oceanic regions blue or transparent animals characterize the uppermost 150 meters; at 150 to 500 meters silvery or grayish fishes predominate in the Atlantic; below that are very dark colored or black fishes and red prawn. Of course, at such a depth, with all the longer rays of sunlight absorbed in the upper waters, red would appear black. The upper levels of red or black fish correspond to levels of loss of most of the rays of sunlight at 500 to 750 meters, or at levels higher in northern than in southern waters (for the northern hemisphere). This, of course, does not tell us how the fishes get their colors.

As almost everyone knows, many oceanic fishes are provided with organs for the emission of light. These may be scattered over the sides of the body in characteristic pattern or they may be borne on long waving stalks, as with some of the pediculates. Such organs are never formed in fresh water fish and but rarely in coastal fishes or in those of northern waters. Presumably they have a use, since some of the light organs are highly specialized, with reflectors and lenses.[3] The common notion that they serve like lanterns in the dark abyss receives little support when it is learned that such organs are not characteristic of abyssal species.[4] They occur rarely, if at all, in deep

3. E. N. Harvey has dealt extensively with bioluminescence in *Living Light* (Princeton University Press, 1940), and in earlier works. An interesting but brief discussion of the subject is found on pages 833-36 of Sverdrup, Johnson, and Fleming, *The Oceans*.

4. "When abyssal forms [fishes] do produce light, it is usually only a faint glow due to a special luminosity of the film of slime which covers the body of any fish." —Gordon Lynn Walls, *The Vertebrate Eye and its Adaptive Radiation* (Bull. No. 19, Cranbrook Institute of Science, 1942), p. 398.

bottom-living fishes. On the other hand, they are "specially characteristic of fishes belonging to the upper 500 meters in warm oceanic waters."[5] We have previously mentioned the bathymetric distribution of species of Cyclothone. It happens that the gray species (*C. signata*) living above 500 meters has much better developed light organs than the several black species living below that depth. Among the scolopolids, the species of the surface water possess the largest light organs. Among mollusks, the pelagic squid have good light organs, while the octopods of the bottom are without them. Luminous fishes are predominantly oceanic, in the upper waters, and among the salmon-form fishes and the Pediculati.

The degree of development of visual organs is also puzzling. Abyssal hauls have brought up blind fish, fish with small eyes, and those with very large eyes. In general, according to Hjort, large and well-developed eyes are found chiefly in fishes living above 500 meters; imperfect visual organs characterize those living below that depth. Nevertheless some of the deepest-living fishes, such as *Macrurus armatus* (p. 267, above) have extremely large eyes, and, according to Walls, some bathypelagic and benthonic fishes have (relatively) the largest eyes of any vertebrates. He adds that "The eyes of deep-sea fishes are probably by far the most sensitive in existence."[6] On the other hand, one deep-sea fish *Ipnops murrayi* is "the only vertebrate known whose eyes have gone without leaving any trace whatever."

We have seen something of the spawning and feeding migrations of salmon, shad, and eel. Marine fishes must engage in some sort of migratory movement. Because of the high specific gravity of sea water, the eggs of most marine fishes are "emersal" (meaning that they rise toward the surface), as contrasted with the "demersal" eggs of fresh water fishes which settle on the bottom. When over spawning grounds the eggs rise to the surface, or, at least, to higher levels, they and the helpless larvae hatching from them must be carried by the currents to other regions. Later, with the attainment of greater weight of body and more effective swimming powers, the bottom fish may find the bottom and the pelagic fish may roam at will in search of food and other necessities of life. For the continued maintenance of populations, there must be at least a breeding

5. Murray and Hjort, *op. cit.*, p. 677.
6. Walls, *op. cit.*, pp. 395-96.

migration back to favorable spawning grounds. We have, then, migrations for feeding and migrations for spawning, in addition to the involuntary transport of fish, particularly of the eggs and young, when they are merely carried by the currents. Marine fishes of nearly all kinds must, then, be "in circulation" within areas of greater or lesser extent.

Great movements of fish populations have been a matter of common knowledge since the beginnings of fisheries, although there has been too little precise knowledge regarding them. In comparatively recent years, a great deal of scientific study of the broader movements of fishes has been in progress, particularly by various methods of marking and tagging with small buttons or bands. To cite only one example, it is now known as the result of such studies that cod from the region of Nantucket, and even from north and east of Cape Cod, make a southwestward fall migration toward North Carolina, and return in the spring. Others come into the Nantucket region from the offshore banks.[7] Herring may feed, and be the object of fishery, hundreds of miles from their spawning ground. The migrations of herring, mackerel, and halibut are of much concern to fishermen. Seasonal migrations often involve both horizontal and vertical submersal movements. The common mackerel, for example, hibernates in deep cold offshore waters. In the spring it moves coastward to feed and breed in the upper waters at the beginning of summer. Apparently the North Atlantic mackerel on the American side goes *southward* in the fall to find the deep *cold* offshore waters and *northward* as it returns to the summer spawning areas nearer the continental shores. Its movements can hardly be governed alone by temperature or pressure gradients.

There are also diurnal vertical movements, as with herring that swim near the bottom by day and rise to the surface at night. This recalls the vertical movement of plankton (mentioned in Chapter XV, p. 215). Squid are known to engage in vertical migrations.

In the northern hemisphere, many fishes of commercial importance develop sexually in the late months of the year, when the colder currents drive the warmer waters downward; they spawn in the earlier (winter) months of the following year. Since the eggs

7. William C. Schroeder, "Migrations and Other Phases in the Life History of the Cod off Southern New England" (*Bulletin of the United States Bureau of Fisheries*, No. 46, 1930, pp. 1-136).

rise toward the surface waters and the developing larvae drift, they can be taken in the plankton nets. Here, indeed, is one method of ascertaining the presence of particular kinds of fish in the deeper waters—by capturing the spawn in fine-meshed nets drawn at the surface. It is necessary, of course, to have precise recognition-characters for eggs and larvae, so that they can be identified to species as accurately as one can identify the adult fish. The systematic study of early stages is, therefore, an important phase of oceanography and of fishery science. It is equally necessary to have knowledge of currents and drifts in order not to be misled as to the relations between the locations of drifting young and of the fish by which they were spawned.

It is not only man that may spread nets for the capture of eggs and young fish. Many kinds of marine organisms, from copepods to grown fish and whales, are equiped with fine filtering appliances for the capture of food, and any digestible component of the plankton of appropriate size is grist to their mill. Innumerable pelagic organisms of other types are equipped to seize individual microorganisms and feed upon them. Accordingly, there is enormous depletion of the populations of the drifting eggs and young fish by predators of all kinds. Yet the cod, the flounder, and other fishes must in some way maintain the species. Nothing illustrates more clearly the profound fact of the vicissitudes of life in the open sea than the number of eggs discharged by a cod: this has been estimated at 5,000,000, as an average. To maintain the population of cod indefinitely it is only necessary that a pair of these survive to replace the breeding pair. If even two pair regularly replaced the parental pair, it would be only a relatively short time before the whole ocean would be packed and overflowing with adult cod. Let us assume that a female cod fish deposits eggs only five times in different years. Obviously, then, the chances are over ten millions to one against the final survival of any one cod that enters upon life as a fertilized egg.[8]

The basic question of the function in nature of organic reproduction comes into question. We must not think of a fish as having a *purpose* in spawning: they mate and spawn in response to inner

8. The biomathematical critic will recognize the implied assumption that all female cod spawn—and the inclusion among vicissitudes of the losses of adult as well as of young fish.

promptings of nature, without knowledge of the eventual results. Nevertheless, if we admit that the whole system of nature is an orderly one, it is proper to speak, if not of the "purpose," at least of the *service* of reproduction. Viewed in that light, the service of reproduction of a particular fish or other marine organism is incidentally to perpetuate the species; mainly, it produces a feed crop for carnivores. The farmer does not grow corn just to get seed for another crop. His farming operations have a broader function. Nature is a farmer; one of ten million eggs of the cod serves for seed. The other ten million minus one, serve to nourish other organisms— some of which, in turn, may become the food of cod. This is not a foolish or fanciful play of the imagination. It is something very real. In a somewhat crude, but perhaps a practical way, it affords an illustration of the complex web of organic life in the sea—a closely-woven web, which is attached, all around, to the physical conditions of salinity, temperature, and movements of masses of water and to the chemistry, physics, and dynamics of the sea.

Mollusks: the Squid

Departing from an order of treatment based upon systematic position in the animal kingdom, we may turn for a little while to a group of invertebrates which play somewhat the same part in marine economy as do the fishes. The squid feed upon fish and are eaten by fish. With the fish they afford sustenance to the higher vertebrates to be considered last. Squid are highly specialized mollusks. The more familiar mollusks are clams, snails, and conchs, possessing external shells secreted by a "mantle," and creeping or burrowing by means of a large muscular "foot." The squid have a shell, but it is internal and known as the "pen." The mantle is an envelope encircling most of the body, enclosing a branchial chamber and well-provided with musculature. Paradoxically, the "foot" is modified to form a recognizable "head,"[9] from which extend a ring of ten long muscular arms provided with powerful suckers and well adapted for seizing and holding prey. There are usually well-developed eyes, as appropriate for active pelagic animals; but some blind squid are known from great depths. Many have organs for the emission of light. They are usually provided with sacks filled with a

9. The class name, Cephalopoda, means head-foot.

black inky fluid, which can be expelled forcibly: in the ink-be-clouded water the squid may escape the more readily from its enemies. Someone has said facetiously that the squid, provided with "pen" and "ink," was the original fountain-pen. The natural sepia ink of commerce is taken from a relative of the squid. Some squid may throw out a luminescent substance that makes a "fiery cloud." The mantle cavity, an elongate sac between the body proper and the mantle, expands and contracts with action of the strong muscles of the mantle. Slow movements of this nature serve the purpose of respiration, but a violent contraction of the mantle drives the water out with such force that the animal is thrust rapidly backward. By this sort of "jet propulsion," a squid travels in reverse with real velocity.

A near relative of the squid is the octopus (many species) which has, as the name implies, eight arms, useful for capture of prey and for creeping over solid surfaces. The octopods are benthonic. Other near relatives are the chambered or pearly nautilus, and the argonaut or paper nautilus discussed on an earlier page.

All squids live in the sea, and there are many species, of diverse forms and sizes, from midgets to the giant squid, which seems to be nearly 50 feet in total length and is sometimes called "pirate of the ocean." Hjort found in a whale's stomach a piece of squid tentacle with a diameter of 17 centimeters (7 inches) and he mentions the report of a part of an arm discharged from the whale and having a length of 18 feet.[10] For many reasons squid are most important in the fauna of the ocean. They may be exceedingly numerous in coastal waters or far off shore: enormous numbers may be seen following shoals of herring and gorging themselves with the fish. Cod stomachs may be found full of squid; cod fishermen and others esteem them highly for bait. They constitute a principal food for the larger toothed whales—the cachalot (sperm whale) and the bottle-nose. The deeper layers of the open ocean, commented Hjort "contain multitudes of larger crustaceans and squids, and here only squid-hunting whales like the cachalot are found in numbers." Again, he mentions seeing squid for many miles "moving in the surface waters like luminous bubbles, resembling large milky white electric lamps being constantly lit and extinguished."

10. Murray and Hjort, *op. cit.*, p. 651.

Squid seem to occur at all depths, with, generally, the smaller ones in the upper waters and the larger in deeper. Certain species have wide distribution, having been taken in both the Atlantic and the Indian Ocean.

In some countries squid are esteemed for food. Cooked for the table, they have a delicious flavor, but it requires no little culinary art to overcome the natural toughness of the meat.

Some Lower Vertebrates

We cannot try to deal with all life in the sea, but some other vertebrate groups should be mentioned. We have passed entirely over the vertebrates of the lowest class which has relative small importance in the oceans. These are the cyclostomes, or vertebrates with circular, suctorial mouths and without even the rudiments of hinged jaws or paired limbs; such are the hagfishes and lampreys, which differ fundamentally from fish proper and should not be confused with them. The hagfishes, (with gill openings far back from the head) are all marine. The lampreys (with gill openings near the head) are sometimes known as "lamper eels," because their bodies are eel-like in form, except for the great difference in the mouth and for the absence of paired fins. Some spend their entire lives in fresh water; still others live in the sea but ascend rivers for the purpose of spawning. Most of the lampreys feed as adults upon the blood of fishes, to which they attach themselves by their mouths to rasp away the flesh with the use of the horny "teeth" on their tongues.

Beyond the fish in the scheme of classification are the classes of Amphibia, Reptilia, Aves, and Mammalia. Amphibia (salamanders and frogs) are not found at all in the sea, but are exclusively animals of fresh water and land. Reptiles, developed upon land, have invaded the sea, where the class is represented offshore by snakes and turtles. Iguanas (lizards) and crocodiles make forays into coastal waters of the southwest Pacific, but play a small part in marine economy. They interest us particularly as showing with other marine reptiles that in all of the four orders comprising most of the existing reptiles some representatives have been able to get back to the sea. Marine snakes, with tails flattened from side to side to make efficient organs of propulsion, are found in tropical waters. They do not have to repair to the shores for breeding, since they bring forth their young alive. They may attain a length of more than 2 meters (approximately 7 feet), and some are highly poisonous.

Sea turtles are notably specialized for life in water, with their limbs transformed into powerful paddles. They have been found at least 250 miles from land. Most of them, if not all, still come ashore for spawning, making their way awkwardly over sand beaches to deposit eggs in one or several clutches and usually more than a hundred per clutch. The eggs are placed in deep holes excavated in the sand above high-tide line, covered with several inches or a foot of packed sand, and left to their fate. The young, hatched from the eggs after some months, must burrow up through the sand, find their way down to the sea, and begin swimming lives independently.

The sea turtles fall into four general types, each with one or two species. Loggerheads have been known to attain a weight of 850 pounds, but specimens over 300 pounds in weight are rare. They are carnivorous and little valued as food. Green turtles, usually, are not so large, yet a specimen 4 feet in length and 850 pounds in weight, has been reported. Those now commonly caught in the Atlantic weigh 150-200 pounds. Green turtles are mainly vegetarian in habit and are highly esteemed as food for man. The smaller tortoise-shell turtle is peculiar in having the horny covering of the shell made of thick, translucent plates, which overlap in shingle fashion and are marked with variegated colors. These give the valuable "tortoise shell" of commerce. Largest of all are the great leatherback turtles, which may attain a length of 8 feet and a weight of more than 1,000 pounds. They keep to deeper water, except when coming ashore for deposition of eggs. They are known to devour jellyfish. Most of these turtles have a world-wide distribution in the warmer waters.[11]

Sea Fowl

About the birds of the sea whole volumes have been written. They are of many kinds and habits—alike only in that they find food in the sea, and, therefore, are important components of the community of sea life as a whole. Although not strictly a part of the nekton,

11. Clifford H. Pope, *Turtles of the United States and Canada* (Alfred A. Knopf, 1939. Pp. 343, 99 figs.)

they are best considered in this connection. Cormorants perch upon exposed rocks or float upon the water and dive after fish. Gulls and terns snatch small fish and debris from the surface. Pelicans light upon the sea surface and thrust long bills and necks into the water to seize their prey, which are carried in capacious pouches. Gannets and boobies make spectacular plunges from aloft to disappear and reemerge with the captured fish. The man-o-war bird darts upon other birds carrying fish from the water, causes them to drop the prey, and catches the fish in midair. Diving petrels spend much of the time floating inconspicuously or swimming beneath the surface for food. Albatrosses, principally of the southern hemisphere, soar or glide through the air, keeping for long periods barely above the crests of the waves with only a rare stroke of the wings. Penguins, most highly specialized of all, have completely lost the power of flight; the wings are transformed into paddles for diving; the body is beautifully streamlined and its coat of feathers presents somewhat the appearance of a thick coat of hair. Penguins walk awkwardly, but effectively enough, on the rocks of the lower shore line, where they nest in caverns barely above the wash of the waves. Because of their toddling walk, Peruvians call them "pajaro-niños," or baby-birds.

For all the different kinds of sea birds the ocean is the chief or only place of feeding. Some merely fly out from land to eat; others live on or over the sea the greater part of their lives; but all return to solid earth for breeding. There is again great diversity in breeding habit—with nests of different kinds, made variously on the level shore lands or the more or less even tops of islands, on the sides of cliffs rising abruptly from the sea, in the niches of relatively small rocks jutting above the wash of the waves, in shore caverns, or even in burrows made in the ground a little distance back from shore.

Some species occur in vast numbers in places where the sea is particularly fertile in plankton and in small fish and crustacea. A single nesting-ground of cormorants on one of the islands off the coast of Peru was measured roughly and found to cover 60,000 square meters, or about 15 acres. The number of nests per square meter averaged barely over three; the average number of birds per nest was presumed to be four—a pair of adults and two fully grown young. With twelve birds per square meter, the number of birds occupying the breeding ground would have been over 700,000. At later times the rookery was very much larger. When such a flock of birds arose to darken the sky and to stream, seemingly endlessly, over the ocean in search of schools of anchobetas, one naturally exclaimed, "millions." Generally we exaggerate in the presence of such numbers, but it is certain that a million is not too large an estimate for the number of cormorants in a single flock in that region. Yet this was only one (and probably the largest) of numerous rookeries in that general region—and this particular cormorant was only one of several kinds of birds that fed on the fishes of the surface waters off the coast of Peru in the Humboldt current. Some other regions have more or less comparable populations of birds; smaller populations are found along coasts everywhere, in addition to those which, for the time, are on the sea at substantial distances from land. The inevitable conclusion is that a prodigious volume of fish is taken from the sea to support avian life—doubtless much more than are taken in all the commercial fisheries of the world.

The take of fish by birds is not all lost to the organic world in the sea, for much of it must return to the water in the form of droppings, dead bodies, and other wastes. Where, however, the topographic and meterological conditions are favorable, deposits of bird manure may accumulate on land to great heights. When the deposits of guano on the coast and islands of Peru were discovered to European and American commerce about a century ago the accumulations were a hundred or more feet in thickness on some islands. Many millions of tons of this highly valuable fertilizer were "mined," loaded onto vessels, and transported to the northern hemisphere.[12] The peculiarly high quality of Peruvian guano derives chiefly from the fact that it never rains on the islands, and the cool, sea-moistened air blowing from the cold Humboldt current (p. 131, above) over islands warmed by a tropical sun is "rarefied" and dried. The richly nitrogenous guano is baked almost immediately, with no formation

12. According to the best estimates more than ten million tons of Peruvian guano, worth many millions of dollars, were mined and exported from a single group of islands during a period of twenty years, 1851–72. Recently, more than a hundred thousand tons seem to be deposited each year, along the entire coastal region of Peru. See articles by the author in the *National Geographic Magazine*, (June, 1920) and in *Science*, Vol. LXXXII (1935); and Robert Cushman Murphy's *Bird Islands of Peru*, (Putnams, 1925), and "The Peruvian Guano Islands Seventy Years Ago," in *Natural History*, Vol. XXVII (1927).

of ammonia to be lost to the atmosphere. In other regions of great populations of birds, rains may wash the manure into the sea, or there may be sufficient moisture in the atmosphere to cause the loss of the nitrogenous components in the form of ammonia, leaving guano which is predominantly phosphate. Valuable deposits of phosphate guano are found in various parts of the world.

Sea Otters, Sea Lions, and Sea Cows

The warm-blooded, air-breathing, hair-covered animals that incubate and nourish the young within their bodies and later nurse them from mammary glands, are primarily adapted for life on land. Yet quite a number of mammals, in at least four different orders, have acquired secondary adaptations to life in the sea.

The sea cows, manatees, and dugongs, constituting the order of Sirenia, with stout bodies, fore limbs modified as flippers, and no hind limbs, live near shores, or in the lower parts of rivers in tropical or semitropical regions, where they browse upon the aquatic vegetation. We shall not here consider them further. The Cetacea, including whales, porpoises, and dolphins, have become so highly specialized for life in the sea that they cannot survive at all when their bodies are not supported by water. We shall devote a special section to them. The Carnivora and, more notably, the Pinnipedia have representatives living mainly in the sea, but repairing to the land for breeding.

The carnivores of most general marine habit are the sea otters, 4 or 5 feet in length, which yield one of the most valuable of all furs, and which were so avidly hunted in past times that, long ago, they were brought nearly to extinction. They are said now to be coming back under conditions of strict protection. They have been found only along the shores of the North Pacific. The polar bears of Arctic ice and waters should be mentioned, but their range of distribution is narrow. Neither the otter nor the polar bear can play any great part in the marine economy.

In the order of Pinnipedia, the seals and, to a lesser extent, the walrus are of some real significance in the community of life in the sea. The name Pinnipedia refers to the fact that the limbs are modified as flippers, or *pinnas*. The walruses constitute the family Odobenidae, characterized by the very elongated canine teeth projecting as prominent tusks from the upper jaw. They, like the polar bears, are confined to the Arctic. The seals fall into two families. Those that have external ears, although small ones, constitute the eared seals (Otariidae), or sea lions and fur seals; the latter are particularly highly prized for their undercoat of fine fur beneath the coarser hair. Those without external ears and with hind limbs useless for locomotion on land are the earless seals or true seals (Phocidae). Among these are the harbor seal, harp seal, and hooded seal of northern waters, Arctic, Atlantic or Pacific, and several species of far southern waters, including the great elephant seal. The last-mentioned may have a length of 20 feet.

Sea lions occur abundantly on the west coasts of North and South America, the upper South Atlantic coast of South America, and the Pacific coast of Asia from Japan northward, but are entirely absent from the North Atlantic. With their highly modified paddle-like limbs they are powerful swimmers passing back and forth from rocks to sea. The fur seals roam widely. They have a double coat of hair, including the soft under-fur, and are adapted to continued life in cold waters. They return to land only for the purpose of rearing young and mating for the next year. The breeding grounds of the northern fur seal are chiefly on the Pribilof Islands in the Bering Sea. Others occur in high southern latitudes, particularly in South Pacific, Indian Ocean, and Antarctic waters. Because of the great depletion of the fur seals from uncontrolled hunting upon land and sea, international treaties were adopted, some thirty-odd years ago, prohibiting all pelagic sealing and permitting only government-controlled killing of surplus "bulls" on the breeding grounds. Under wise and scientific administrations of the fur-seal "fishery," the population is now markedly replenished.

The Whales

Largest of all the members of the nekton are the whales, and among them are the most massive of all animals that live or are known ever to have lived. The blue or sulphur-bottom whale attains a length of 79 feet and a weight of 60 to 80 tons. There are two types of whales as distinguished by structure and habit of feeding. The "right whales" of whalers, and others related to them, have no teeth on the jaws, but are equipped with a fine straining apparatus composed of innumerable frayed sheets of "whalebone" (baleen) suspended from the upper jaw on both sides. With the great mouths open as the whale swims, water, carrying the small animals of the plankton, flows in and passes out through the giant strainer. Repeated catches of the minute organisms of the plankton taken in this way afford sufficient nourishment to build a huge body with exceptional rapidity, to support high expenditure of energy, and to enable the storage beneath the skin of voluminous masses of insulating oily blubber. Some whalebone whales feed exclusively on such small organisms as copepods, and pteropods, and the small shrimplike "kril" (euphausiids), all of which, where encountered in conspicuous numbers, the whalers know as "whale feed," and recognize as indicators of the proximity of whales. A ton of such food has been found in the stomach of a blue whale.

Other whalebone whales take such small fishes as the boreal capelin and young herring, and even, sometimes, shark and sea fowl; the fin whale and the hump backs are in this latter group of fish feeders.

Whales of another type have teeth on one or both jaws. The smaller "toothed whales," the porpoises and dolphins of coastal waters, with teeth on both upper and lower jaws, feed on fish; but the larger sperm whale, or cachalot, and the bottle-nose, with teeth only on the lower jaw, are believed to feed mainly on squid. These great whales have remarkable diving powers; according to the most creditable reports, they may "sound," or dive vertically and with great speed, to a depth of nearly half a mile. In so doing they pass from a region with pressure of barely more than one atmosphere to a level where the pressure is the equivalent of about 80 atmospheres. The physiological methods by which they speedily adjust themselves to such extraordinary change of pressure are yet a mystery. The giant squids, which seem to be a prominent part of their food, are believed to live only at great depths.[13] Parenthetically, it is only the cachalot among the whales that could have swallowed Jonah or any other man.

13. The two types of whales differ also in that the nostrils of the toothed whales have a common opening on the top of the beak: when they "blow," or expel air from the lungs, a single spray of vapor appears. From the well-separated external nasal openings of the whalebone whales, two divergent blows appear. Thus, by the single or double "blow," sperm whales and right whales may be distinguished at a distance.

Whales roam widely in pursuit of food, particularly the sperm whale, which is taken in the Pacific, Atlantic, and Indian oceans. Humpback whales, which are of medium size, are found mostly near the coasts. Right whales are taken largely in the colder waters of high northern or southern latitudes, as around Greenland in the north and the Falkland Islands in the south; but some have been taken in the Gulf of Mexico, off the coast of Brazil, and in coastal waters elsewhere. In the open seas of low, tropical latitudes only the sperm whale is regularly sought. Except during periods of parturition and nursing, the whalebone whales must find regions of rich plankton development, and these are not in the open sea in warmer regions. They are said to find in some instinctive way, and to follow, shoals of particular kinds of plankton organisms. A classical example of evidence of migrations was the discovery of whales in Barents Sea, north of Russia, in two different years, bearing in their bodies bomb lances presumed to have been planted in them in waters somewhere off the American coast. At least, most whales are known to be very migratory, some calving in tropical seas and feeding at other times in Arctic or Antarctic waters. Some seem restricted to Arctic or near Arctic waters while others wander far from polar seas. Whalebone whales make "seasonal migrations from tropical calving grounds to the feeding grounds in the colder waters of Arctic and Antarctic Seas."[14]

All life is remarkable, but the whales have features of structure and habit that are of exceptional interest. They are the most highly specialized of all mammals. Although undoubtedly descended from terrestrial animals, they have attained the highest degree of adaptation to life in water. Hair has been lost except for a few small hairs developing and remaining only temporarily on the unborn foetus. The fore limbs are paddle like and adapted for steering and balancing; modified hind limbs have been completely lost except for small internal vestiges in some. Propulsion is effected by the hinder part of the body, which is extended by the tail flukes, spread horizontally. Although breathing the free air, they may dive to great depths, and they are entirely helpless when out of water: the very weight of the body on the lungs causes early suffocation for a stranded whale. When man ascends mountains, or descends into the water, he has

14. Remington Kellogg, *Adaptation of Structure to Function in Whales* (Carnegie Institution of Research, Publication No. 501, 1938, pp. 649-82).

great difficulty in enduring change in pressure to the extent of much less than one atmosphere; yet some whales may pass rapidly through depths involving quick change of pressure in amount equivalent to many atmospheres.

Although whales are warm blooded, they may live in icy water, protected, not by a coat of fur, but by the even better insulation afforded by a coat of blubber a foot thick beneath the skin. In cold, or at least cool, briny homes, they bring forth their young in active condition and suckle them from mammary glands. The young, which at birth may be 7 meters (over 20 feet) in length and a couple of tons in weight, may, at weaning six months later, be twice as long and ten or eleven times as heavy. By nursing, and then feeding upon organisms of near-microscopic size, they may put on weight at the rate of about 30 tons a year, to mature at the age of two years. Such growth, as the physiologist Krogh has said, is "unparalleled in the animal kingdom." The whales easily display the very maximum of metabolic efficiency in the sea—or anywhere!

Summary.

1. Fishes are most abundant where nutritive conditions are most favorable, as near continents, in regions of divergence of currents, or where warm and cold streams converge. The shallower waters generally are far richer in fishes than is the abyssal plain.

2. In respect to breadth of distribution, abyssal fishes have widest ranges; but a deep area cut off from the main area by subsurface ridges, as the Norwegian Sea, may have a distinct deep-water fauna.

3. In the Norwegian Sea deep fishes are subject always to temperatures below the freezing point of fresh water.

4. Cold water fishes living at higher levels in high latitudes may be found at greater depths beneath warmer surface waters in lower latitudes.

5. The coloring of fishes shows some relation to translucency of the water, to depth, and to the faunal or floral environment.

6. Organs for emission of light are particularly characteristic of fishes of the upper levels rather than of those of the dark depths.

7. Although eyes are generally best developed in fishes of the surface waters, some deep-living fishes have very large eyes.

8. Because they are likely to be carried by currents, particularly

as eggs and young, and for other reasons, fishes engage much in horizontal and vertical migrations, seasonal or diurnal.

9. The vast majority of fish are born to serve as food for other animals.

10. Squids are important elements of the nekton and play a significant part as food of fishes and whales. Many have organs for emission of light.

11. Vertebrates of the nekton, other than fishes, are the lampreys and hagfishes (which are not fishes), reptiles of various kinds and some mammals.

12. Sea fowl of many kinds play a great part in the bionomics of the sea as also do seals, sea lions, and whales.

13. The several kinds of whales differ in the kinds of food taken. The cachalot seems to subsist largely upon squid. Other kinds take small fish that go in dense schools. Most of the whalebone whales feed on the small organisms of the plankton, which they strain from the water in great bulk. The largest of whales are plankton-feeders and, upon such food, they grow at rates unparalleled anywhere else in the animal kingdom.

Selected Bibliography

(Comprising titles of books most freely drawn upon in this volume and a few others valuable for special reference.)

Adams, K. T. *Hydrographic Manual.* U. S. Dept. of Commerce Coast and Geodetic Survey, Special Publication No. 143. Rev. ed., Washington, 1942. Pp. xiv, 940. 190 figs., 42 tables.

Bigelow, Henry B. *Oceanography; Its Scope, Problems, and Economic Importance.* New York, Houghton Mifflin, 1931. Pp. vi, 263.

Boulenger, E. G. *A Natural History of the Seas.* New York, Appleton-Century, 1936. Pp. 215. Well illustrated.

Clarke, F. W. *Data of Geochemistry.* U. S. Geological Survey, Bull. No. 616, 1916.

Coker, R. E. "Life in the Sea," *The Scientific Monthly,* XLVI (1938), 299-322, 416-32.

Daly, Reginald Aldworth. *The Floor of the Ocean.* Chapel Hill, The University of North Carolina Press, 1942. Pp. x, 177.

Ekman, Sven. *Tiergeographie des Meeres.* Akad. Verlagsgesellsch. M. B. H., Leipzig, 1935. Pp. 542.

Flattely, F. W., C. W. Walton, and J. Arthur Thomson. *The Biology of the Sea-Shore.* London, Sidgwick and Jackson, Ltd., 1922. Pp. xvi, 336. 16 pl., 23 figs.

Fowler, G. Herbert and E. J. Allen (Eds.) *Science of the Sea. An Elementary Handbook of Practical Oceanography.* (Second Edition.) Prepared by the Challenger Society, Oxford, Clarendon Press, 1928. Pp. xxiii, 502, 220 figs. 11 charts.

Gran, H. H. "Phytoplankton Methods and Problems," Cons. Perm. Internat. Explor. Mer., Journ. Conseil., VII (1932), 343-58.

Haeckel, Ernst. *Planktonic Studies: A Comparative Investigation of the Importance and Constitution of the Pelagic Fauna and Flora.* Washington, U. S. Commission of Fish and Fisheries, Report for 1889-91,

(1893), pp. 565-641. Tr. by George Wilton Field from *Plankton-Studien*, publ. in Jena, 1890.

Haight, F. J. *Coastal Currents along the Atlantic Coast of the United States*. U. S. Dept. of Commerce, Coast and Geodetic Survey, Special Publication, No. 230. Washington, 1942. Pp. iv, 73.

Harvey, H. W. *Biological Chemistry and Physics of Sea Water*. Cambridge, University Press, 1928. Pp. x, 194.

———. *Recent Advances in the Chemistry and Biology of Sea Water*. Cambridge University Press, 1945. Pp. vii, 164.

Henderson, L. J. *The Fitness of the Environment*. New York, Macmillan, 1924. Pp. xv, 317.

Herdman, Sir William A. *Founders of Oceanography and Their Work. An Introduction to the Science of the Sea*. London, Edward Arnold & Co., 1923.

Hesse, Richard. *Ecological Animal Geography*. New York (Wiley) and London, 1937. Pp. xiv, 597. An authorized, rewritten edition based on *Tiergeographie auf oekologischer Grundlage* (Jena, G. Fischer, 1924), prepared by W. C. Allee and Karl P. Schmidt.

Johnstone, James. *Conditions of Life in the Sea*. Cambridge, University Press, 1908. Pp. iv, 332.

———. *An Introduction to Oceanography*. London, 1928. Pp. 368.

———. *Life in the Sea*. Cambridge, University Press, 1911. Pp. vii, 150.

Krummel, Otto. *Handbuch der Ozeanographie*. Stuttgart, Engelhorn, 1907, 1911. 2 vols. Pp. 526; 764.

Lohmann, H. "Die Probleme der Modernen Planktonforschung," *Verh. der Deutschen Zool. Ges.*, 1912, pp. 16-109.

Marmer, H. A. *The Sea*. New York, Appleton, 1930. Pp. x, 312.

Maury, M. F. *The Physical Geography of the Sea*. Sixth ed. New York, Harper, 1856. Pp. xvi, 348. 13 pl.

Mears, Eliot G. *Pacific Ocean Handbook*. Stanford University, Delkin, 1944. Pp. vii, 192. Many maps.

Meisel, Max. *Bibliography of American Natural History. The Pioneer Century, 1769-1865*. Brooklyn, Premier Publishing Co., 1924-1929. 3 vols.

Meek, Alexander. *The Migration of Fish*. London, Arnold, 1916. Pp. xviii, 427.

Murphy, Robert Cushman. *Bird Islands of Peru*. New York, Putnam's, 1925. Pp. xx, 362.

———. *Oceanic Birds of South America*. New York, American Museum of Natural History, 1936. Pp. xxiv, 1245. 2 vols.

Murray, John. "The General Conditions of Existence and Distribution of Marine Organisms," *Annual Report of the Smithsonian Institution for 1896*, Washington, 1898, pp. 397-469.

———. *The Ocean; a General Account of the Science of the Sea*. New York, Henry Holt, 1913. Pp. 256. 12 colored pl.

Murray, Sir John, and Dr. Johan Hjort (with contributions from A.

Appellöf, H. H. Gran, and B. Holland-Hansen). *The Depths of the Ocean*. London, Macmillan, 1912. Pp. xx, 821, 4 maps, 9 pl.

Osborn, Fairfield. *The Pacific World*. New York, Norton, 1944. Pp. 218.

Ricketts, Edward, and Jack Calvin. *Between Pacific Tides*. London, Stanford University Press, 1939. Pp. xxii, 320. 45 pl. 112 figs.

Russell, F. S., and C. M. Yonge. *The Seas*. London and New York, Frederick Warne & Co., 1928 and 1936. Pp. xiii, 379. 127 pl.

Schultz, Leonard P. with Edith M. Stern. *The Ways of Fishes*. New York, Van Nostrand, 1948. Pp. xii, 264.

Steuer, Adolf. *Leitfaden der Planktonkunde*. Leipzig and Berlin, Teubner, 1911. Pp. 382. One color pl., 279 figs.

Sverdrup, H. U. *Oceanography for Meterologists*. New York, Prentice-Hall, 1942. Pp. xv, 246. 4 charts.

Sverdrup, H. U., Martin W. Johnson, and Richard H. Fleming. *The Oceans, Their Physics, Chemistry, and General Biology*. New York, Prentice-Hall, 1942. Pp. x, 1087. 7 charts.

Tanner, Z. L. *Deep Sea Exploration*. "A General Description of the Steamer Albatross, Her Appliances and Methods," *Bulletin of the U. S. Fish Commission*, xvi (1896), 257-428. 39 pl., 76 cuts.

———. "On the Appliances for Collecting Pelagic Organisms, with Special Reference to Those Employed by the United States Fish Commission," *Bulletin of the U. S. Fish Commission*, xiv (1894), 143-51. 4 pl.

———. *Report on the Construction and Outfit of the United States Fish Commission Steamer, Albatross*. Washington, U. S. Fish Commission Report for 1883, pp. 3-116. Front., 55 pl., 20 figs.

Taylor, Harden F. "Resources of the Ocean," *The Journal of the Franklin Institute 214* (2): August, 1932.

Thomson, C. Wyville. *The Depths of the Sea*. London, Macmillan, 1873. Pp. xxi, 527.

Vaughan, Thomas Wayland, and others. *International Aspects of Oceanography, Oceanographic Data and Provisions for Oceanographic Research*. Washington, National Academy of Sciences, 1937. Pp. xvi, 225.

Wilson, Douglas. *Life of the Shore and Shallow Sea*. London, Ivor Nicholson and Watson, Ltd., 1937. Pp. 150.

ZoBell, Claude. *Marine Microbiology. A Monograph on Hydrobacteriology*. Waltham, 1946. (Chronica Botanica)

SOME RECENT, READABLE AND SIGNIFICANT BOOKS ON THE SEA

Bigelow, Henry B. and W. T. Edmondson. *Wind Waves at Sea Breakers and Surf*. Washington, U. S. Navy Hydrographic Office, Publication No. 602, 1947.

Carson, Rachael. *The Sea Around Us.* New York, Oxford University Press, 1950.

Coleman, John S. *The Sea and Its Mysteries.* London, C. Bell and Sons, Ltd., 1950.

Ekman, Sven. *Zoogeography of the Sea.* London, Sidgewick and Jackson, Ltd., 1953.

Index

Abalones, utilization, 251
Aberdeen, Fishery Board, 37
Absorption, selective, 172
Abyssal benthic, 181, 245
Abyssal pelagic zone, 181
Abyssal waters, temperature, 98
"Adiabatic" warming, 98
Aegean Sea, use of dredge in, 20
Agar, produced from red algae, 201
Agassiz, Alexander, 41-43; cruises directed, 41; directed scientific work by "Albatross," 42; organizer, apparatus designer, and zoologist (summary of works), 55; Gulf Stream studies, 126; on azoic zone, 30; wire rope, 251
Agassiz, Louis, stimulated interest in Marine Zoology, with United States Coast and Geodetic Survey, on continental and oceanic areas, 40
Agulhas Current, 134-135
"Air-mapping," pioneered by Hydrographic Office, United States Navy, 47
"Albatross," 41, 43-45; explorations by Alexander Agassiz, 42, 43
Alepocephalidae, 262
Aleutian Current, 133
Algae, distribution, 198; exceed animal plankton, 212; filamentous, 199; green, brown, red, 243;
Alkalinity, variable, 88

Allee, W. C., vii, 82, 180
Allen, Winifred E., cited on temperature effects, 103; quoted on Noctiluca, 221; quoted on productivity of plankton, 185
"All-mouth," 270
All-Union Scientific Research Institution, of Marine Fisheries and Oceanography, 35
Amino acids, synthesis by plants, 183
Ammodytes, 268
Amphibia, not in sea, 291
Amphipoda in plankton, 228
Amundsen Roald, attainment of South Pole, 15; sailing of North West Passage, 15
Anacanthini, 266
Anaplopoma, 276
"Anchobetas," 159, food of guano birds, 262
Anchovies, 261, feed on plankton, 142
Angler fish or goosefish (*Lophius piscatorius*), 270
Anguilla, 263
Animal feed, from fish and fish wastes, 274
Annelida, in plankton, 224
Antarctic, as abyssal water supply, 90
Antarctic, bottom water traced into North Atlantic, 129, 135; source of bottom water, 60, 126; faunal

zones, 258; German deep sea expedition, 32; greatest producer of icebergs, 136; penetration of, 15; transverse movement, 135

Antarctic continent, first recognized by Wilkes, 46

Antarctic convergence, 141

Antarctic Current, 134

Antarctic Drift, 121, 122, 125, 131

Antarctic intermediate waters, in South Pacific and Indian Oceans, 135

Antarctic Ocean, arbitrary boundary, 63; circulation of, 134

Antennarius, 272

Antiboreal, zone of life, 259

Antilles Current, joins Florida Current, 127

Apodes, 263

Arabians, preservation of ancient knowledge, 14

Arago, Laboratory at Bonyuls-Sur-Mer, 38

Archibenthic, in benthos, 245; on continental slope, 181

Arctic, area of sea ice, 136; source of dense bottom water, 126

"Arctic," soundings in North Atlantic, 1851-1856, 40

Arctic Ocean, salinity of, 82, 135; surrounded by land masses, 63, 135

Arctic life, 256

Arctic region, source of cold bottom water, 60

Arctic waters, Canadian research, 53; meet Gulf Stream, 54; rich in dissolved gasses, 90

Argonaut, 226

"Armauer Hansen," 34

Arthropoda, 227; few species found in sea, 186

Artificial pearls, from fish scales, 274

Ascidians, larvae in plankton, 235

Atherina, 268

Atkins, W. R. H., 37; cited on materials in solution, 84

Atlantic Boreal, zone, of life, 258

Atlantic Ocean, coastal contacts, broad, continental slope, 63; dense bottom water source, 126; deep

water, 61; distribution of oxygen, 90; German deep sea expedition, 32; gross features, 59; "intermediate water", 136; receives major portion of fresh water drainage, 65; salinity, 82; surface temperature, 99; tides, 151

"Atlantis," 51

Atlantis, the legend, 12

Atmosphere, 122; reservoir of heat, 94; studied by Maury, 23; interchange of energy with sea, 161

Azoic area, Forbes theory, 20, 193; nonexistent, 27, 109

Azoic region, revised theory invalid, 30

Azores, 33

Bache, Alexander, Director United States Coast and Geodetic Survey, 40; with United States Coast and Geodetic Survey, 48; studied Gulf Stream, 126

"Bache," ship of United States Coast and Geodetic Survey, 48; made West Indian explorations, 49

Bacteria, in the deep, 205; in plankton, 179; use of dissolved organic matter, 85; of decomposition, 84; nitrogen-fixing, 86

Baffin, W., search for Northwest Passage, 14

Baird, Spencer F., "founder" of United States Commission of Fish and Fisheries, 43, 46

Balboa, discovery of Pacific, 14

Baltic, salinity of, 81

Bandfish (Cepola), 267

Banks, fisheries, 259

Barents Sea, richness of life, 214; temperature change, 257; great fisheries, 282

Barnacles, in benthos, 243, 244; larvae in plankton, 229

Barracuda (Sphyraena), 268

Barriers to plant and animal migration, 62

"Bathybius," 27

Bathymetrical map, first for North

Atlantic, 23
Bathypelagic zone, 181
Bathythermograph, 101
Bayfield, Captain, exploration of Gulf of St. Lawrence, 53
Bay of Fundy, Canadian research, 53; "tides" of, 153
Bay of St. Malo, "tides" of, 153
"Beagle," voyage of, 18; cruise mentioned, 209
Bêche-de-mer, 252
Beers, C. D., viii
"Belgic," 35
Belknap, Rear Admiral G. E., commanded U. S. S. "Tuscarora," 40; used piano wire for sounding, 70
Bellinghausen, exploration of Antarctic region, 15
Belone, 266
Benguela Current, map, 121; effect on land climate, 124
Benthic, 245
Benthic region, subdivisions, 181
Benthos (defined), 178, 241
Bergen Museum, published results of North Atlantic expedition, 28
Bering, V., search for Northwest Passage, 14
Bicarbonates, 88
Bigelow, Henry B., first director of Woods Hole Oceanographic Institution, 51; investigation of Gulf of Maine, 49; quoted on accumulation of globigerina ooze, 116
Bingham Oceanographic Collection, 50
Bingham Oceanographic Laboratory, established at Yale, 50
Birds, 294; guano-producing, 159
Birge, E. A., improved centrifuge, 34
Bjerknes, J. A., at Bergen (Geophysical Institute), 38
"Black cod," 276
"Blake," ship of United States Coast and Geodetic Survey, 48, use of steel cables for dredging, 42; explored Caribbean and Gulf of Mexico, 41; explorations by Alexander Agassiz, 42; observations of

Gulf Stream, 127; wire rope, 251
Blind fish, 286
Blue-green Algae, 199
Blue-green radiation, penetration of, 172-193
Blueness, due to scattering of radiation among molecules, 173
Bonito, 267
"Bore," 153
Boreal zone, fisheries, 259
Börno Research Station, in Sweden, 38
Bost, R. W., vii
Bottle-nose whale, 297
Bottom, distribution of fishes, 257
Bottom deposits, 112-119; formation of, 18; examined in Maury's program, 23
"Bottom grabs," 113
Bottom sampler, 250
Bottom-sampling tube, 113
Bottom, temperatures, 98
Bottom water, variations in salinity, 82, 126
Brachiopoda, larvae in plankton, 224
Brazil Current, map, 121
British Isles, use of dredge in waters adjacent to, 20
Brooke, Midshipman, preparation of sounding apparatus, 23; improved sounding apparatus, 47, 69
Brooks, W. K., cited on simplicity of plant bodies, 91; quoted on microorganisms as basic food, 193
Brown algae (Phaeophyceae), 199
Bryozoa, in benthos, 240; larvae in plankton, 224
Bulletin of the Bingham Oceanographic Collection, 51
Bulletins et Annales de l'Institute Oceanographique, 33
Bureau of Fisheries, supersedes Fish Commission, 48; Fish and Wildlife Service, 48
Byrd, Captain Richard, expedition to Antarctica, 16

Cable, first international, 24
Cachalot, 297
Calcium carbonate oozes, 119

Calanoids, in plankton, 232

Calanus finmarchicus, in plankton, 233

Calanus hyperboreus, 234; in plankton, 230; surface plankter, 233

Calcium carbonate, precipitated by red algae, 201

California Current, map, 121; 132-133; receives Aleutian Current, 133; studied by Scripps Institution, 50

"Callao Painter," 132

Cameras, for photographing bottom, 113

Canada, Dominion of, oceanographic research, 53-54

Canadian Arctic Expedition, 53

Canaries, discovery, 12

Canaries Drift, 13, 129; map, 121

Capelin, affected by temperature, 257

Cape of Good Hope, rounding of, 14

Caranx, 268

Carbon dioxide, and photosynthesis, 89

Carbon dioxide, in organic production, 86; in solution, 88; interchange between atmosphere and sea, 89; relation to acid-base equilibrium, 88

Carbonates, 88

Carbonic Acid, in solution, 88

Caribbean Sea, path of Gulf Stream, 127

Carnegie Institution of Washington, study of Terrestrial Magnetism, 7

Carpenter, W. B., 26

"Catalyst," ship of University of Washington Oceanographic Laboratories, 52

Catch Basin, 78

Central North Atlantic eddy, 129

Centrifuge, 236

Cephalopoda, 226

Cepola, 268

Cero, 268

Chaetognatha, in plankton, 224

Chaetopterus, 244

Chalk deposits, 116

"Challenger," 24; bottom deposit findings, 109; deep-sea sediment, 27; dredging and trawling, 250; exploration of marine plankton, 210; sounding methods, 69; study of bottom deposits, 114

Challenger Expedition, shows theory of azoic area to be invalid, 30; reimbursement of cost, 28; work of John Murray, 27

Challengerida, 27

Challenger Reports, by John Murray, 27

Charlottenlund Slot, 38

Chauliodes, wide distribution, 262

Chaunax, 272

Chemical analysis, of sea water, 79

Chemicals, deposition of, 83

Chemistry of sea waters, 78; biological relations, 92

Chesapeake Bay, extent of shoreline, 60

Chiasmodus niger, distensible stomach, 269

Chimaeras, 260

China, Department of Oceanography, 35

Chip log, 123

Chlorine, disproportion of, 83

Chlorinity, 80

Chlorophyceae, 199

"Christmas Island," phosphate mines, 28

Chun, Carl, directs oceanographic investigations, 32; improvement of apparatus, organizer of expedition, 55; improvement of closing net, 31

Circulation of sea water, 120; affected by salinity, 83; affects organisms, 187; effect of salinity on, 77; in Pacific, 130-131; oceanic, conceived by Maury, 23

Cladocera, 229; affected by viscosity, 105

Clams, utilization, 261

Clarke and Gellis, bacteria as food of copepods, 205

Clarke, G. L. and R. H. Oster, cited on light penetration, 87

Climates, affected by Gulf Stream, 128; affected by interchanges of energy between sea and land, 161; affected by water movements, 124; Maury's observations on, 23

Climbing perch, 266

Clione limacina, in polar waters, 226

"Closing net," 30, 31, 276

Clupeidae, 274

Clupeoids, 261

Coalfish, 276

Coast Guard, 45; collaboration with Fish Commission, 45

Coast Survey, 45; collaboration with Fish Commission, 45; investigation of velocity of sound in sea water, 71

Coccolith oozes, 119

Coccolithophores, in plankton, 179; rate of sinking, 85

Coccolithophoridae, 205

Cod, important food fish, 266; migration of, 287

Codium, 199

Codlike fishes, commercial sources of vitamins, 274

Coelenterata, as macroplankton, 222

Coker, Robert E., publications cited, 159, 265, 294

"Cold Wall," off United States Coast, 128

Collected Reprints from the Woods Hole Oceanographic Institution, 52

Color, adaptive to environment, 284

Commerce, 56; interest of United States Exploring Expedition, 7, 46

Commercial oils, from fishes, 274

Committee on Oceanography, Canadian, 53

Communities, different in the several oceans and parts of the oceans, 65

Communities of animals, mapped by Forbes, 20

Compensation depth, defined, 87

Composition, from chlorinity, 80

Compressibility of water, 111

Conchs, utilization, 251

"Congrio," 267

Continental edge, 67

Continental shelf, 67, 112; deposits, 114

Continental slope, 67

Continental terrace, 67

Contributions to Canadian Biology, 53

Convection currents, 126, 141

Convergence of currents, causes sinking, 141

Cook, James, search for Northwest Passage, 14

Copeland, Charles W., made final designs for "Albatross," 43

Copepods, affecting distribution of herring, 7; carried in currents, 102; affected by temperature, 102; affected by viscosity, 105; food consumed, 213; food of whales, 207; in plankton, 230; make sea appear red or brown, 173; rate of sinking, 85; tolerance of pressure and lack of sunlight, 63

Copper, in crabs, 78

Coral Islands, 6; origin of, 18

Coral reefs, origin of, 27

Coral sands, 114

Corals, building reefs, 223; endure only small salinity changes, 182; in plankton, 223

Core sample, 113

Cormorants, 294

Coryphaena, 268

Costello, D. P., viii

Council of the Royal Society, 26

Counter Equatorial Current, map, 121 (See Equatorial Countercurrent)

Crabs, utilization, 252

Crinoids, in benthos, 246

Croakers, 276

Crustacea, in plankton, 228

Ctenophora, in plankton, 223

Current meters, 123

Currents, effect on temperature, 96; identified by salinity, 124; identified by temperature, 124; map, 121

Cusk eels, 268

"Cyclomorphosis," 105, 202

Cyclopoids, in plankton, 232

Cyclostomes, 291

Cyclothone, 262; correlation of light organs with depth, 286

Cyclothone signata, correlation of size with depth, 284

Cystoflagellates, 221

Daily tides, 148

Da Gama, Vasco, voyage, 14

"Dana," 34

Dana, James Dwight, 46; United States Exploring Expedition, 40

Danish Committee for Fisheries Investigations and the Study of the Sea, 38

Darwin, Charles, voyage of the "Beagle," 18, 209

Davis, John, search for Northwest Passage, 14

Decapods, larvae in plankton, 228

Decomposition, effect on oxygen content, 90

Deep-sea fishes, in benthos, 246

Deep water, 126

Deep waters, rise of (see also Upwelling), 86

Deeps, 67

De Fant, A., 38, 55

Deflection of wind-driven currents, 139

Del Cano, Sebastian, succeeds Magellan, 14

"Demersal," eggs, 286

Denmark, oceanographic operations, 32, 56

Density, 106; affected by evaporation, 168; affected by temperature, 98, 99; defined, 81; effect on form, 106; in relation to salinity, 80; streamlining, 187

Deposition of chemicals, 83

Deposits, 112; from icebergs, 118; deficiency of solid organic wastes in the depths, 85; of extra-terrestrial origin, 118; studies by Murray, 27

"Depot of Charts and Instruments," predecessor of Hydrographic Office, United States Navy, 45

Depth, effect on pressure, 109; and topography, 65 ff.

Depths of the ocean, Maury's observations on, 23

"Desert areas," 177

Desert areas, bluest parts of sea, 173

Desert dust, in deposits, 118

"Deutschland," expedition in Atlantic and Antarctic, 34

"Devilfishes," 226

Diatom, 27

Diatom ooze, 114-116

Diatoms, believed to form basic substances of vitamins, 202; affected by temperature, 102; affected by viscosity, 105; found in sea, 17; make sea appear yellowish, 173; production in enriched sea water, 192

Diatoms, on bottom, 243; rate of sinking, 85; source of food for small vegetarian animals, 202

Diaz, Bartholomew, voyage of, 14

Dinoflagellate algae, description and occurrence, 204; make sea appear red or brown, 173

Diurnal tides (see semi-daily tides)

"Discovery," 34

"Discovery II," 34

Dissolved gas content, source of knowledge of currents and drifts, 65

Divergence, 141

"Dogfish," 260

Dohrn, Anton, "Naples Station," 36

Dohrn, Reinhard, revitalizing "Naples Station," 36

Dolphin (Coryphaena), 269

"Dolphin," soundings in North Atlantic, 40

Dolphins, 295, 297

Dredge, "Agassiz" or "Blake," 42; for bottom fauna, 243; deep-sea, 113

Dredging, use of steel wire rope (Alexander Agassiz), 42

"Drift Anchor," 122

"Drift Bottles," 122

Drift bottles, used by Prince of Monaco, 33

Drift buoys, 123

Drifts, 122; identified by temperature, 124; identified by salinity, 124; Maury's observations on, 23

Drumfishes (Sciaenidae), 267, 276

Dugongs, 295

Earthquakes, cause "tidal waves," 156; cause waves of great velocities, 144

East Australian Current, map, 121

Eastern Hemisphere, includes greater bulk of land, 57-59

Echinodermata, studies of led to use of plankton net, 225

Eddies, faunal interchange with oceanic currents, 218

Eddy, in Indian Ocean, 134

Eddy viscosity, 103

Edinburgh, Medical School, 25

Edreobenthos, 242

Eel, in fresh and salt water, 182; life history, 263

Eelgrass, 206; habitat of fishes, 265

Eels, 276

Eggs, "emersal" and "demersal", 107

Ehrenberg, C. G., study of microscopic life in sea, 17

Ekman, Gustav, 34; organization of Biological Commission in Sweden, 38

Ekman, Sven, 55; on polychaete worm, 248; quoted on angle of deflection, 140

Ekman current meter, 123; dredge, 113

Elasmobranch fishes, osmotic pressure of body fluids, 182

Elasmobranchs, isotonic with sea water, 259

Electrical conductivity, in relation to salinity, 80

Elephant seal, 296

El Niño, 132

Elopidae, 262

Elver, 263

Emden Deep, 67

"Emersal eggs," 286

Emory, Samuel, viii

Enemies, necessity, 181; usefulness, 188

Energy, transformations, source, 160; interchanges, 161

Energy in circulation, 120

England, discovery, 12

Enteromorpha, 199

"Enterprise," collected bottom samples, 41

Epipelagic zone, 181

Equator, cold waters in depth, 98

Equatorial Countercurrent, 125; Atlantic Ocean, 127; in Indian Ocean, 134; Pacific Ocean, 132; map, 121

Equatorial Currents, 121

Eratosthenes, geography of earth, 13

Escallops and eelgrass, 206

Escallops, utilization, 251

Eulittoral, 187, 245

Euphausiids, 228; food of whales, 297

Eurybathic, animals, 248

Euryhaline, 182

Eurythermal, defined, 214

Evaporation, storage of heat, 94; cooling effect, 99; depends on vapor pressure, 165; effect on salinity, 83; energy transformation, 161

Everest, Mount, former sea bottom, 73

Exocoetus, 265

Extinction coefficient, 172

Eyes, (See Light Organs)

Falkland Current, 135

Fats, storage of energy, 183

Fauna e Flora del Golfo di Napoli, 36

Fertilizer, from fish and fish wastes, 274

Fierasfer, 269

File fish, 273; characteristic of Sargasso Sea, 284

Fire-fighting foams, from fish scales, 274

"Fish Commission," 43-45, 48

Fisheries, 56; prompting oceanographic studies, 6; in regions of upwelling, 142

Fisheries Laboratory at Lowestoft, Suffolk, 37

Fisheries Research Board of Canada, 53

Fisheries Science, linked with oceanography, 7

Fishery Board for Scotland at Aberdeen, 37

"Fish Hawk," Fish Commission vessel, 43

"Fishing frogs," 272

Fiske, John, characterization of voyages of Columbus and Magellan, 14

Flatworms, in plankton, 223

Floor of ocean, 67, 112

Florida Current, 127

Flotation, 108

"Flotation processes" of animals, 107

Flounderlike fishes, 266, 275

Flounders, benthonic mode of life, 269

Flying fishes, 265

Flying gurnards, 267

Foerst, H. M., improved centrifuge, 34

Fog, advection, 166

Foraminifera, deposits, 112; in plankton, 219

Forbes, Edward, biographical sketch, 19; linkage with Thomson and Murray, 25; concept of organic communities, 54; mentioned, 20, 29, 30

"Fram." drift of, 15, 35, 136

France, seaside stations, 38

Franklin, Benjamin; mapped Gulf Stream, 40, 126

Franklin, John, search for Northwest Passage, 14

Freezing point, affected by salinity, 96; effect on weight, 96-98; lowered by pressure, 98; variations of, 96

Friday Harbor Laboratories, 52

Frobisher, Martin, search for Northwest Passage, 14

Frog fishes, 272

Fur seals, 296

Fussler, Karl, vii

Ganoids, 260

Garpike, 266

Gases, in solution, 86

Gastrostomus bairdii, 264

Geophysical Institute at Bergen, 38

Geopolitics, and oceanography, 6

Geosphere, 122

Germany, oceanography, 37

"Gettysburg," 40

Gibraltar, Straits of, 12

Girard, Charles, 46

Globigerina bulloides, in plankton, 219

Globigerina ooze, 27, 114, 115, 116; contains coccolithophores, 205; rich in food material, 248

Glue, from fish and fish wastes, 274

Goldsborough, L. M., 45

Goosefish, 270

Gould, A. A., 46

"Grampus," 45

Gran, H. H., 55; at Oslo, 38; distribution of algae, 198; quoted on copepods, 232; quoted on temperature effects, 102

Grand Banks, meeting place of Arctic waters and Gulf Stream, 54; Newfoundland, turning point of Gulf Stream, 127; region of icebergs, 136

Gravity distributed heat, 171

Gray, Asa, 46

Great Britain, oceanographic operations, 37

Greeks, knowledge of oceans, 12

Greeley, A. W., search for North Pole, 15

Green algae (Chlorophyceae), 199

Greenland Area, 61

Greenland Sea, investigation of, 17

Greenness, due to calcareous matter, 173

Guano, return of organic substances to land, 294

Guano birds, 132, 159; feeding on anchobeta, 262

Guano deposits, traceable to nutritive materials brought up by upwelling, 142

Gudger, E. W., cited on sturgeon, 260; quoted on angler fishes, 272

"Guide," investigation of velocity of sound in sea water, 71

Guinea Current, map, 121

Gulf of Aden, 134

Gulf of Bothnia, salinity, 81

Gulf of Mexico, receives South Atlantic water, 61; tides, 151

Gulf of St. Lawrence, Canadian research, 53; cold waters, 129

Gulf Stream, 126-130; effect on climate, 128; effect on land climate, 124; effect on temperature, 96; map, 129; mapped by Benjamin Franklin, 40; Maury's observations, 22, 23; meets cold Arctic waters, 54; salinity, 129

Haddock, 275

Haeckel, Ernst, criticism of Hensen, 32; ecological classification of marine life, 209; proposed terms "benthos" and "nekton," 178; quoted on Crustacea, 228

Hagfishes, 291

Hake, 275

"Halcyon," 45

Halfbeak, 266

Halibut, 269

Halibut, migration, 287

Halobates, on surface of the sea, 227; seafaring neuston, 180

Halosphaera, 202; in plankton, 209

Haplomi, 264

Harpacticoids, in plankton, 231

Harvey, E. N., cited on bioluminescence, 285

Harvey, H. W., 37; chemistry of sea, 78; cited on downward drift of phosphates and nitrates, 191; cited on materials in solution, 84, 86

Hawaiian Islands, of volcanic origin, 67

Hayes, Harvey C., developed sonic depth-finder, 48, 70

Hazlett, Captain E. E., vii

Heat, absorption (greater in summer), 166; distribution, 95, 171; in atmosphere, 94; transfer to atmosphere, 166; transport, 164

"Heat Budget", 168

Heat capacity of water (see also temperature), 94, 124, 162

Heating, energy transformation, 161

Heat of evaporation, 164

Heat of melting, 95

Heat storage, 94

Heck, N. H., cited on velocity of sound in sea water, 71

Hedgpeth, Joel W., on Forbes, 20; on the "Albatross," 44

Helland-Hansen, B., 34, 38, 55; on "adiabatic" warming, 98; on light penetration, 172; divined occurrence of internal waves, 154

Hemirhamphus, 266

Henley, Catherine, vii

Hensen, Victor, at Kiel, 38; improvement of closing net, 31; plankton net, 33; proposed term "plankton," 179, 210; quantitative methods and organization of planktology, 55; study of plankton, 32

Herdman, Sir William A., 37; acknowledgment to, 11; quoted, 20, 23, 26; quoted on Alexander Agassiz, 42; quoted on Forbes's influence, 20; quoted on John Murray, 28; quoted on Monaco, 33; quoted on Murray's book, 29

Herodotus, story of Phoenician mariners, 12

Herpetobenthos, 242

Herring, 261; distribution affecting centers of population, 6; migration of, 287

Herringlike fishes (Clupeidae), 274

Hesiod, lands in ocean, 12

Hesse, Richard, W. C. Allee, and Karl P. Schmidt, cited on salinity of Red Sea, 82

Heteromi, world wide distribution, 265

Heteropods, in pteropod ooze, 117; in the plankton, 225

Hexactinellidae, in benthos, 245

Hildebrand, Samuel F., quoted, 273

Hippocampus, 265

"Hirondelle", 32

"Hirondelle II", 32

Histrio, 272

Hjort, Johan, 28, 38, 55, 268; food of whales, 234; on correlation of size with depth, 284; on development of visual organs, 286; on distribution of fishes, 282; squid in whale's stomach, 290; investigations for Canada, 54; North Atlantic Expedition, 28; on a deep-sea eel, 264; on "bottom" in mid-water, 215; on classification of fishes, 259; on distribution of pelagic crustacea, 214; on examination of stomachs, 236; on fish of Sargasso Sea, 213; on Globigerina ooze, 248; on Salpa, 235; on plankton, 234; on distribution of copepods, 215; on copepods, 232; on Crustacea, 228; on detritus, 213; on influence of Wyville Thomson Ridge, 284

Holoplankton, defined, 211

Holothuroids, in benthos, 246

Horse mackerel (*Caranx trachurus*), 267

Horse Shoe Crab, 227

Hudson, Henry, search for Northwest Passage, 14

Hudson Bay, Canadian research, 53

Hughes, Carrie Ola, vii

Hull, University of, Department of Zoology and Oceanography, 37

Humm, Harold J., 201

Humboldt Current, 131-132; cool water at low latitude, luxuriance of organic life, 185; effect on temperature, 96; studied by Scripps Institution, 50; support to avian life, 294; relation to rainfall, 294; Peru Current, 125; map, 121

Huntsman, A. G., quoted, 54

Huxley, T. H., 36

Hydrobiology, Forbes concern with, 24; subdivision of oceanography, 5; influenced by Victor Hensen, 32

Hydrogen, ion concentration, 88

Hydrographic Biological Commission, Sweden, 38

Hydrographic Department of the Admiralty, 37

Hydrographic Department of the Imperial Japanese Navy, 35

Hydrographic Office, United States Navy, 45-48; Maury's work, 24; collaboration with Fish Commission, 45

Hydroids, in benthos, 246

Hydrosphere, 122

Hypertonic, 182

Hypotonic, 182

Iceberg, collision of "Titanic," 6; effect on temperature, 96; from Antarctic and Arctic oceans, 136; indicators of currents, 122; indirect effect on water movements, 125

Ice Formation, 96

Imperial Marine Observatory (Kobe), 35

India, reached by da Gama, 14

Indian Ocean, boundaries, 63-65; circulation, 133-134; German Deep Sea expedition, 32; gross features, 59; Monsoon winds, 134; high salinity areas, 82; surface temperature, 99; tide, 151; waters from Antarctic, 135

Infra-red, penetration, 172

"Ingolf," 35

Insects, few in the sea, 227

Institute and Museum für Meereskunde at Berlin, 38

Institute of Physical Oceanography, 35

Intermediate water, 126; in North Atlantic, 136

Internal waves, 154-156

"Internal waves," affecting life in the depths, 246

International Aspects of Oceanography, list of institutions, 35, 39

International Commission for Exploration of the Sea in Copenhagen, source of normal water standard, 81

International Hydrographic Bureau, 33

International Ice Patrol, 6, 45, 47, 49

International Passamaquoddy Fisheries Commission, 54

Interplanetary particles, on ocean floor, 118

Intertidal, divisions of the littoral, 245

Intertidal zone, defined, 181

Iodine, 93; in seaweed, 78

Ionization, 79

Ipnops murrayi, no trace of eyes, 286

Ireland, discovery, 12

Iselin, Columbus, Gulf Stream studies, 127; Director of Woods Hole Oceanographic Institution, 51

Isotonic, 182

Istiophorus, 269

Italy, 37, 38

Japan Current, 133

Jellyfishes, in plankton, 179

"John Dory," 270

"John Mariggle," 262

"John Murray Expedition," 34

Johnstone, James, 185, 186

Jones, C. S., viii

Journal of Marine Research, 51

Journal of the Biological Board, 54

Journal of the Fisheries Research Board of Canada, 53

Juday, Chancey, improved centrifuge, 34

Kelly, exploration of Gulf of St. Lawrence, 53

Kelps, 201

Kelvin, Lord, piano wire in sounding, 70

Ketchum, Bostwick, 191

Kiel, Germany, 37

King Crab, 227

Kingfish (cero), 267

"King of the mackerels" (Ranzania), 273

Kjellman, quoted on vegetation in the Arctic, 186

Kofoid, C. A., 49; quoted on Biological Stations, 37; on Alexander Agassiz, 42; on azoic area, 31

Kril, 228; food of whales, 297

Krogh, August, cited on organic matter in solution, 85; on organic substance in the deeps, 85; on rate of sinking, 108, 109

Krummel, Otto, 55

Kuroshio, 133; map, 121

Labrador, fisheries of off-coast banks, 282; mixture of currents, 214

Labrador Current, meets Gulf Stream, 127; transports icebergs, 136

Labrador Sea, origin of North Atlantic deep water, 61

Lampreys, 291

Land, compared with oceans, 65; washed into the sea, 73; interchanges of energy with sea, 161

Longley, William H., quoted on *Histrio gibba*, 273

Lankester, E. Ray, 36

Lapworth, Charles, quoted on coastal contacts, 63

Larvacea, in plankton, 235

Latitude, affect on radiation received, 170

Latitude, and temperature, 99

Leptocephalus, 263

Life in the depths, 246

"Lightning," evidence of Wyville Thomson Ridge, 29

Light organs, 262, 263, 265, 270, 285, 286, 289, 290 (See also Luminescence)

Limulus, 227

Ling, 275

Littoral region, subdivisions, 180

Littoral zone, commercial fisheries, 259; benthos, 242

Liverpool Biological Committee, 37

Lobsters, utilization, 252

Lohmann, Hans, at Kiel, 38; centrifuge, 33, 55; quoted on significance of microscopic life, 18; use of centrifuge, 210, 236; work on Salpas, 236

Lophius, 270

Lowestoft, Fisheries Laboratory, 37

Luminescence, 205, 221, 236 (See also Light Organs)

"Mabahis," 34

McClure, completion of North West Passage, 15

McEwen, George F., on upwelling, 141

Mackerel, 267, 287

Mackerel-like fishes, 266, 267

Macroplankton, 211

Macruridae, most important and numerous of bottom fishes, 267

Macrurus armatus, geographical range, 266; made soundings, 69

Malay Archipelago, studies by Wallace, 30

Manatees, 295

"Mar brava," havoc on coast of Peru, 142

Marine Biological Association of San Diego, 49; of the United Kingdom, 36

Marine Biological Station at Millport, 37

Markham, search for North Pole, 15

Marmer, H. A., acknowledgment to, 11; on deflection of St. Lawrence waters, 129; on proportions of land and sea, 59; on temperature changes, 95; on angle of deflection, 140; on heights of waves, 144; on temperature and latitude, 99; on tides of various oceans, 151; with United States Coast and Geodetic Survey, 48

Marshall, Nelson, viii

Martin, Flossie, vii

Martin, George W., on temperature effects, 102

Maury, Lt. Matthew Fontaine, biographical sketch, 20; founder of oceanography, 17; head Depot of Charts and Instruments, 46; service to oceanography, saw sea as an object of diversified scientific study, 54; sensed integrated circulation system, 137

Mediterranean Sea, effect of evaporation, 20; Forbes observations in, 20; increased salinity and density, 128; origin of North Atlantic water, which passes to South Atlantic, 61; salinity and temperature at depths, 82; sounded by Strabo, 69; source of deep, saline water, 126

Medusa, 222

Meisel, Max, *Bibliography,* 7, 46, 47

Melting, latent heat, 95

Menhaden, 261

Merluccius, 275

Meroplankton, defined, 212

Merriman, Daniel, 51

Mesopelagic zone, 181

"Messenger," for bottom sampler, 250; for dredge, 113; on closing net, 31; on reversing thermometer, 100

"Meteor," 34

Meteorites, on ocean floor, 118

Meteorology, affecting the ocean, 6; associated with oceanography, 4

"Michael Sars," expedition, 28, 34; on luminescence, 262; on Salpa as food of herring, 235; taking scopelids, 265; used steel line with trawl, 277

Microplankton, or net plankton, 211

"Mid-Atlantic Swell," 67

Midge larvae, 227

Migrations, 215, 216, 287; barriers, 62; feeding, 286; of whales, 297

Millport, Biological Station, 37

"Milwaukee Depth," 67

Mississippi River, compared with Gulf Stream, 127

Mites, 227

Mixed tides, 148

Mola mola ("giant sunfish"), 273

Mollusca, larvae in plankton, 225

Mollusks, deposits of skeletons, 117; with light organs, 286

Monaco, aquarium and museum, 33

Monaco, Prince Albert Honoré Charles, 32, 33; used "pelagic trawl," 278

"Monaco Deep," 33

Monsoon Drift, map, 121

Monsoons, in Indian Ocean, 125

Monsoon winds, of Indian Ocean, 134

Moon, a cause of tides, 146; effect of declination on tides, 150

Mosby, M., at Bergen (Geophysical Institute), 38

Mount Everest, elevation compared with depth of sea, 67

Mozambique current, map, 121

Mud dredge, 250

Muds, red, green, and blue, 114

Müller, Johannes, plankton net, 18, 33, 55, and 209

Müller, O. F., modification of dredge, 20

Müller net, invention of, 24

Mullet, jumping (Mugil), 259, 268, 276

Muraenidae, 264

Murman Branch of the State Oceanographic Institution, 35

Murphy, Robert Cushman, quoted on upwelling, 131; on birds, 294

Murray, Sir John, 29, 55; association with "Challenger," 25; Challenger Reports, 27; on increment of bottom deposits, 119; classification of deposits, 114; established station at Millport, 37; "father of modern oceanography," 27; financial aid to oceanography, 28; on distribution of marine organisms, 246; on marine deposits of extra-terrestrial origin, 118; on Alexander Agassiz, 43; quoted on, 185; on "the great feeding ground," 248

Murray, Sir John and Johan Hjort, *The Depths of the Ocean*, acknowledgement to, 11, 28, 29; on biology, 178; on distribution of algae, 198; on internal waves, 155; directed expedition of the "Michael Sars," 34; on detritus, 213; on Macruridae, 267; on specific gravity, 106; on animals of the deep, 246; on food of copepods, 213; on fishes, 259

Museum of Comparative Zoology at Harvard, 45; Gulf of Maine investigation, 49; published results of "Albatross" cruise, 41

Mussels, in benthos, 243; utilization, 251

Myctophum, 265

Mysida, 228

Nannoplankton, 211; defined, 34; production and volume, 193

Nansen, Fridtjof, 55; drift of the "Fram," 35; divined occurrence of internal waves, 154; improvement of closing net, 31; search for North Pole, 16

"National," North Atlantic Cruise, 32

National Academy of Science, 35, 51

National Botanical Garden, 46

National Observatory, compilation of logs, 21

National Research Council of Canada, sponsor for Committee on Oceanography, 53

Naucrates, 268

Nautilus, pearly, or chambered, 227

Navigation, problems of, 6

Navigators, aided by Maury, 21

Neap tides, 146

Negretti and Zambra, reversing thermometer, 100

Nekton, 255; (defined) 179

Nelson, Thurlow C., vii; quoted on internal waves, 154

Nemathelminthes, in plankton, 224

Nemerteans, in plankton, 223

Neritic deposits, 114

Neritic life, 258

Neritic zone, 181; commercial fisheries, 259

"Nero," soundings in Pacific, 41

Net-plankton, 193; a subdivision of the plankton, 210

Neuston (defined), 179

Newfoundland, great fisheries on off shore banks, 214, 282

Nitrates, distribution, 191

Nitrogen, for nutriment, 91; in solution, 86

Nitrogenous compounds, depletion of, 84

Noctiluca, luminescence, 221

Nomeus, 268

Nordenskiold, Baron, sailed Northwest Passage, 15

Normal water, standard prepared, 80

North American Council on Fisheries Investigations, 54

North Atlantic, circulation of, 126;

extent of terrigenous bottom, 247; first bathymetrical map, 23; surface currents, 33

North Atlantic Current, 127; map, 121

North Atlantic Eddy, surface salinity of, 82

North Equatorial Current, 121, 125; map, 89; Atlantic Ocean, 127; furnishes Gulf Stream waters, 127; in Indian Ocean, 134; receives California Current, 133

Northern Hemisphere, greater land area, 59; salinity, 82

North Pacific, salinity relative to Atlantic, 82

North Pacific Current, receives Japan Current, 133

North Pacific Exploring Expedition, 46

North Pole, search of, 15

North Sea, fisheries, 6

Northwest Passage, search of, 14

Norway, fisheries, 6; oceanographic operations, 38; warmed by Gulf Stream, 128

Norwegian Current, map 89

Norwegian Sea, abyssal fauna, 283; bottom temperature, 98

Nutrient matter, lost in the depths, 85

Nutriment, from weak solution, 91

Ocean currents, map, 121

Oceanic areas as barriers, 259

Oceanic zone, 258; zones, 181

Oceanographic Institute in Paris, founded by Prince of Monaco, 33

Oceanographic Laboratories of the University of Washington, 47

Oceanography, 5, 6, 7, 17, 24, 25

Oceanography and Meteorology, 4

Oceans, area, 65; reservoir of heat, 94; continuity, 62; interrelations, 60

Octopods, lack of light organs, 286

Octopus, 226; utilization, 251

Ophiodon, potent producer of vitamin A, 275

"Organic Cycle," 190

Organic matter in solution, 84, 85

Orstedt, investigation of Trichodesmium, 18

Oscillation, natural periods of, 151

Osmotic Pressure, bony fishes, 259; differs in fresh and salt waters, 182

Ostracods, in plankton, 229

Ostwald, Wolfgang, cited on transparency of organisms, 189

Otter trawl, for deep fauna, 249

"Overturn," 90; deep oxygen supply, 193; caused by convection currents, 141; location, 99

Oxygen, barrier to distribution, 256; in solution, 86; in solution by depth, 90; solubility of, 87; supply to bottom, 193

Oyashio, 133

Oysters, in benthos, 241, 243, 244; utilization, 251; withstand changes in salinity, 182

Pacific ocean, coastal contacts, 63; circulation, 130; deep water, 133; gross features, 59; red clay deposits, 118; surface salinity, 82; surface temperature, 99; temperate zone, 258; tide, 151; waters from Antarctic, 135

Palolo worm, in plankton, breeding behavior, 225

Palumbo, designs closing net, 30-31; plankton net, 33

Paper Nautilus, 226

Papers in Physical Oceanography and Meteorology, 52

Paris, University of, 38

Parr, Professor Albert E., 50, 200, 201

Parry, W. E., search for North Pole, 15; search for Northwest Passage, 14

Peabody Museum of Natural History, 50

Peary, Robert Edwin, reaches North Pole, 15

Pedicel fishes (Pediculati), 270

Pediculates, bear light organs, 285

Pediculati, 270

Peje-rey, 268

Pelagic region, subdivisions, 181

Penekese station, 35

Penguins, 294

Perch-pike fishes, 265, 266

Percomorphoidea, 266

Peridineae, causing red seas, 221; food of Salpas, etc., 221

Periwinkles, utilization, 251

Permanent International Council for the Exploration of the Sea, 39

Perry Expedition to Japan, 46

Peru, no continental shelf, 67

Peru Current, 131-132; effect on land climate, 124; (Humboldt), map, 121

Petersen, C. G. J., 39; bottom sampler, 250; dredge, 113; "young fish trawl," 278

Peterson, Eugen von, improvement on closing net, 31

Pettersson, Hans, with Börno Research Station in Sweden, 38

Pettersson, Otto, 34; found relationship between occurrence of herring in certain Swedish fiords and internal waves, 158; Biological Commission in Sweden, 38

Phaeophyceae, 199

Phifer, L. D., quoted on Washington Oceanographic Laboratories, 52

Phoenicians, reaching Sargasso Sea, 12

Phoronidea, larvae in plankton, 224

Phosphate guano, 28

Phosphate mines, 28

Phosphates, depletion of, 84; distribution, 191; for nutriment, 91

Phosphorescence (See Luminescence), 236

Phosphorus, depletion, 183

Photoelectric cells, 172

Photosynthesis, affected by temperature, 102; energy returned to sea, 169; process providing all energies of plants and animals, 183; storage of short-wave radiation, 166; wave lengths used, 172

Photosynthetic zone, 87; enriched by upswelling, 141

Physical Geography of the Sea, textbook by Maury, 21

Physophora, in deep-sea, 223

Piano wire, used in sounding, 70

"Piggott gun," 113

Pike, 269

Pikelike fishes, 264

Pilchard, 261

Pillsbury, J. E.; Gulf stream studies, 126; with U.S. Coast and Geodetic Survey, 48

Pilot fish, 268, 269

Pinnipedia, 295

"Pipefishes," 265, 284

"Planet," nitrogen content at depths, 91

Plankton, 208, 270; affected by rise of deep water, 86, 142; defined, 179; occurrence at all depths, 31; source of knowledge of current and drifts, 65; nets, used in the depths, 249

"Plankton Expedition," 32; based at Kiel, Germany, 38

Plato, concerning Atlantis, 12

Platyhelminthes, in plankton, 223

Plectognathi, 273

Pleuronectoidae, 269

Plymouth Laboratory, 84

Poisonous fish, 266, 273

Poisonous snakes, 293

"Pola," 35

Polar bears, 295

Polar Scientific Research Institute of Marine Fisheries and Oceanography, 35

Pollack, 266, 275

Pompano, 267

Pope, Clifford H., cited on turtles, 293

"Porcupine," 29

Porcupine fishes, 273

Porpoises, 295, 297

Port Erin, 37

Portuguese man-of-war, houses nomeus, 268; a sea-faring neustont, 180; in plankton, 223

Prawns, 284

Pressure, 109; cause of water movement, 124-125; effect on temperature, 111; on viscosity, 104, 110; recorded by reversing thermometers, 101

"Princesse Alice," 32
"Princesse Alice II," 32
"Progressive wave," 152
Protochordata, in plankton, 235
Protozoa, feeding, 213; in the plankton, 219; rate of sinking, 85
Pterophryne, 272
Pteropod ooze, 114-117
Pteropods, 118; food of whales, 297; in the plankton, 225, 226
Ptolemy, classical oceanography, 13
Puffers, 273
"Pyramid of life," 198
Pyrosoma, luminosity, 236
Pytheas, knowledge of tides, 13

Quahogs, utilization, 251

Radiation, 161; balance maintained, 171; penetration, 171; range of wave lengths for energy changes in sea, 162; varies with time, place, and latitude, 169
Radiolaria, 27; found in sea, 17; shells forming ooze, 220
Radiolarian deposits, 112; ooze, 114-117
Ranzania, 273
Rays, 260
Red algae (Rhodophyceae), 199
Red clay, 27, 118; barren region, 248
Redfield, Alfred C., 191
Redfish, 267, 276
Red mullets (surmullet), 267
Red Sea, color, 18, 199; influences Antarctic, 61; interchange with Indian Ocean, 134; salinity and temperature at depths, 81; source of deep saline water, 126
"Red Seas," caused by red shrimp, 173; caused by Peridineae, 221
Red snapper, 276
Reflection of solar energy, 162
Refraction, 170, 173
Refractive index and salinity, 80
Remora, 267
Rennell, James, on North Atlantic currents, 21
Report of Canadian Fisheries Expedition, 54

Report of tides and currents in Canadian waters, 53
Reptiles, 291
Reservoirs of heat, 164; the sea, 168
Resultats des Champagnes Scientifiques, 33
Revelle, Roger R., on classification of bottom deposits, 119
Reversing thermometer, protected and unprotected, 100, 101
Rhizosolenia, cyclomorphosis, 202
Rhodophyceae, 199
Ribbonworms, in plankton, 223
Richter, C., improvement of reversing thermometer, 100
Ringgold, Commander, command of North Pacific Exploring Expedition, 46
Ritter, Dr. William E., 49
River herring, 262
River water, favors algal growth, 198
Robbins, W. J., quoted on radiation absorbed by green plants, 166
Rockfishes, (Scorpaenidae), 258, 267, 275
Rockweeds, 201
Rodgers, Lt., Command of North Pacific Exploring Expedition, 46
Rosefish, 267, 276
Ross, John, Search for Northwest Passage, 14
Ross, Sir James, Exploration of Antarctic region, 15; made soundings, 69
Rotation of the earth, affecting currents, 125
Rotifers, in neritic plankton, 224; change of form, 105
Roundworms, in plankton, 224
Royal Prussian Biological Station, 37
Russell, F. S., 37; quoted on copepods in plankton, 232
Russell, F. S. and Yonge, C. M., *The Seas,* cited on biology, 178
Russia, oceanographic studies, 35, 38

Sablefish, 276
Sagitta, in plankton, 224
Sailfish (Istiophorus), 267
Sailing directions, of Maury, 22

Sailing Directions for the Gulf and River St. Lawrence, 53

Salinity, 65, 80, 81, 82, 256; effect on freezing point, 96; identifying water masses, 124; of Arctic, 135; of the Gulf Stream, 129, 130; range of, 81; surface and deep waters, 82

Salmonoids, 261

Salmons, 275; in fresh and salt water, 182

Salpas, in plankton, 235, 236; tunics housing amphipods, 228

Sand eels, 268

Sand launces, 268

Sarda, 267

Sardine, 261

Sargasso fish, characteristic of Sargasso Sea, 272, 284

Sargasso Sea, map, 121, 129; accumulation of sargassum, 201; "bottom" in mid-waters, 215; characteristic surface fauna, 284; habitat of fishes, 265; known to Phoenicians, its location, 12; plankton, 234; surface salinity, 82, 213; water from Gulf Stream, 128

Sargassum weed, 201; affords shelter for animals, 189; detritus giving, 213; in plankton, 179

Sars, G. O., dredging operations, 34

Sars, Michael, dredging operations, 34

Schmidt, Johannes, 39, 55; on life history of eels, 263

Schmitt, Waldo, 44

Schott, Gerhard, 55

Schroeder, William C., cited on migration of cod, 287

Schultz, Dr. L. P., 259 n.

Schütt, Fr., on plants of ocean currents, 217; on color of seas, 185

Scienidae, 276

Scomber, 267

Scombriform fishes, 267

Scopelids, 264; correlation of light organs with depth, 286

Scoresby, Wm., investigation of Greenland Sea, 17; search for North Pole, 15

Scott, Captain Robert F., voyage of, 15

Scripps Institution of Oceanography, 47, 49, 50

Sea-basses (Serranidae), 267, 276

Sea-cows, 295

Sea-cucumbers, utilization, 252

Sea-horse, 265, 284

Sea ice, of Arctic, 136; reflects more strongly than water, 170

Sea-lions, 296

Seals, 295, 296

Sea otters, 295

Sears Foundation, 51

Sea turtles, 293

Sea urchins, utilization, 252

Seaweeds, utilization, 252

Secchi disc, for determining light penetration, 172

Sedimentation, 112; on continental shelf, 114

Seiches, 151; modifies progressive wave form of tide, 152

Seines, 276

Seiwell, H. R., on internal waves, 155; on oxygen, North Atlantic oxygen, 90

Semidaily tides, 148

Sepia ink, 290

Serranidae, 276

Service, Jerry H., on velocity of sound in sea water, 71

Set line, 276

Shackleton, voyage, 15

Shad, in fresh and salt water, 182, 261

Sharks, 260

Shark's pilot (Remora), 268

Shark's teeth, in bottom sediment, 109, 112

Sheepshead, 267, 276

"Shelter," for animal life, 188

Shore Stations, an Atlantic, 35

Shrimp, in benthos, 246; utilization, 252

"Siboga," 35

Sigsbee, C. D., beam trawl, 41, 249; devised apparatus, 41; water bottle, 41; with United States Coast and Geodetic Survey, 48; wire rope, 251

Sigsbee sounding machine, 41, 70

Silica, depletion, 84, 183

Silicious oozes, 119

Silversides, 268

Sinking movements, effect on temperature, 96

Sinking rate of minute organisms, 85

Sinking velocity, 194, 108

Siphonophores, in plankton, 223

Sirenia, 295

Size of body, in relation to concentration of nutritive substances, 91; other conditions, 102, 105, 108, 184, 187, 197, 233, 284

Smelts, 261

Smithsonian Institution, 45

Snakes, 291

Snappers, 267

Sodium, disproportion of, 83

Solar radiation, 161

Solenichthoidea, 284

Soles, 269

Sonic depth-finder, developed, 70

Sonic sounder, for locating schools of fish, 279

Sonic sounding, developed by United States Navy, 47

Sound, velocity in sea water, 71

Sounding apparatus, Brooke, 23, 69

Sounding Lead, 69

Sounding Machine, Sigsbee, 41, 70; Tanner, 44, 70

Soup-fin shark, producer of vitamin A, 276

South Equatorial Current, 121, 125; Atlantic Ocean, 127; Gulf Stream water supply, 127; in Indian Ocean, 134; receives Humbolt current, 132

Southern hemisphere, greater sea area, 59; salinity, 82

South Pole, reached by Amundsen and Scott, 15

Spanish mackerel, 268

Specific gravity, 106; defined, 81; effect on sinking, 104

Spectrophotometers, 172

Sperm whale, 297

Spiny-rayed fishes (Acanthopterygii), 266

Sponges, in benthos, 240, 245; utilization, 252; not prominent in plankton, 222

Spots, 276

Sprat, 261

Spring tides, 146

Squeteagues ("sea trout"), 276

Squid, as food of whales, 33; blind, 289; consume herring, 290; food for cod, 290; food of toothed whales, 297; giant, 290; light organs, 286, 289; in marine economy, 289; vertical migrations, 287

"Standing wave" type of tide, 152

Stazioni Zoologica di Napoli, 35, 36

"Stem thermometer," 101

Stenohaline, 182

Stenothermal, defined, 214

Sternoptychidae, 262

Steuer, Adolph, cited on pteropod ooze, 118

Stoke's Law, 107

Stomias, 262

Stomiatidae, wide distribution, 262

Storms, cause "tidal waves," 156; Maury's observations on, 23

Strabo, depth sounding in Mediterranean, 13, 69

Straits of Florida, outlet to Gulf Stream, 127

Straits of Gibraltar, outlet of dense Mediterranean water, 128. See Gibraltar

Strata of water, 126

Stratification, caused by salinity variations, 84; knowledge of, 25

"Streamlining," 105

Streamlining, reduces "drag," 187

Sturgeons, 260

Sublittoral, in benthos, 245

Sublittoral zone, defined, 181

Subtropical convergence, 141

Summer, Francis B., 180

Sun, effective radiation varies with altitude, 170; source of energy, 160

Sunfish, giant, 273

"Surf," 145

Surface temperature, variations, 170

Surface water, 126

Surf whitings, 276

Surmullet, 267

Sverdrup, H. U., on back radiation, 170; on internal waves, 155; on penetration of radiation, 171; on pressure effect on temperature, 111; on radiation of heat, 161; on radiation used in photosynthesis, 169; on Red Sea water in Indian Ocean depths, 134; Director of Scripps Institution of Oceanography, 50; on equatorial counter current, 132; on evaporation, 95; on probable influences of Red Sea on Antarctic, 61; quoting Schütt, 217; on generation of surface waves, 143

Sverdrup, H. U., Martin W. Johnson, and Richard H. Fleming, *The Oceans*, cited on fishes, 259; on bacteria, 205; on bioluminescence, 285; on continental terrace, 67; on eurybathic animals, 248; for normal water standard, 81; on copepods, 232; on internal waves, 156; on biology, 178, 183

Sweden, oceanographic operations, 38

Swells, 142; cause irregularity of waves, 145

Swordfish (*Xiphias gladius*), 267

Synaphobranchus, 264

"Talisman," 34

Tangles, for bottom fauna, 249

Tanner, self-closing net, 31; sounding machine, 70

Tanner, Z. L., 43, 44

Tarpon, 262

Taylor, Harden F., vii; on chemistry, 93; on dietetic quality of ocean fish, 274; on temperature, 257

Temperate zones, for fisheries, 259

Temperature, 93-103; affected by pressure, 111; affecting distribution of animals, 102, 214, 257; effect on animal form, 102; on animal size, 102; effect on photosynthesis, 102; effect on viscosity, 103; identifying water masses, 124; in the depths, 82, 96, 97, 98; range, 95; seasonal and diurnal variation, 95, 96; source of knowledge of currents and drifts, 65. (See also Heat)

"Ten-pounder," 262

Terrigenous bottom, for fisheries, 259

Terrigenous deposits, 114, 119, 244

Tester, Albert L., cited on use of sonic sounder, 279

Tetragonurus, poisonous flesh, 268

Thermographs, 101

Thermometers, reversing and others, 100

Thermosounder, 101

Thompson, Thomas G., director of University of Washington Oceanographic Laboratories, 52

Thomson, C. Wyville, 24-27; 55; Wyville Thomson Ridge, 29

Thunnus, 267

"Tidal current," 153

"Tidal Waves," caused by earthquakes and storms, 156-157

Tides, 146-159; affected by natural period of oscillation, 151; biological relations, 157; largest waves, 146; "progressive wave" type, 152; standing wave type, 152

Tilefish, 256, 267

Tintinnoids, in plankton, 221

"Titanic," loss of, 6, 47

Tomopteris, planktonic habit, 225

Topography, affected by biology, 6

"Tortoise shell" of commerce, 293

Tow-net, Tanner, 44 (see also Müller, Johannes and Hensen, Victor)

Townsend, Charles S., directed Scientific work by "Albatross," 43; quotes on "Albatross," 44

Trace elements, 92

Transition zones of life, 259

Transparency, means of concealment, 189

Traps, 276

"Travailleur," 34

Trawl, pelagic, "young fish," 277; Sigsbee, 41; Tanner, 44

Trawler, fishing vessel, 277

Trawl line, 276

Trawls, for bottom fauna, 249

Trepang or bêche-de-mer, utilization, 252

Trichodesmium, 18, 199

Triggerfish, poisonous to men, 273

Trochelminthes, in neritic plankton, 224

Tropical convergence, 141

Tropical zones of life, 259

Trunkfishes, 273

Tsientang River in China, famous "bore," 153

Tsingtao Observatory, 35

Tuna (Tunny), 267, 268, 275

Tunicates in plankton, 235

Turbulence, 103

Tuscarora, 41, 70

Ultraplankton, 211

Ultraviolet, penetration of, 172

Ulva (sea lettuce), 199

University Biological Station at Drøbak, 38

University of Oslo, 38

University of Washington Oceanographic Laboratories, 52

United States Coast and Geodetic Survey, 40, 48; forecasts of tides, 152

United States Coast Guard, 6, 49

United States Exploring Expedition, exploration of Antarctic region, 15; first great government scientific expedition, 46; object, 7; soundings and dredgings, 40

United States National Museum, 45

U.S.S. "Tuscarora," 40

Upper water, 126

Upwelling, 92, 140-142, 243; along African coast, 130; along California coast, 141; along coast of Peru, 141; along coast of West Africa, 141; Pacific coast and South America, 131; biological relations, 159; effect on temperature, 96

Utterback, Clinton L., director of University of Washington Oceanographic Laboratories, 52

"Valdivia," collection of radiolaria, 221; investigations in Atlantic and Indian Oceans, 32

Van Leeuwenhoek, Antoni, describing plankters, 209

Vaughan, Thomas Wayland, 35; cited on oxygen in Pacific, 90; head of Scripps Institution of Oceanography, 50

Vegetation, single-celled, 197

Velella, in plankton, 223

Vertical movements of fish, diurnal, 287

"Vetter Pisani," used closing net, 34

Vikings, discoverers, 14

"Vincennes," 45

Viscosity, 103-105; affecting distribution of animals, 214; streamlining, 187; biological effects, 104; effect on animal movement, 104; effect on animal size, 105, 107

Visual organs, (See Light Organs)

Vitamins, 202; from fishes, 275, 276; synthesis by plants, 183

"Vitiaz," 35

Volcanic dust in deposits, 118

Volcanic muds, 114

Volcanoes, cause of "tidal waves," 156

Von Humboldt, Alexander, study of microscopic life in the sea, 17; characterization of Maury's studies, 21

Waksman, S. A., cited on marine bacteria, 205

Wallace, Alfred Russell, study of animal life in Malay Archipelago, 30

Walls, Gordon Lynn, quoted on bioluminiscene, 285; cited on eyes of deep-sea fish, 286

Walrus, 295

Washington, 34

Water, compression of, 111; heat capacity, heat of evaporation, 164

Water bottles, 100; described, 79; Sigsbee, 41

Water strider, 227

Watts, W. W., quoted on coastal contacts, 63

Waves, 142-145; biological relations of, 157; caused by wind, 142; great velocities caused by earthquakes, 144; height, 144; increase reflection of radiation, 170; length, 144; parallel to shore, 145; periods, 144; progressive wave, 152; standing wave, 152; velocities, 144

Weather, affected by interchanges of energy between sea and land, 161; daily reports, 24 (See also Atmosphere and Meterology)

Weber, Max, expedition in Dutch East Indies, 35

Wedell, exploration of Arctic region, 15

West Australian Current, map, 89

Western Hemisphere, greater sea area, 57-59

West Wind Drift, 121, 131

Whalebone whales, 262

"Whale Feed," 118, 209, 297

Whale fisheries, 46

Whales, bearing whale-bone, 118; ear bones on red clay, 109; feeding on Clione, 226; feed on squid, 290; in regions of euphausiid crustacea, 229; investigation by Prince of Monaco, 33; largest of nekton, 296; migrations, 17, 297; preying on animals, 234; sperm, streamlining, 106; tolerance of pressure changes, 110; tolerance of temperatures, 62; whalebone, food, 262

Wheelworms, in neritic plankton, 224

Whitecraft, Thomas H., cited on sonic sounding, 48, 70

Whiting, 266

Wilkes, Charles, head of Depot of Charts and Instruments, 45; United States Exploring Expedition, 40; commanding United States North Pacific Expedition, 7

"Willebrord Snellius," 34

"William Scoresby," 34

Wind, a cause of waves, 142; data concerning, 21; Maury's observations, 23; transports heat via water vapor, 164

Wire rope, used on the "Blake," 251

Woods Hole Oceanographic Institution, 47, 51; source of normal water, 81

Worms, in benthos, 243; larval stages in plankton, 224

Wüst, Georg, 38, 55; Gulf Stream studies, 127

Wyville, Thomson Ridge, discovery, 29; as barrier, 284

Xiphias, 267

"Yellow substances," absorb radiation, 172, 173

Yucatan Channel, 127

Zeids, 270

ZoBell, Claude E., on bottom temperature, 98; on marine bacteria, 205

Zones of life, 73, 180, 181, 258

Zostera, 206

HARPER TORCHBOOKS / The Bollingen Library

Rachel Bespaloff   ON THE ILIAD. Introduction by Hermann Broch   TB/2006

Elliott Coleman, *ed.*   LECTURES IN CRITICISM: *By R. P. Blackmur, B. Croce, Henri Peyre, John Crowe Ransom, Herbert Read, and Allen Tate*   TB/2003

C. G. Jung   PSYCHOLOGICAL REFLECTIONS. Edited by Jolande Jacobi   TB/2001

Erich Neumann   THE ORIGINS AND HISTORY OF CONSCIOUSNESS. *Vol. I*, TB/2007; *Vol. II*, TB/2008

St.-John Perse   SEAMARKS. Translated by Wallace Fowlie   TB/2002

Jean Seznec   THE SURVIVAL OF THE PAGAN GODS: *The Mythological Tradition and Its Place in Renaissance Humanism and Art.* Illustrated   TB/2004

Heinrich Zimmer   MYTHS AND SYMBOLS IN INDIAN ART AND CIVILIZATION   TB/2005

HARPER TORCHBOOKS / The Academy Library

James Baird   ISHMAEL: *A Study of the Symbolic Mode in Primitivism*   TB/1023

Herschel Baker   THE IMAGE OF MAN: *A Study of the Idea of Human Dignity in Classical Antiquity, the Middle Ages, and the Renaissance*   TB/1047

Jacques Barzun   THE HOUSE OF INTELLECT   TB/1051

W. J. Bate   FROM CLASSIC TO ROMANTIC: *Premises of Taste in Eighteenth Century England*   TB/1036

Henri Bergson   TIME AND FREE WILL: *An Essay on the Immediate Data of Consciousness*   TB/1021

H. J. Blackham   SIX EXISTENTIALIST THINKERS: *Kierkegaard, Jaspers, Nietzsche, Marcel, Heidegger, Sartre*   TB/1002

Walter Bromberg   THE MIND OF MAN: *A History of Psychotherapy and Psychoanalysis*   TB/1003

Abraham Cahan   THE RISE OF DAVID LEVINSKY. A novel. Introduction by John Higham   TB/1028

Helen Cam   ENGLAND BEFORE ELIZABETH   TB/1026

Joseph Charles   THE ORIGINS OF THE AMERICAN PARTY SYSTEM   TB/1049

T. C. Cochran & William Miller   THE AGE OF ENTERPRISE: *A Social History of Industrial America*   TB/1054

Norman Cohn   THE PURSUIT OF THE MILLENNIUM: *Revolutionary Messianism in Medieval and Reformation Europe and its Bearing on Modern Totalitarian Movements*   TB/1037

G. G. Coulton   MEDIEVAL VILLAGE, MANOR, AND MONASTERY   TB/1022

Wilfrid Desan   THE TRAGIC FINALE: *An Essay on the Philosophy of Jean-Paul Sartre*   TB/1030

Cora Du Bois   THE PEOPLE OF ALOR: *A Social-Psychological Study of an East Indian Island. Vol. I*, 85 illus., TB/1042; *Vol. II*, TB/1043

George Eliot   DANIEL DERONDA. A novel. Introduction by F. R. Leavis   TB/1039

John N. Figgis   POLITICAL THOUGHT FROM GERSON TO GROTIUS: 1414-1625: *Seven Studies.* Introduction by Garrett Mattingly   TB/1032

Editors of *Fortune*   AMERICA IN THE SIXTIES: *The Economy and the Society*   TB/1015

F. L. Ganshof   FEUDALISM   TB/1058

G. P. Gooch   ENGLISH DEMOCRATIC IDEAS IN THE SEVENTEENTH CENTURY   TB/1006

Francis J. Grund   ARISTOCRACY IN AMERICA: *A Study of Jacksonian Democracy*   TB/1001

W. K. C. Guthrie   THE GREEK PHILOSOPHERS: *From Thales to Aristotle*   TB/1008

Marcus Lee Hansen   THE ATLANTIC MIGRATION: 1607-1860   TB/1052

Alfred Harbage   AS THEY LIKED IT: *A Study of Shakespeare's Moral Artistry*   TB/1035

J. M. Hussey   THE BYZANTINE WORLD   TB/1057

Henry James   THE PRINCESS CASAMASSIMA. A novel. Intro. by Clinton Oliver.   TB/1005

Henry James   RODERICK HUDSON. A novel. Introduction by Leon Edel   TB/1016

Henry James   THE TRAGIC MUSE. A novel. Introduction by Leon Edel   TB/1017

William James   PSYCHOLOGY: *The Briefer Course.* Edited with an Introduction by Gordon Allport   TB/1034

Arnold Kettle   AN INTRODUCTION TO THE ENGLISH NOVEL. *Vol. I, Defoe to George Eliot*, TB/1011; *Vol. II, Henry James to the Present*, TB/1012

Samuel Noah Kramer   SUMERIAN MYTHOLOGY: *A Study of Spiritual and Literary Achievement in the Third Millennium B.C.* Illustrated   TB/1055

Paul Oskar Kristeller   RENAISSANCE THOUGHT: *The Classic, Scholastic, and Humanist Strains*   TB/1048

L. S. B. Leakey   ADAM'S ANCESTORS: *The Evolution of Man and His Culture.* Illustrated   TB/1019

Bernard Lewis   THE ARABS IN HISTORY   TB/1029

Ferdinand Lot   THE END OF THE ANCIENT WORLD AND THE BEGINNINGS OF THE MIDDLE AGES   TB/1044

Arthur O. Lovejoy	THE GREAT CHAIN OF BEING: *A Study of the History of an Idea* TB/1009
Robert Lowie	PRIMITIVE SOCIETY. Introduction by Fred Eggan TB/1058
Niccolo Machiavelli	HISTORY OF FLORENCE AND OF THE AFFAIRS OF ITALY: *From the Earliest Times to the Death of Lorenzo the Magnificent.* Introduction by Felix Gilbert TB/1027
J. P. Mayer	ALEXIS DE TOCQUEVILLE: *A Biographical Study in Political Science* TB/1014
John U. Nef	CULTURAL FOUNDATIONS OF INDUSTRIAL CIVILIZATION TB/1024
Jose Oretga y Gasset	THE MODERN THEME. Introduction by Jose Ferrater Mora TB/1038
J. H. Parry	THE ESTABLISHMENT OF THE EUROPEAN HEGEMONY: 1415-1715: *Trade and Exploration in the Age of the Renaissance* TB/1045
Robert Payne	HUBRIS: *A Study of Pride.* Foreword by Herbert Read TB/1031
Samuel Pepys	THE DIARY OF SAMUEL PEPYS: Selections, edited by O. F. Morshead; illustrated by Ernest H. Shepard TB/1007
Paul E. Pfeutze	SELF, SOCIETY, EXISTENCE: *Human Nature and Dialogue in the Thought of George Herbert Mead and Martin Buber* TB/1059
Georges Poulet	STUDIES IN HUMAN TIME: *Montaigne, Molière, Baudelaire, Proust, et al.* TB/1004
George E. Probst, *Ed.*	THE HAPPY REPUBLIC: *A Reader in Tocqueville's America* TB/1060
Priscilla Robertson	REVOLUTIONS OF 1848: *A Social History* TB/1025
Ferdinand Schevill	THE MEDICI. Illustrated TB/1010
Bruno Snell	THE DISCOVERY OF THE MIND: *The Greek Origins of European Thought* TB/1018
C. P. Snow	TIME OF HOPE. A novel TB/1040
Perrin Stryker	THE CHARACTER OF THE EXECUTIVE: *Eleven Studies in Managerial Qualities* TB/1041
Percy Sykes	A HISTORY OF EXPLORATION. Introduction by John K. Wright TB/1046
Dorothy Van Ghent	THE ENGLISH NOVEL: *Form and Function* TB/1050
W. H. Walsh	PHILOSOPHY OF HISTORY: *An Introduction* TB/1020
W. Lloyd Warner	SOCIAL CLASS IN AMERICA: *The Evaluation of Status* TB/1013
Alfred N. Whitehead	PROCESS AND REALITY: *An Essay in Cosmology* TB/1033
Louis B. Wright	CULTURE ON THE MOVING FRONTIER TB/1053

HARPER TORCHBOOKS / The Science Library

Angus d'A. Bellairs	REPTILES: *Life History, Evolution, and Structure.* Illustrated TB/520
L. von Bertalanffy	PROBLEMS OF LIFE: *An Evaluation of Modern Biological and Scientific Thought* TB/521
David Bohm	CAUSALITY AND CHANCE IN MODERN PHYSICS. Foreword by Louis de Broglie TB/536
R. B. Braithwaite	SCIENTIFIC EXPLANATION TB/515
P. W. Bridgman	THE NATURE OF THERMODYNAMICS TB/537
Louis de Broglie	PHYSICS AND MICROPHYSICS. Foreword by Albert Einstein TB/514
J. Bronowski	SCIENCE AND HUMAN VALUES TB/505
A. J. Cain	ANIMAL SPECIES AND THEIR EVOLUTION. Illustrated TB/519
R. E. Coker	THIS GREAT AND WIDE SEA: *An Introduction to Oceanography and Marine Biology.* Illustrated TB/551
T. G. Cowling	MOLECULES IN MOTION: *An Introduction to the Kinetic Theory of Gases.* Illustrated TB/516
A. C. Crombie, *Ed.*	TURNING POINTS IN PHYSICS TB/535
W. C. Dampier, *Ed.*	READINGS IN THE LITERATURE OF SCIENCE. Illustrated TB/512
H. Davenport	THE HIGHER ARITHMETIC: *An Introduction to the Theory of Numbers* TB/526
W. H. Dowdeswell	ANIMAL ECOLOGY. Illustrated TB/543
W. H. Dowdeswell	THE MECHANISM OF EVOLUTION TB/527
C. V. Durell	READABLE RELATIVITY TB/530
Arthur Eddington	SPACE, TIME AND GRAVITATION: *An Outline of the General Relativity Theory* TB/510
Alexander Findlay	CHEMISTRY IN THE SERVICE OF MAN. Illustrated TB/524
H. G. Forder	GEOMETRY: *An Introduction.* Illus. TB/548
Gottlob Frege	THE FOUNDATIONS OF ARITHMETIC TB/534
R. W. Gerard	UNRESTING CELLS. Illustrated TB/541
Werner Heisenberg	PHYSICS AND PHILOSOPHY: *The Revolution in Modern Science* TB/549
C. Judson Herrick	THE EVOLUTION OF HUMAN NATURE TB/545
Max Jammer	CONCEPTS OF SPACE TB/533
Max Jammer	CONCEPTS OF FORCE TB/550
S. Korner	THE PHILOSOPHY OF MATHEMATICS: *An Introduction* TB/547
David Lack	DARWIN'S FINCHES: *The General Biological Theory of Evolution.* Illustrated TB/544

D. E. Littlewood	THE SKELETON KEY OF MATHEMATICS: *A Simple Account of Complex Algebraic Theories* TB/525
J. E. Morton	MOLLUSCS: *An Introduction to Their Form and Function.* Illustrated TB/529
O. Neugebauer	THE EXACT SCIENCES IN ANTIQUITY TB/552
J. R. Partington	A SHORT HISTORY OF CHEMISTRY. Illustrated TB/522
H. T. Pledge	SCIENCE SINCE 1500: *A Short History of Mathematics, Physics, Chemistry, and Biology.* Illustrated TB/506
John Read	A DIRECT ENTRY TO ORGANIC CHEMISTRY. Illustrated TB/523
O. W. Richards	THE SOCIAL INSECTS. Illustrated TB/542
George Sarton	ANCIENT SCIENCE AND MODERN CIVILIZATION TB/501
Paul A. Schilpp, *Ed.*	ALBERT EINSTEIN: *Philosopher-Scientist.* Vol. I, TB/502; Vol. II, TB/503
P. M. Sheppard	NATURAL SELECTION AND HEREDITY. Illustrated TB/528
Edmund W. Sinnott	CELL AND PSYCHE: *The Biology of Purpose* TB/546
L. S. Stebbing	A MODERN INTRODUCTION TO LOGIC TB/538
O. G. Sutton	MATHEMATICS IN ACTION. Foreword by James R. Newman. Illustrated TB/518
Stephen Toulmin	THE PHILOSOPHY OF SCIENCE: *An Introduction* TB/513
A. G. Van Melsen	FROM ATOMOS TO ATOM: *The History of the Concept* Atom TB/517
Friedrich Waismann	INTRODUCTION TO MATHEMATICAL THINKING. Foreword by Karl Menger TB/511
W. H. Watson	ON UNDERSTANDING PHYSICS: *An Analysis of the Philosophy of Physics.* Introduction by Ernest Nagel TB/507
G. J. Whitrow	THE STRUCTURE AND EVOLUTION OF THE UNIVERSE: *An Introduction to Cosmology.* Illustrated TB/504
Edmund Whittaker	HISTORY OF THE THEORIES OF AETHER AND ELECTRICITY. Vol. I, *The Classical Theories,* TB/531; Vol. II, *The Modern Theories,* TB/532
A. Wolf	A HISTORY OF SCIENCE, TECHNOLOGY, AND PHILOSOPHY IN THE SIXTEENTH AND SEVENTEENTH CENTURIES. Illustrated. Vol. I, TB/508; Vol. II, TB/509
A. Wolf	A HISTORY OF SCIENCE, TECHNOLOGY, AND PHILOSOPHY IN THE EIGHTEENTH CENTURY. Vol. I, TB/539; Vol. II, TB/540

HARPER TORCHBOOKS / The Cloister Library

Tor Andrae	MOHAMMED: *The Man and His Faith* TB/62
Augustine/Przywara	AN AUGUSTINE SYNTHESIS TB/35
Roland H. Bainton	THE TRAVAIL OF RELIGIOUS LIBERTY TB/30
C. K. Barrett, *Ed.*	THE NEW TESTAMENT BACKGROUND: *Selected Documents* TB/86
Karl Barth	DOGMATICS IN OUTLINE TB/56
Karl Barth	THE WORD OF GOD AND THE WORD OF MAN TB/13
Nicolas Berdyaev	THE BEGINNING AND THE END TB/14
Nicolas Berdyaev	THE DESTINY OF MAN TB/61
Anton T. Boisen	THE EXPLORATION OF THE INNER WORLD: *A Study of Mental Disorder and Religious Experience* TB/87
J. H. Breasted	DEVELOPMENT OF RELIGION AND THOUGHT IN ANCIENT EGYPT TB/57
Martin Buber	ECLIPSE OF GOD: *Studies in the Relation Between Religion and Philosophy* TB/12
Martin Buber	MOSES: *The Revelation and the Covenant* TB/27
Martin Buber	THE PROPHETIC FAITH TB/73
Martin Buber	TWO TYPES OF FAITH: *The interpenetration of Judaism and Christianity* TB/75
R. Bultmann, et al.	KERYGMA AND MYTH: *A Theological Debate.* Ed. by H. W. Bartsch TB/80
Jacob Burckhardt	THE CIVILIZATION OF THE RENAISSANCE IN ITALY. Illustrated Edition. Introduction by Benjamin Nelson and Charles Trinkaus. Vol. I, TB/40; Vol. II, TB/41
Emile Cailliet	PASCAL: *The Emergence of Genius* TB/82
Edward Conze	BUDDHISM: *Its Essence and Development* TB/58
Frederick Copleston	MEDIEVAL PHILOSOPHY TB/76
F. M. Cornford	FROM RELIGION TO PHILOSOPHY: *A Study in the Origins of Western Speculation* TB/20
G. G. Coulton	MEDIEVAL FAITH AND SYMBOLISM [Part I of "Art and the Reformation"]. Illustrated TB/25
G. G. Coulton	THE FATE OF MEDIEVAL ART IN THE RENAISSANCE AND REFORMATION [Part II of "Art and the Reformation"]. Illustrated TB/26
H. G. Creel	CONFUCIUS AND THE CHINESE WAY TB/63
Adolf Deissmann	PAUL: *A Study in Social and Religious History* TB/15
C. H. Dodd	THE AUTHORITY OF THE BIBLE TB/43
Johannes Eckhart	MEISTER ECKHART: A Modern Translation TB/8
Mircea Eliade	COSMOS AND HISTORY: *The Myth of the Eternal Return* TB/50

Mircea Eliade	THE SACRED AND THE PROFANE: *The Significance of Religious Myth, Symbolism, and Ritual Within Life and Culture*	TB/81
Morton S. Enslin	CHRISTIAN BEGINNINGS	TB/5
Morton S. Enslin	THE LITERATURE OF THE CHRISTIAN MOVEMENT	TB/6
G. P. Fedotov	THE RUSSIAN RELIGIOUS MIND: *Kievan Christianity, the 10th to the 13th Centuries*	TB/70
Ludwig Feuerbach	THE ESSENCE OF CHRISTIANITY. Introduction by Karl Barth	TB/11
Harry E. Fosdick	A GUIDE TO UNDERSTANDING THE BIBLE	TB/2
Henri Frankfort	ANCIENT EGYPTIAN RELIGION: *An Interpretation*	TB/77
Sigmund Freud	ON CREATIVITY AND THE UNCONSCIOUS: *Papers on the Psychology of Art, Literature, Love, Religion.* Edited by Benjamin Nelson	TB/45
Maurice Friedman	MARTIN BUBER: *The Life of Dialogue*	TB/64
O. B. Frothingham	TRANSCENDENTALISM IN NEW ENGLAND: *A History*	TB/59
Edward Gibbon	THE TRIUMPH OF CHRISTENDOM IN THE ROMAN EMPIRE [J. B. Bury Edition, illus., Chapters 15-20 of "The Decline and Fall"]	TB/46
C. C. Gillispie	GENESIS AND GEOLOGY: *A Study in the Relations of Scientific Thought, Natural Theology, and Social Opinion in Great Britain, 1790-1850*	TB/51
Maurice Goguel	JESUS AND THE ORIGINS OF CHRISTIANITY I: *Prolegomena to the Life of Jesus*	TB/65
Maurice Goguel	JESUS AND THE ORIGINS OF CHRISTIANITY II: *The Life of Jesus*	TB/66
Edgar J. Goodspeed	A LIFE OF JESUS	TB/1
H. J. C. Grierson	CROSS-CURRENTS IN 17TH CENTURY ENGLISH LITERATURE: *The World, the Flesh, the Spirit*	TB/47
William Haller	THE RISE OF PURITANISM	TB/22
Adolf Harnack	WHAT IS CHRISTIANITY? Introduction by Rudolf Bultmann	TB/17
R. K. Harrison	THE DEAD SEA SCROLLS: *An Introduction*	TB/84
Edwin Hatch	THE INFLUENCE OF GREEK IDEAS ON CHRISTIANITY	TB/18
Friedrich Hegel	ON CHRISTIANITY: *Early Theological Writings*	TB/79
Karl Heim	CHRISTIAN FAITH AND NATURAL SCIENCE	TB/16
F. H. Heinemann	EXISTENTIALISM AND THE MODERN PREDICAMENT	TB/28
S. R. Hopper, *Ed.*	SPIRITUAL PROBLEMS IN CONTEMPORARY LITERATURE	TB/21
Johan Huizinga	ERASMUS AND THE AGE OF REFORMATION. Illustrated	TB/19
Aldous Huxley	THE DEVILS OF LOUDUN: *A Study in the Psychology of Power Politics and Mystical Religion in the France of Cardinal Richelieu*	TB/60
Flavius Josephus	THE GREAT ROMAN-JEWISH WAR, with *The Life of Josephus.*	TB/74
Immanuel Kant	RELIGION WITHIN THE LIMITS OF REASON ALONE.	TB/67
Soren Kierkegaard	EDIFYING DISCOURSES: A Selection	TB/32
Soren Kierkegaard	THE JOURNALS OF KIERKEGAARD: A Selection. Edited by A. Dru	TB/52
Soren Kierkegaard	PURITY OF HEART	TB/4
Soren Kierkegaard	THE POINT OF VIEW FOR MY WORK AS AN AUTHOR: *A Report to History*	TB/88
Alexandre Koyré	FROM THE CLOSED WORLD TO THE INFINITE UNIVERSE	TB/31
Walter Lowrie	KIERKEGAARD. *Vol I*, TB/89; *Vol. II*, TB/90	
Emile Mâle	THE GOTHIC IMAGE: *Religious Art in France of the 13th Century.* Illustrated	TB/44
T. J. Meek	HEBREW ORIGINS	TB/69
H. Richard Niebuhr	CHRIST AND CULTURE	TB/3
H. Richard Niebuhr	THE KINGDOM OF GOD IN AMERICA	TB/49
Martin P. Nilsson	GREEK FOLK RELIGION	TB/78
H. J. Rose	RELIGION IN GREECE AND ROME	TB/55
Josiah Royce	THE RELIGIOUS ASPECT OF PHILOSOPHY: *A Critique of the Bases of Conduct and Faith*	TB/29
George Santayana	INTERPRETATIONS OF POETRY AND RELIGION	TB/9
George Santayana	WINDS OF DOCTRINE *and* PLATONISM AND THE SPIRITUAL LIFE	TB/24
F. Schleiermacher	ON RELIGION: *Speeches to Its Cultured Despisers*	TB/36
H. O. Taylor	THE EMERGENCE OF CHRISTIAN CULTURE IN THE WEST: *The Classical Heritage of the Middle Ages*	TB/48
P. Teilhard de Chardin	THE PHENOMENON OF MAN	TB/83
D. W. Thomas, *Ed.*	DOCUMENTS FROM OLD TESTAMENT TIMES	TB/85
Paul Tillich	DYNAMICS OF FAITH	TB/42
Ernst Troeltsch	THE SOCIAL TEACHING OF THE CHRISTIAN CHURCHES. Introduction by H. Richard Niebuhr. *Vol. I*, TB/71; *Vol. II*, TB/72	
E. B. Tylor	THE ORIGINS OF CULTURE [Part I of "Primitive Culture"]. Introduction by Paul Radin	TB/33
E. B. Tylor	RELIGION IN PRIMITIVE CULTURE [Part II of "Primitive Culture"]. Introduction by Paul Radin	TB/34
Evelyn Underhill	WORSHIP	TB/10
Johannes Weiss	EARLIEST CHRISTIANITY: *A History of the Period* A.D. 30-150. Introduction by F. C. Grant. *Vol. I*, TB/53; *Vol. II*, TB/54	
Wilhelm Windelband	A HISTORY OF PHILOSOPHY I: *Greek, Roman, Medieval*	TB/38
Wilhelm Windelband	A HISTORY OF PHILOSOPHY II: *Renaissance, Enlightenment, Modern*	TB/39